ROADABLE AIRCRAFT

FROM **WHEELS** TO **WINGS**

A Flying Auto & Roadable Aircraft
Patent Search

to Doug

Palmer Stiles
Osh '06

Edited by

PALMER STILES

1994

Custom Creativity, Inc.
Melbourne, Florida

ROADABLE AIRCRAFT: FROM WHEELS TO WINGS

Copyright 1994 by Palmer Stiles

Second Edition, August 1994
Current Printing:
8 7 6 5 4 3 2 1

Printed in the United States of America.
Book Design: Christina Pechstein
Cover Design: Christina Pechstein
Front Cover Photo: Aerocar IV, Molt Taylor (2,767,939) by Jere Pechstein
Back Cover Photos: top: Aircar, Martin (3,029,042) by B.W. Preston
     center: A. Del J. Gero, Sr. (2,609,167) by A. Del J. Gero, Sr.
     bottom: Aerocar III, Molt Taylor (2,767,939) by Pat Ortiz

Published in North America b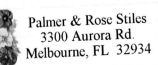.S. 1, Melbourne, Florida 32940

Palmer & Rose Stiles
3300 Aurora Rd.
Melbourne, FL 32934

Additional copies may be ordered from the publisher for $20.00 plus 3.00 shipping and handling. Florida residents please add $1.20 (6%) state sales tax.

For Joan

ACKNOWLEDGEMENTS

Very few accomplishments are solo efforts. A book that compiles the work of many others is of course indebted to them. A letters patent is an act of the U.S. Goverment giving "intellectual title" for a concept for 17 years in exchange for disclosing the concept. The disclosure document (patent) then becomes public domain. A design patent (prefaced by the letter D) gives rights to the inventor only for the ornamental appearance of the object and runs for fewer years. It has been my priviledge to to get to know some of the living patent holders represented here. I would like to know more of them.

Many thanks to these who have been an inspiration and have aided the editor in his research and in the preparation of this volume: Molt & Neil Taylor(2,767,939) have done more for the movement over a longer period than anybody else. He graciously gave his time for a video interview and permission to use His Aerocar IV concept for the cover. He and his mentor Robert Fulton(2,430,869) were the only ones to achieve full U.S. Government certification for their machines. Fulton provided a very professional autobiographical video originally made for French Television. Ed & Sandra Sweeney loaned the Aerocar IV model and gave permission for its use on the cover as well as making other valuable connections. Tom Faulconer was a partner of the late Ted Hall (2,562,490 & 2,562,491)and supplied much information on their efforts. Mel Kosanchick encouraged the publication and was the launch customer for the first edition.

Ron Borovec is the current leader of the roadable movement thru his publishing of Roadable Aircraft magazine and sponsorship of Oshkosh forums. He reviewed the first edition and has given it free advertizing. A. Del J. Gero(2,609,167) furnished the pictures of his model on the back cover. B.W. Preston furnished the pictures of the Martin(3,029,042) Aircar also on the back cover. Dr. Branko Sarh(4,986,493) has sponsored Society of Automotive Engineers (SAE) technical sessions on flying autos. Joseph F. Peters and Galen Barefoot of the U.S. Patent and Trademark Office helped uncover some patents that would have been missed. Others who have helped in many ways are Joe Yasecko, Kip Anderson, Ogden Martin, Dr. Gordon & Marzenda McComb, Oralee Stiles, Art & Mary Beth Coffey, Ed Bruski, Gary & Dawn Bullard, Bill Chana, Dr. Steven Crow, Johnnie Eskue, Jim Fox, Ken & Jean Fox, Harvey & Dot Miller (4,269,374 &5,050,817), Robert & Ola Smurthwaite, Paul Moller (5,115,996), Ross Nolan, K.P. Rice, Bill Schugt, Michael Siewart, A.J. Smith, Bruce Crower, Erwin Stockwell, Richard Strong(2,923,494 & 3,612,440), Joe & Esther Szakacs(Des 331, 893), Ken Wernicke, Pat Ortiz, and Don Wooley(5,201,478).

Finally, faculty colleagues, administrators, and staff at Florida Institute of Technology (Florida Tech) gave their individual and institutional support: Vicki Borton, Nancy Chmelir, Roslyn Bursey, Dan Simpson, and Drs. Sepri, Russell, Engblom, Subramanian, Kalajian, Sullivan, Revay & Weaver. My wife Joan and our sons Jonathan & Colin gave much support. Jere and Christina "Cricket" Pechstein did the photography, layout, and consulting on the book itself.

Palmer Stiles
Melbourne, Florida, June 1994

CONTENTS

INTRODUCTION

We are pleased to present this second, updated edition of *Flying Auto and Roadable Aircraft Patent Search.* When driving down the road or snarled in traffic, we look up and dream of having a machine that we can fly as well as drive. This book was compiled to address that desire. Presented here are some of the works of 70+ individuals who have pursued that dream. Most of these patents are condensed. Otherwise, this volume would have over 650 pages and a prohibitive price tag.

If you were to hire a patent search firm to find these U.S. patent numbers, it would cost hundreds of dollars — plus the cost of the individual copies, which are now $3.00 each. Seventy-six patents are represented here. They range in length from Mills at 2 pages to Eickman at 64. Ten are complete. There are certain to be other relevant patents that were not found during several searches. Also, no patents from other nations are included. If there is sufficient response to this edition, perhaps subsequent editions will correct some of the omissions.

It is possible that the editor and the reader will differ about which of the patents should have been condensed. In that case, you are encouraged to contact:

U.S. Department of Commerce
Patent and Trademark Office
Washington, D.C. 20231

Send the patent numbers with $3.00 each and they will send you complete copies. Some large libraries have the more recent patents on microfilm or perhaps CD ROM which can be copied on site.

The patents are in numerical order, except for the design patents starting with the letter D, in chronological order. A standard (letters) patent is good for 17 years from date of issue. The more recent patents are subject to maintenance fees which, if not paid periodically, could cause permanent expiration.

The comparison chart relates common features of the designs. Very few of these have reached the hardware or flight stage to the editor's knowledge. Those which have are shown in column 5. The first of these to receive full U.S. Government certification was Fulton's (2,430,869). He has several patents on details of the same design called the Airphibian. Only one is included. The only other design to be certified was Taylor's (2,767,939). His five Aerocars have been the most successful of all the designs so far. Rutan's patent (4,641,800) is not a roadable aircraft but was included because of its swinging canard. Because of the editor's personal bias against vertical takeoff machines, only a few were included. Unfortunately, none of the patented vehicles in this book or other non-patented ones have ever reached full commercial production.

The editor is a longtime enthusiast of roadable aircraft who teaches mechanical and aerospace engineering at Florida Tech (Florida Institute of Technology). He has learned it is easier to study history than make it, but has ambitions to do just that. It is his passionate desire that this volume will serve as a catalyst for many to join him in pursuing the DREAM of a practical, fast, affordable, and commercially available roadable aircraft.

PALMER STILES
1994

COMPARISON CHART
Patents by Number

Patent No.	Name	YEAR FILED	YEAR ISSUED	FLOWN	NUMBER OF ENGINES	FLIGHT ONLY	ROAD ONLY	BOTH	NUMBER OF PROPS	DUCTED FAN OR CHANNEL	T:TRACTOR P:PUSHER B:BOTH	NUMBER OF ROTORS	NUMBER OF WHEELS	WHEEL(S) DRIVEN	DETACHABLE FLIGHT SECTION	COMPLETE ROADABILITY	WINGLESS	TWINTAIL BOOMS	CANARD	USES COMMERCIAL AUTO	AMPHIBIOUS	COMPLETE PATENT	OTHER PATENT(S) SAME VEHICLE	GAS TURBINE	PAGES IN ORIGINAL	PAGES INCLUDED
D106,939	Waterman	1937	1937	X	1			1	1		P		3	2	X										2	1
D153,331	Zuck (2)	1946	1949		1			1	1		P		4	2		X						X	X		4	4
D155,569	Bailey	1947	1949		1			1	2		P		4	?		X				X		X	X		2	2
D331,893	Szakacs	1991	1992		?	?	?	?	2	?	P		3	?		X							X		2	2
1,286,679	Longobardi	1918	1918		?	?	?		3		B	3							X	X					5	3
1,731,757	Tubbe	1926	1929		1			1	1		P		3			X									8	3
1,756,463	Jezek	1928	1930		1	1	?	1	1		T		4	?		X									6	4
1,816,653	Nelsch	1930	1931		1			1	1		T		3			X									6	4
1,998,148	Vieru	1934	1935		1			1	1		T		3			X									5	2
2,135,073	Gerhardt	1937	1938		1			1	1		P	1	3	1		X	X								6	2
2,215,003	Johnson (1)	1938	1940		1			1	1		P		7	2	X			X		X					18	4
	Johnson (2)	1938	1940		2	1		1	2		P		7	2	X			X								
	Johnson (3)	1938	1940		2	1		1	2		T		7	2	X					?						
2,241,577	Beals	1939	1941		1			1	1		P		4	2	X			X							17	3
2,338,751	Zuck (1)	1939	1944		1			1	1		T		3			X									8	5
2,373,467	Frakes	1943	1945		3	2	1		2		T		4	2	X				?	X					15	1
2,402,468	Thompson, G	1943	1946		1			?	1		T		4	?	X										6	2
2,410,234	Read	1943	1946		3	2	1		2		T		7	2	X					X					8	2
2,424,769	Page	1945	1947		1			1	1		P	1	4	2		X									8	2
2,427,936	Wales	1943	1947		1			1	0			2	3	1	X										10	2
2,430,869	Fulton	1945	1947	X	1			1	1		T		7	2	X								X		12	9
2,434,068	Geisse	1944	1948		1			1	10		P		?	?	X	X		X			X				3	3

COMPARISON CHART
Patents by Number

Patent No.	Name	YEAR FILED	YEAR ISSUED	FLOWN	NUMBER OF ENGINES	FLIGHT ONLY	ROAD ONLY	BOTH	NUMBER OF PROPS	DUCTED FAN OR CHANNEL	T:TRACTOR P:PUSHER B:BOTH	NUMBER OF ROTORS	NUMBER OF WHEELS	WHEEL(S) DRIVEN	DETACHABLE FLIGHT SECTION	COMPLETE ROADABILITY	WINGLESS	TWINTAIL BOOMS	CANARD	USES COMMERCIAL AUTO	AMPHIBIOUS	COMPLETE PATENT	OTHER PATENT(S) SAME VEHICLE	GAS TURBINE	PAGES IN ORIGINAL	PAGES INCLUDED
2,446,528	Clark	1944	1948		1			1	1		T		3	2	X										10	3
2,462,462	Boggs	1944	1949		1			1	1		P		7	2	X			X							7	3
2,494,547	Fish	1946	1950		1			1	1		P		6	2	X			X							14	4
2,539,489	Smith	1947	1951		?				?		?		7	?		X									5	3
2,544,021	Holland (1)	1948	1951	X	1			1	1		T		3	0		X						X			4	4
2,562,490	Hall (1)	1945	1951	X	1			1	1		T		3	2	X			X							40	5
2,562,491	Hall (2)	1947	1951	X	2	1	1		1		T		7	2	X								X		9	9
2,563,731	Masterson	1945	1951		1			1				1	3	1		X	X				X				8	5
2,573,271	Perl	1947	1951		1			1	1		P		4	2		X							X		6	6
2,593,785	Nye	1945	1952		1			1	1		P		7	2	X			X							5	2
2,609,167	Gero	1948	1952		1			1	1		P		4	0		X									15	3
2,624,530	Hanssen	1946	1953		2	1	1		1		P		3	1	X			X							4	2
2,666,602	Holland (2)	1951	1954	?	1			1	1		T		3	0		X									8	4
2,674,422	Pellarini	1950	1954	X	1			1	1		P		3	0		X						X			3	3
2,675,976	Gerardine	1946	1954		1			1	1		T		?	?	X										8	1
2,681,773	Rethorst	1948	1954		2				?	2	T		3	?	X	?									6	2
2,692,095	Carpenter	1952	1954		1			1	1		T		3	1		X									8	3
2,713,465	Novinger	1953	1955		1			1	1		P		3	2		X							?	X		11	2
2,767,939	Taylor	1952	1955	X	1			1	1		P		7	2	X	X						X			10	10
2,770,427	Schreffler	1952	1956		2	1	1		1		P		3	2		X		X		X					6	2
2,811,323	Rethorst	1953	1957		2				?	2	T		3	?		X							X		12	3

COMPARISON CHART
Patents by Number

Patent No.	Name	YEAR FILED	YEAR ISSUED	FLOWN	NUMBER OF ENGINES	FLIGHT ONLY	ROAD ONLY	BOTH	NUMBER OF PROPS	DUCTED FAN OR CHANNEL	T:TRACTOR P:PUSHER B:BOTH	NUMBER OF ROTORS	NUMBER OF WHEELS	WHEEL(S) DRIVEN	DETACHABLE FLIGHT SECTION	COMPLETE ROADABILITY	WINGLESS	TWINTAIL BOOMS	CANARD	USES COMMERCIAL AUTO	AMPHIBIOUS	COMPLETE PATENT	OTHER PATENT(S) SAME VEHICLE	GAS TURBINE	PAGES IN ORIGINAL	PAGES INCLUDED
2,893,661	Aylor	1954	1959		1			1	1	X	P		4	0		X									6	1
2,923,494	Strong (1)	1958	1960		1			1		X	T		4	?		X									5	3
2,938,681	Palermo	1956	1960		1			1	1		T		2	1		X									5	2
2,940,688	Bland	1956	1960		2	1		1	1		P		3	1		X				X	X				10	3
2,945,646	Sturgeon	1957	1960		1			1	1		T		3	0		X									6	3
3,012,737	Dodd	1960	1961		1			1	1		P		3	0		X									4	1
3,029,042	Martin (1)	1958	1962	X	1			1	1	X	P		4					X			X				6	3
	Martin (2)	1958	1962		1			1		X	P		4							X	X		X			
	Martin (3)	1958	1962		1			1	1	X	P		4	?		X					X					
3,056,564	Zuck (2)	1959	1962		1			1	1		P		3	1	X									X	16	6
3,065,927	Mills	1962	1962		1			1	0			1	4	2	X										2	1
3,083,936	Rethorst	1959	1963		?			?	?	?	T		4	?		X								X	9	4
3,090,581	Einarsson	1959	1963		1			1	3		B		4	2		X	X				X	X			5	5
3,134,560	Halsmer	1961	1964	?	2	1		1	2		B		4	0		X		X							6	3
3,261,572	Gorton	1964	1966		1			1		X	P	2	3	2		X	X				X			X	6	3
3,265,329	Apostolescu(1)	1963	1966		?				0	X			4	?		X	X				X				12	1
3,317,161	Sawyer	1964	1967		3	2	1		0	X	P		4	2		X	X								6	3
3,371,866	Schertz	1966	1968		1			1	1	X	P		4	2		X							X		8	5
3,481,559	Apostolescu(2)	1966	1969		?					X		1	4	?		X	X				X			?	11	1
3,612,440	Strong (2)	1969	1971		1				1	X	T		4	?		X								X	6	4
3,645,474	Arbuse	1970	1972		2	1	1		1		P		7		X			X			X				12	3

COMPARISON CHART
Patents by Number

Patent Number	Name	YEAR FILED	YEAR ISSUED	FLOWN	NUMBER OF ENGINES	FLIGHT ONLY	ROAD ONLY	BOTH	NUMBER OF PROPS	DUCTED FAN OR CHANNEL	T:TRACTOR P:PUSHER B:BOTH	NUMBER OF ROTORS	NUMBER OF WHEELS	WHEEL(S) DRIVEN	DETACHABLE FLIGHT SECTION	COMPLETE ROADABILITY	WINGLESS	TWINTAIL BOOMS	CANARD	USES COMMERCIAL AUTO	AMPHIBIOUS	COMPLETE PATENT	OTHER PATENT(S) SAME VEHICLE	GAS TURBINE	PAGES IN ORIGINAL	PAGES INCLUDED
4,022,403	Chiquet	1976	1977		1			1	0		P		6			?								X	3	2
4,269,374	Miller	1979	1981		1			1	1	?	P		4	2		X	X								8	3
4,358,072	Williamson (2)	1980	1982		1			1	1		P		6	2		X									8	
4,579,297	Ayoola	1984	1986		3	2	1		1	X	P		4	2		X					X			X	9	4
4,627,585	Einstein	1984	1986		2	1	1		1		P		3	?		X					X				7	3
4,641,800	Rutan	1983	1987	X	2	2			2		P		3	0					X					X	10	4
4,856,732	Eickman	1987	1989		?				4				4	0	X	X					X				64	9
4,865,275	Thompson, H	1987	1989		1	1				X	P		0	0	N	X	X				X				18	6
4,881,701	Bullard	1988	1989		1			1			P		4	2		X			X						8	5
4,899,954	Pruzenski	1988	1990		1			1	1		P		4	1		X			X			X	X		8	8
4,913,375	Fitzpatrick	1988	1990		1			1	1	X	P		3	0		X						X			8	5
4,986,493	Sarh	1988	1991		1			1	?		P		4	2		X							X		32	8
5,050,817	Miller (2)	1989	1991		1			1	1		P		5	?		X				X			X		7	7
5,115,996	Moller	1990	1992		8	8	?	?		X	B		3	?		X			?					27	10
5,141,173	Lay	1991	1992		1			1	1	X	P	4	4	4		X	X								13	5
5,201,478	Wooley	1991	1993		1			1	1		P		3	?		X			X						18	7

ALPHA SEQUENCE
Patent Holders and Their Patents

A

Apostolescu	3,265,329
	3,481,559
Arbuse	3,645,474
Aylor	2,893,661
Ayooia	4,579,297

B

Bailey	D155,569
Beals	2,241,577
Bland	2,940,688
Boggs	2,462,462
Bullard	4,881,701

C

Carpenter	2,692,095
Chiquet	4,022,403
Clark	2,446,528

D

Dodd	3,012,737

E

Eickman	4,856,732
Einarson	3,090,581
Einstein	4,627,585

F

Fish	2,494,547
Fitzpatrick	4,913,375
Frakes	2,373,467
Fulton	2,430,869

G

Geisse	2,434,068
Gerardine	2,675,976
Gerhardt	2,135,073
Gero	2,609,167
Gorton	3,261,572

H

Hall	2,562,490
	2,562,491
Halsmer	3,134,560
Hanssen	2,624,530
Holland	2,544,021
	2,666,602

J

Jezek	1,756,463
Johnson	2,215,003

L

Lay	5,141,173
Longobardi	1,286,679

M

Martin	3,029,042
Masterson	2,563,731
Miller	4,269,374
Miller (2)	5,050,817
Mills	3,065,927
Moller	5,115.996

N

Nelsch	1,816,653
Novinger	2,713,465
Nye	2,593,785

P

Page	2,424,769
Palermo	2,938,681
Pellarini	2,674,422
Perl	2,573,271
Pruzenski	4,899,954

R

Read	2,410,234
Rethorst	2,681,773
	2,811,323
	3,083,936
Rutan	4,641,800

S

Sarh	4,986,493
Sawyer	3,317,161
Schertz	3,371,866
Schreffler	2,770,427
Smith	2,539,489
Strong	2,923,494
	3,612,440
Sturgeon	2,945,646
Szakacs	D331,893

T

Taylor	2,767,939
Thompson, G	2,402,468
Thompson, H	4,865,275
Tubbe	1,731,757

V

Vieru	1,998,148

W

Wales	2,427,936
Waterman	D106,939
Williamson	4,358,072
Wooley	5,201,478

Z

Zuck	2,338,751
	D153,331
	3,056,564

CHRONOLOGY
From 1906 to 1994

1906 Trajan Vuia tests flying auto near Paris, France.

1917 Glenn Curtiss Autoplane displayed at Pan-American
   Aeronautic Exposition in New York.

1922 Pierre Tampier operates Hybrid Aeroauto in Paris.

1929 George Spratt flies pivoting wing roadable.

1936 Daniel Zuck builds model of Planemobile.
   Harold Pitcairn flies AC 35.

1937 Waldo Waterman flies Arrowbile.

1938 Jerry Phillips pilots Arrowbile on national tour.

1946 Ted Hall and Tom Faulconer fly Southern Aircraft roadable.
   Daniel Zuck and Stanley Whitaker complete Planemobile I
   Robert Fulton flies Airphibian
   Ted Hall and Tom Faulconer fly Convair Model 116.

1947 Ted Hall and Tom Faulconer fly Convaircar Model 118.

1949 Molt Taylor flies Aerocar.
   Wismer Holland flies roadable Ercoupe.

1950 Luigi Pellarini tours Italy with Aerauto.
   CAA certifies Fulton Airphibian.

1955 Skeets Coleman reveals Aeromarine concept and model.

1956 CAA certifies Taylor Aerocar.
   Dr. Lewis Jackson flies roadable with pivot wing.

1957 Waldo Waterman finishes Aerobile and donates to
   Smithsonian.

1958 Daniel Zuck publishes "An Airplane in Every Garage".
   Ogden Martin flies Triphibious Aircar.

1959 Ed Sweeny rides in Aerocar 102D.
   Joseph Halsmer flies first design.

1961 Molt Taylor forms Aerocar International.
   KISN radio Portland, Oregon buys Aerocar for traffic watch.
   Bob Cummings buys Aerocar 102D for use in his TV show.
   Temco contracts to build 1000 Aerocars but deal collapses.

1963 Joseph Halsmer flies his Model III.

1964 Dr. Lewis Jackson flies 4 place delta type pusher.

1965 Helicopter Technik Wagner flies roadable helicopter in
   Germany.

1966 Molt Taylor flies Aerocar III.

CHRONOLOGY
From 1906 to 1994

1968 Chitty Chitty Bang Bang movie is released.

1970 Erwin Stockwell rolls out Corvair with wings.

1971 Richard Place and Donald Peterson of Ford study the Aerocar.

1973 Smolinski and partner killed in AVE Mizar Pinto.

1974 Dewey Bryan killed in his roadable III at Oshkosh Fly in.
James Bond movie, "Man with the Golden Gun" has flying car sequence.

1976 Waldo Waterman dies.

1978 San Diego Aerospace Museum fire. Many records and at least one roadable vehicle lost.

1983 Ken Fox incorporates Roadable Aircraft Association.
K.P. Rice flies Volante.
Robert Fulton and sons produce video of his life including clips of Airphibian.

1985 John Olander starts Flying Car Association.

1987 Fred Barker writes article in July "Sport Aviation" on Skycycle.

1988 Jack Carpenter completes book"Waldo, Pioneer Aviator".
Bueler Foundation starts restoration of Aerocar prototype.
Don Parham sells info pack on GC 100 Gyrocar concept.
Ed and Sandra Sweeney buy and restore Aerocar 102D.

1989 Harvey Miller and Robert Smurthwaite start on AviAuto RC model.

1990 Sweeneys' Aerocar on cover of Jan "Sport Aviation".

1991 Paul Moller's M400 Volantor featured in cover story in Jan "Popular Mechanics"
EAA releases video "Molt Taylor's Aerocar".
A.J. Smith issues info pack on Aero Caballo with pictures of vehicle partially complete.
July: Aerocar prototype flies and is donated to EAA museum.
August: Ross Nolan informally leads flying car session at
              Oshkosh.

1992 Gary Bullard sells info packs on his GB 2000 canard concept.
July: Ron Borovec launches Roadable Aircraft Magazine.
           Joe Yasecko"s Air Trike RC model crashes on take off.
August: Ron Borovec and Joe Yasecko lead roadable aircraft session at Oshkosh.
           Mel Kosanchick organizes International Roadable Aircraft Association(IRAA).
           Branko Sarh chairs Flying Car session at SAE Future Transportation Technology Conference in Costa Mesa, California. Speakers are Brandt Goldsworthy,

CHRONOLOGY
From 1906 to 1994

Dr Steven Crow, Ed Sweeney, Palmer Stiles, Branko Sarh, and Barry Felrice. Tom Faulconer presents evening session, with caucus afterward.

October: Daniel Zuck dies.

Palmer Stiles at Florida Tech sponsors aerospace engineering student senior design project to build radio controlled model of CaRnard.

December: Palmer Stiles publishes "Flying Auto and Roadable Aircraft Patent Search"

1993 March: Joseph Halsmer dies.

June: CaRnard RC model almost flies.

August: Ron Borovec chairs forum at Oshkosh. Speakers: Palmer Stiles, Molt Taylor, Harry Einstein, Bill Schugt, Nick D'Aquisto.

Peter Garrison article "Can We Ever Make a Car Airworthy" published in August "Flying" magazine.

September: Three senior design roadable projects started at Florida Tech.

October: Dr. Branko Sarh Chairs Flying Car session at SAE Aerotech, Costa Mesa, California . Speakers: Palmer Stiles, Dr. Steven Crow, Merkel Weiss, Dr. Branko Sarh, Mike Czajkowski, John Knepp.

November 1: Kenneth Wernicke's Sky Car full scale mockup written up in "Aviation Week".

December 17: Ken Fox marries on 90th anniversary of Wright's first flight.

1994 Kip Anderson builds scale model of "pancake roadable"

July   Kenneth Wernicke's Sky Car is cover story in Popular Mechanics

Palmer Stiles publishes "Flying Auto and Roadable Aircraft Patent Search" 2nd edition

Ron Borovec leads two roadable aircraft forums at Oshkosh.

Nov. 9, 1937.   W. D. WATERMAN   Des. 106,939

AIRPLANE

Filed Feb. 8, 1937

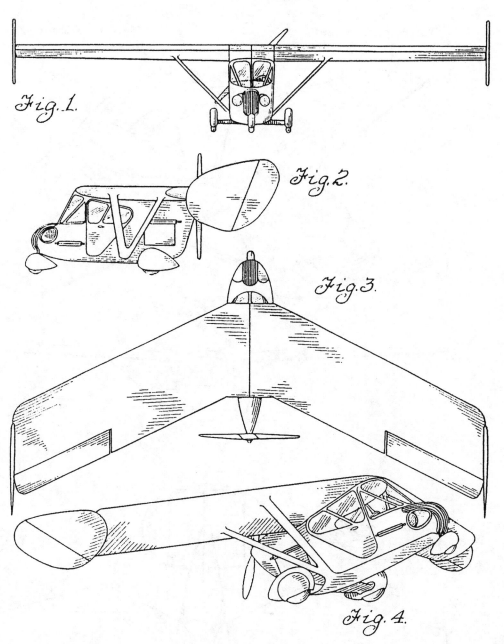

Fig. 1.

Fig. 2.

Fig. 3.

Fig. 4.

INVENTOR.

Waldo D. Waterman

BY W. E. Williams

ATTORNEY.

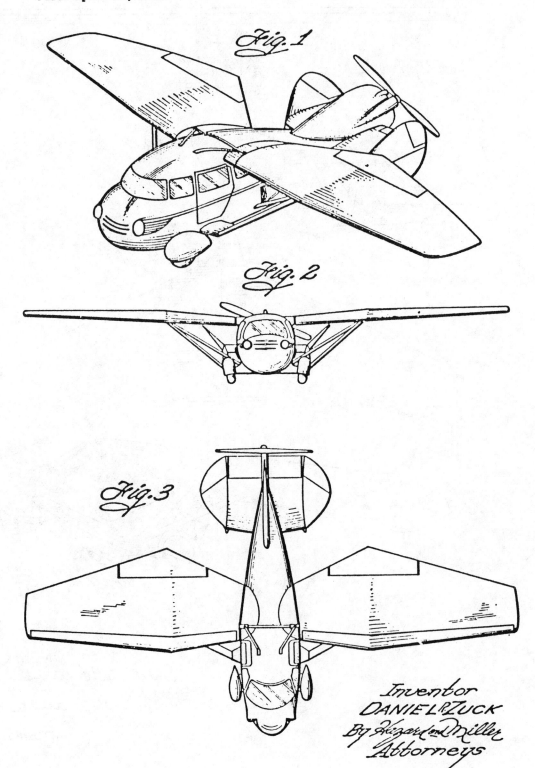

Fig.1

Fig.2

Fig.3

Inventor
DANIEL R. ZUCK
By Hazard and Miller
Attorneys

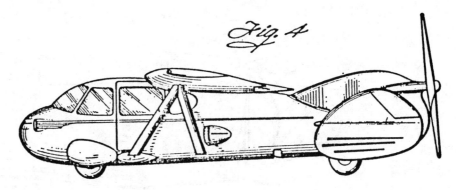

Fig. 4

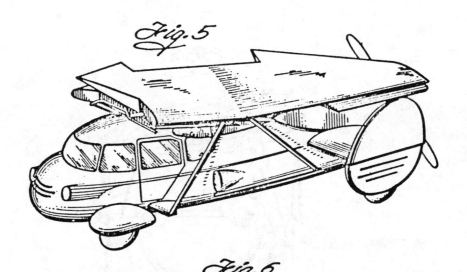

Fig. 5

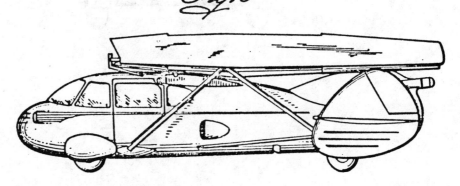

Fig. 6

Inventor
DANIEL R ZUCK
By Hazard on Miller
Attorneys

Fig. 7

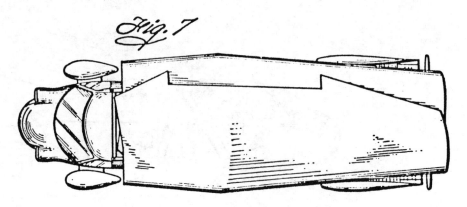

Fig. 8

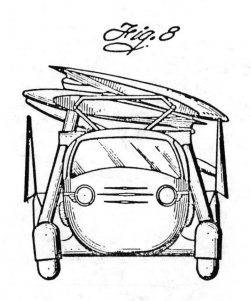

Inventor
DANIEL R ZUCK
By Hazard and Miller
Attorneys

UNITED STATES PATENT OFFICE

153,331

DESIGN FOR AN AIRPLANE

Daniel R. Zuck, Los Angeles, Calif.

Application April 22, 1946, Serial No. 128,832

Term of patent 14 years

(Cl. D71—1)

To all whom it may concern:

Be it known that I, Daniel R. Zuck, a citizen of the United States, residing at Los Angeles, in the county of Los Angeles and State of California, have invented a new, original, and ornamental Design for an Airplane, of which the following is a specification, reference being had to the accompanying drawing, forming part·thereof.

Fig. 1 is a perspective view of the airplane, embodying my new design and illustrating the same as it appears in flight position; Fig. 2 is a view in front elevation of the airplane; Fig. 3 is a top plan view of the same; Fig. 4 is a view in side elevation of the same; Fig. 5 is a perspective view of the same but illustrating the wings in collapsed position; Fig. 6 is a view in side elevation of the plane in collapsed position; Fig. 7 is a top plan view of the airplane in collapsed position; and Fig. 8 is a view in front elevation of the same in collapsed position.

In Figs. 5, 6 and 7 the ailerons are shown as having been removed.

I claim:

The ornamental design for an airplane, as shown.

DANIEL R. ZUCK.

REFERENCES CITED

The following references are of record in the file of this patent:

UNITED STATES PATENTS

Number	Name	Date
D. 94,926	Sikorsky	Mar. 19, 1935
D. 143,969	Gross	Feb. 26, 1946
1,307,318	Petersen	June 17, 1919
2,347,230	Zuck	Apr. 25, 1944

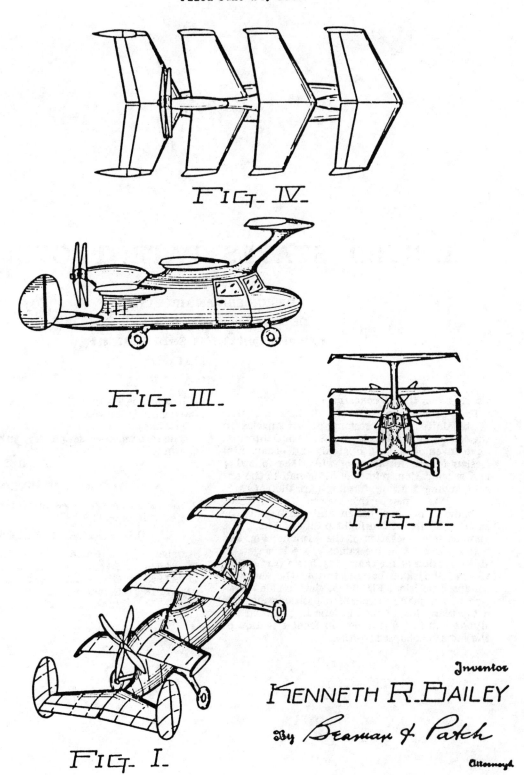

FIG. IV.

FIG. III.

FIG. II.

FIG. I.

Inventor

KENNETH R. BAILEY

By Beaman & Patch

Attorneys

UNITED STATES PATENT OFFICE

155,569

DESIGN FOR A COMBINED AUTOMOBILE AND AIRPLANE

Kenneth R. Bailey, West Dearborn, Mich.

Application June 24, 1947, Serial No. 139,888

Term of patent 14 years

(Cl. D71—1)

To all whom it may concern:

Be it known that I, Kenneth R. Bailey, a citizen of the United States, residing at West Dearborn, in the county of Wayne, and State of Michigan, have invented a certain new, original, and ornamental Design for Combined Automobile and Airplane, of which the following is a specification, reference being had to the accompanying drawing, forming part thereof:

In the drawing,

Fig. I is a starboard rear perspective view of a combined automobile and airplane, showing my new design,

Fig. II is a front elevational view,

Fig. III is a starboard side elevational view, and

Fig. IV is a top plan view thereof.

The port side of the airplane is constructed like the starboard side as shown in Fig. III.

I claim:

The ornamental design for a combined automobile and airplane, substantially as shown and described.

KENNETH R. BAILEY.

REFERENCES CITED

The following references are of record in the file of this patent:

UNITED STATES PATENTS

Number	Name	Date
D. 78,838	Orsett	June 25, 1929

US00D331893S

United States Patent [19]

Szakacs

[11] Patent Number: **Des. 331,893**

[45] Date of Patent: ** Dec. 22, 1992

[54] **COMBINED AIRCRAFT AND ROAD VEHICLE**

[76] Inventor: **Joseph J. Szakacs,** 1714 Washington Pl., San Diego, Calif. 92103

[**] Term: **14 Years**

[21] Appl. No.: **719,579**

[22] Filed: **Jun. 21, 1991**

[52] U.S. Cl. **D12/4; D12/333**

[58] Field of Search D12/4, 333, 330; 244/2, 244/12.6, 36

[56] **References Cited**

U.S. PATENT DOCUMENTS

D. 188,359	7/1960	LeBel	D12/330
D. 217,402	4/1970	Miller	D12/4
D. 226,685	9/1973	Ackerson	D12/333
D. 238,937	2/1976	Szakacs	D12/333
D. 257,629	12/1980	Miller	D12/4
2,681,773	6/1954	Rethorst	D12/4
2,811,323	10/1957	Rethorst	244/36
2,940,688	6/1960	Bland	244/12.6
3,026,066	2/1962	Coates	D12/4
3,083,936	4/1963	Rethorst	D12/4
5,050,817	9/1991	Miller	244/2

Primary Examiner—Wallace R. Burke
Assistant Examiner—Melody Brown

[57] **CLAIM**

The ornamental design for a combined aircraft and road vehicle, as shown and described.

DESCRIPTION

FIG. 1 is a front and side perspective view of a combined aircraft and road vehicle showing my new design;
FIG. 2 is a rear and side perspective view thereof;
FIG. 3 is a front and side perspective view thereof, in an alternate condition; and,
FIG. 4 is a rear and side perspective view thereof, in an alternate condition.
The broken lines are for illustrative purposes only and form no part of claimed design.

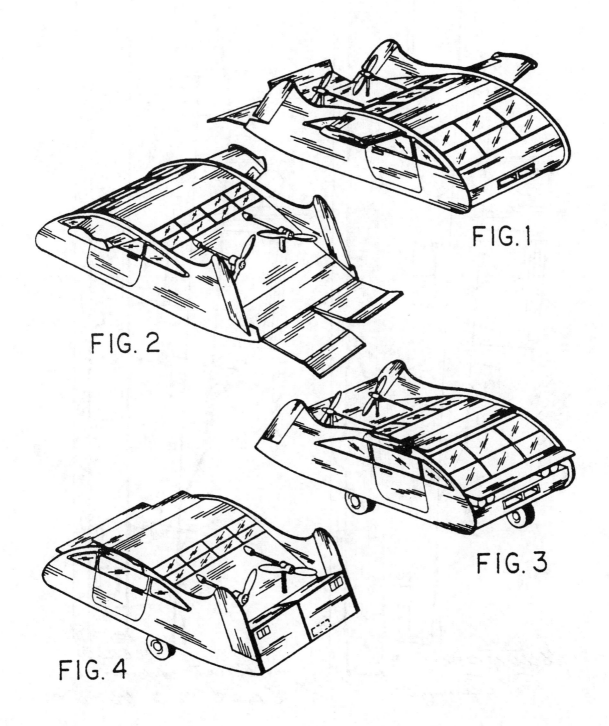

FIG.1

FIG. 2

FIG. 3

FIG. 4

F. LONGOBARDI.
COMBINATION VEHICLE.
APPLICATION FILED JUNE 12. 1918.

1,286,679.

Patented Dec. 3, 1918.
3 SHEETS—SHEET 1.

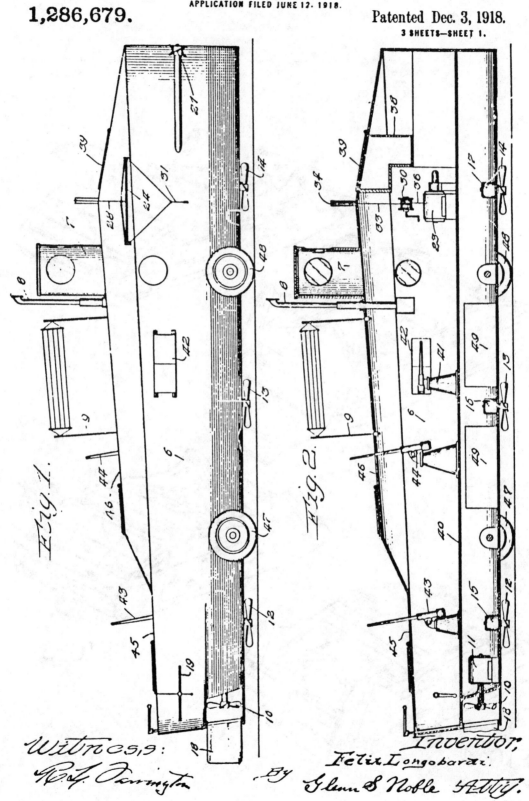

Fig.1.

Fig.2.

F. LONGOBARDI.
COMBINATION VEHICLE.
APPLICATION FILED JUNE 12, 1918.

1,286,679.

Patented Dec. 3, 1918.
3 SHEETS—SHEET 2.

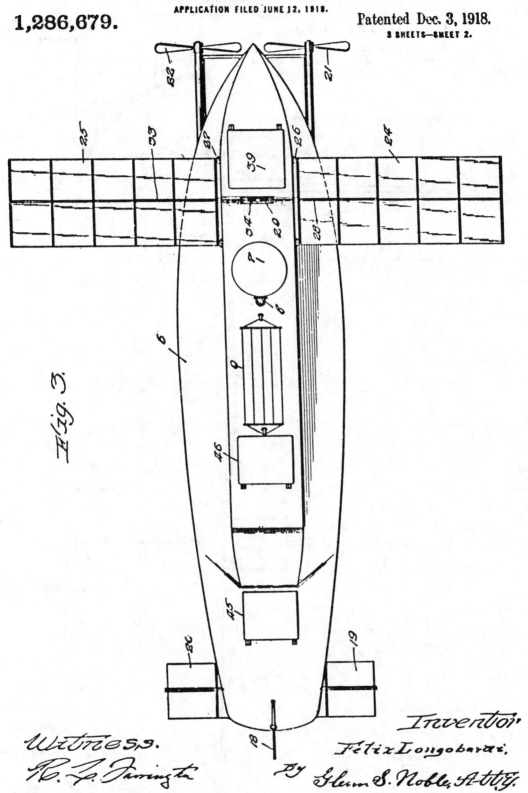

Fig. 3.

F. LONGOBARDI.
COMBINATION VEHICLE.
APPLICATION FILED JUNE 12, 1918.

1,286,679.

Patented Dec. 3, 1918.
3 SHEETS—SHEET 3.

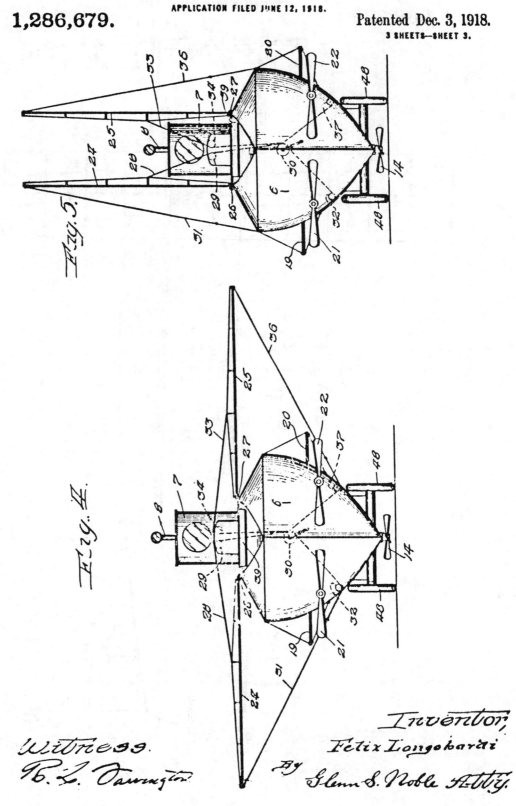

Witness.
R. L. Farrington

Inventor,
Felix Longobardi
By
Glenn S. Noble Atty.

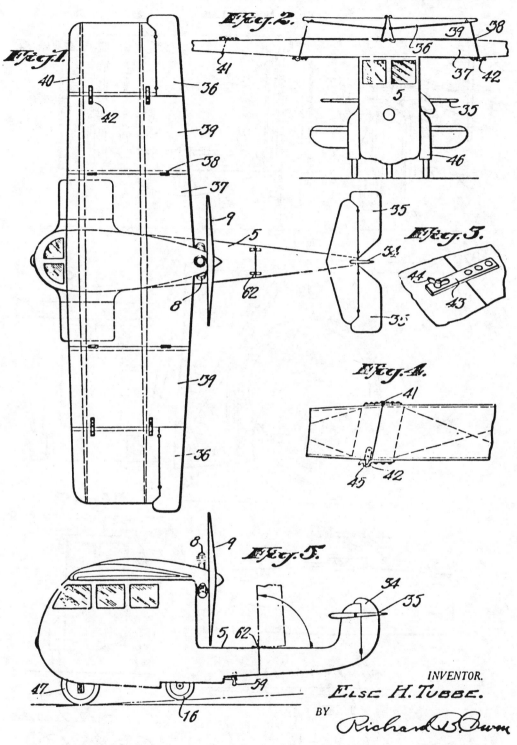

INVENTOR.

Else H. Tubbe.

BY Richard B. Owen

ATTORNEY.

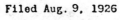

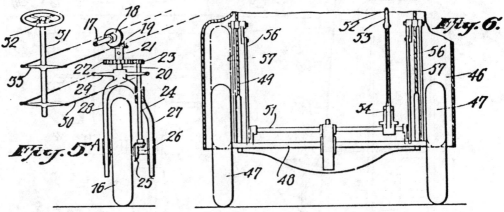

Fig. 5.

Fig. 6.

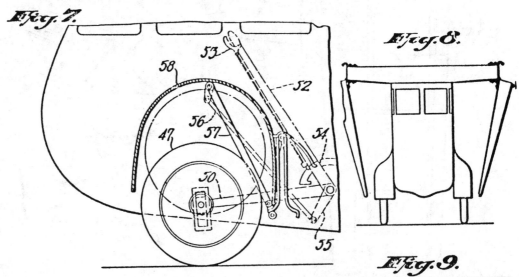

Fig. 7.

Fig. 8.

Fig. 9.

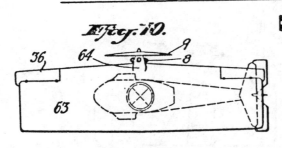

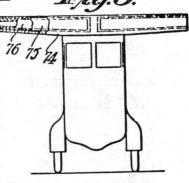

Fig. 10.

Fig. 11.

INVENTOR.

ELSE H. TUBBE.

BY　Richard B. Owen

ATTORNEY.

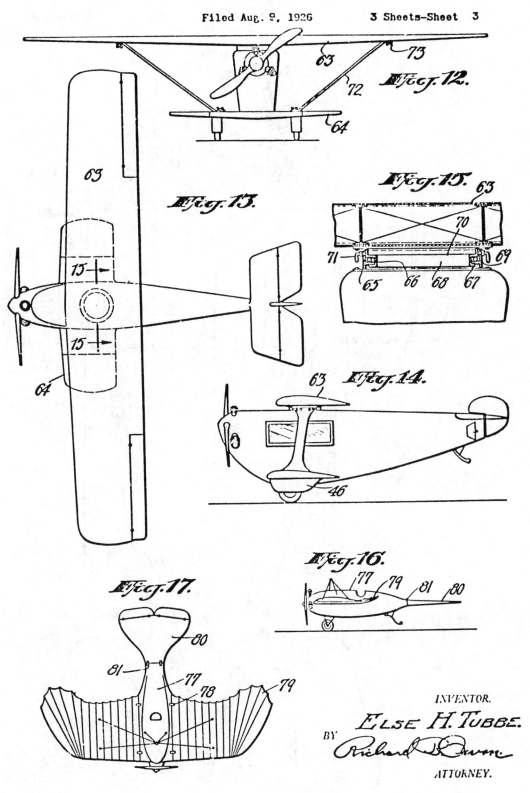

Fig. 12.

Fig. 13.

Fig. 15.

Fig. 14.

Fig. 16.

Fig. 17.

INVENTOR.
ELSE H. TUBBE.
BY
ATTORNEY.

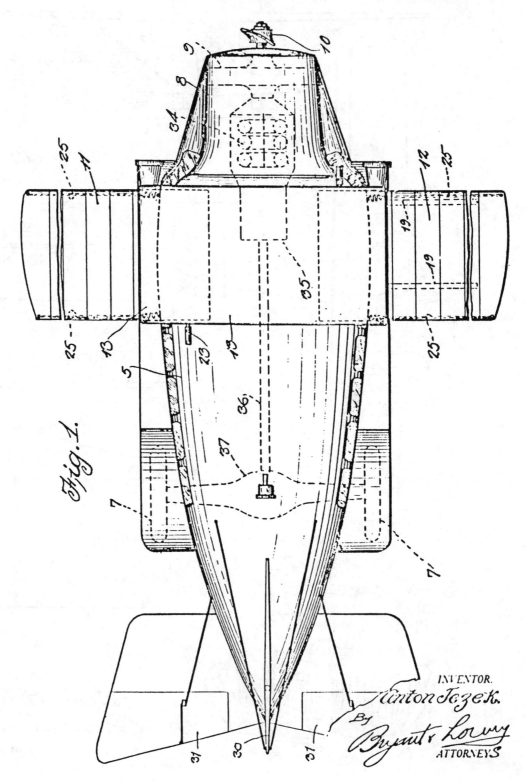

Fig. 1.

INVENTOR.
Anton Jezek.
By
Bryant & Lowry
ATTORNEYS

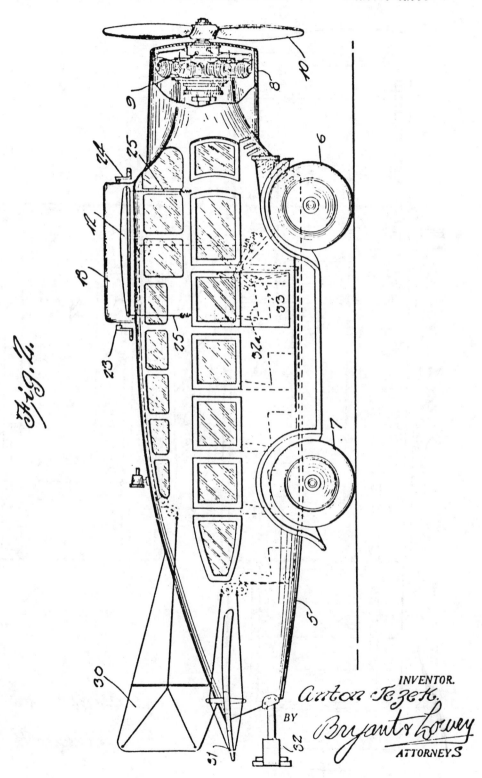

Fig. 4.

INVENTOR.

Anton Jezek

BY Bryant & Lowey

ATTORNEYS

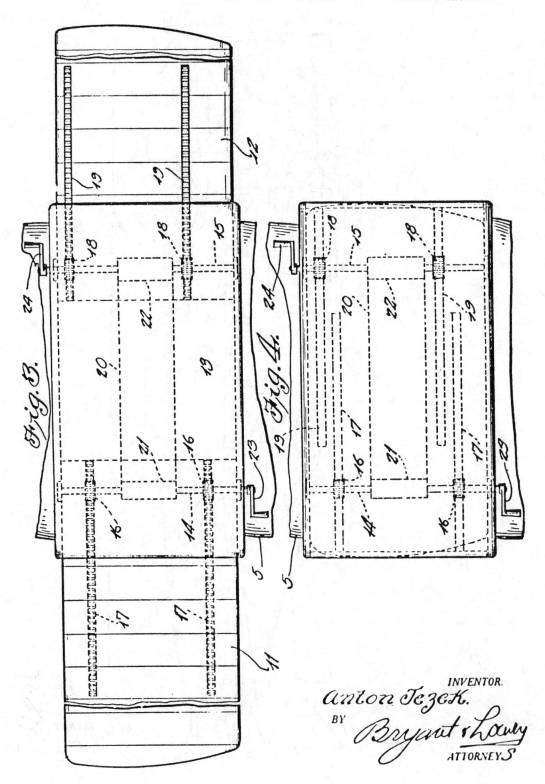

INVENTOR.

Anton Jezek.

BY *Bryant & Lowry*

ATTORNEYS

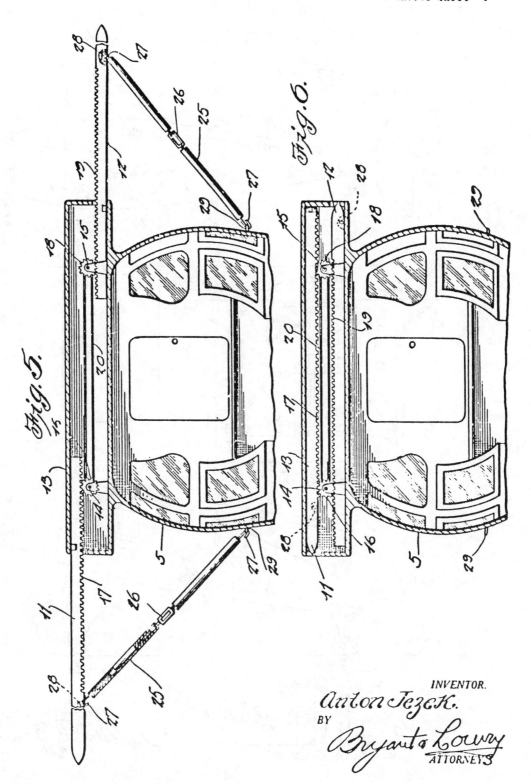

INVENTOR.
Anton Jezek.
BY
Bryant & Lowry
ATTORNEYS

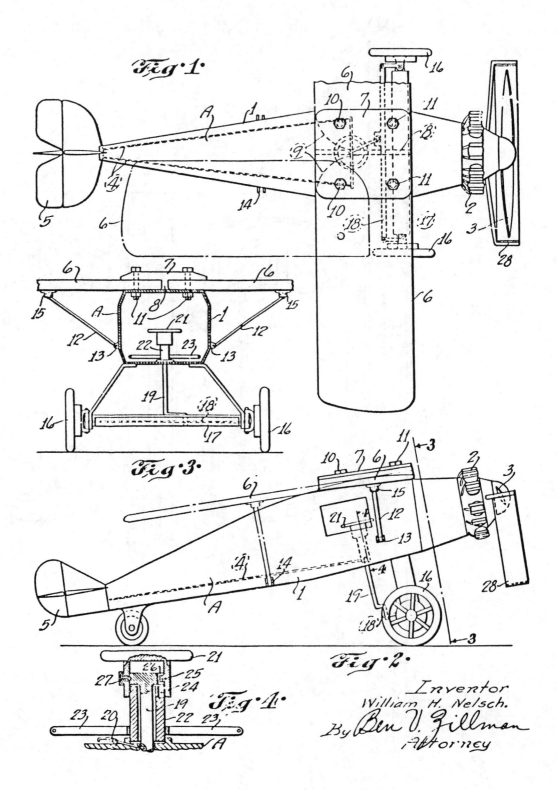

Fig·1·

Fig·3·

Fig·2·

Fig·4·

Inventor
William H. Nelsch.
By Ben V. Zillman
Attorney

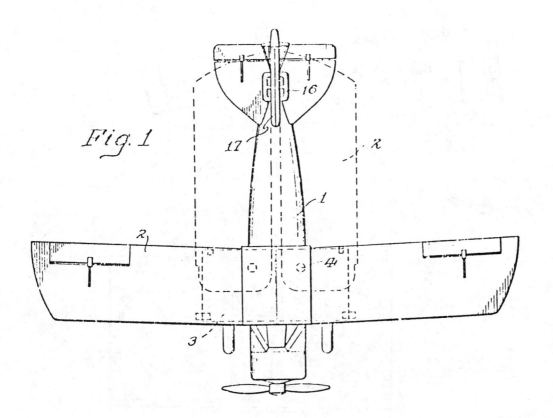

Fig. 1

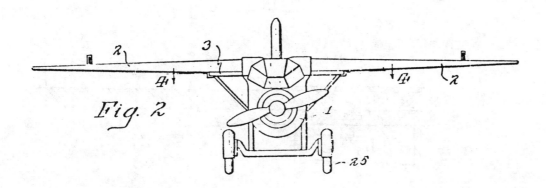

Fig. 2

Inventor
Daniel Vieriu

atty.

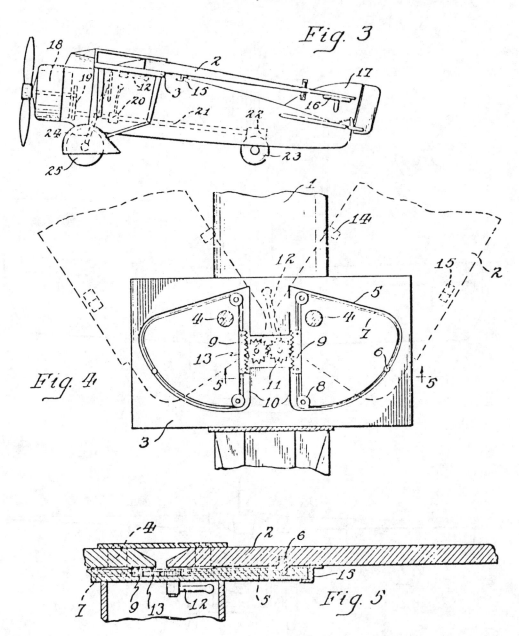

Fig. 3

Fig. 4

Fig. 5

Inventor
Daniel Vieriu

atty.

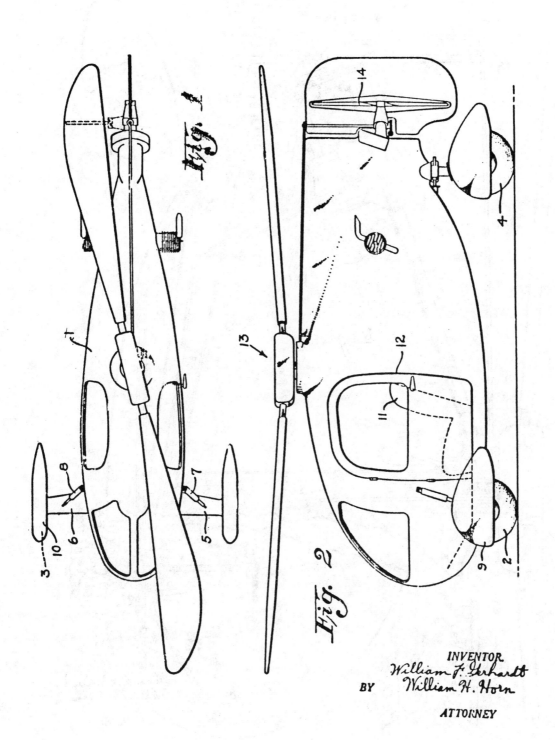

Fig. 1

Fig. 2

INVENTOR
William F. Gerhardt
BY   William H. Horn

ATTORNEY

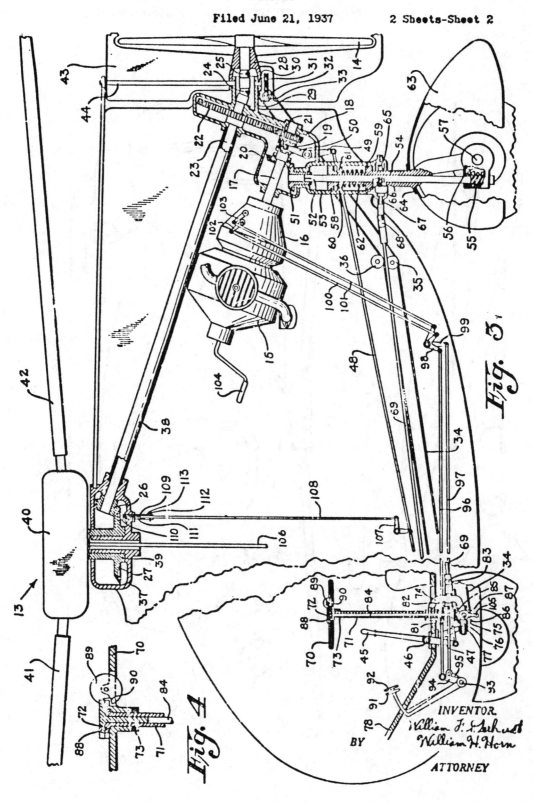

Fig. 3

Fig. 4

INVENTOR.

William F. Gerhardt
William H. Horn

BY

ATTORNEY

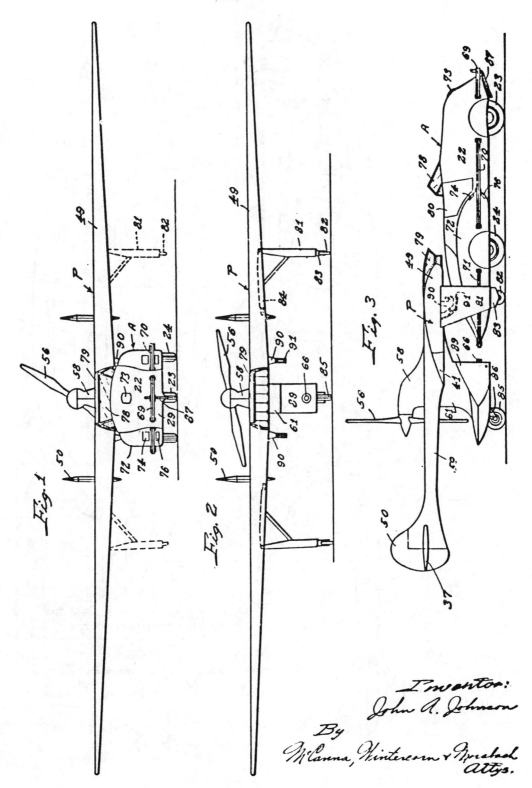

Inventor:
John A. Johnson
By
McCanna, Wintercorn & Myrabach
Attys.

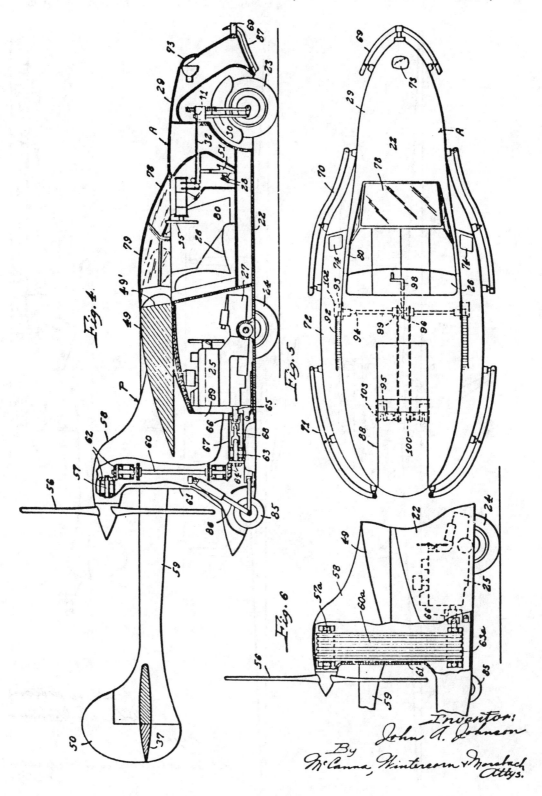

Fig. 4

Fig. 5

Fig. 6

Inventor:
John A. Johnson
By
McCanna, Wintercorn & Morsbach
Attys.

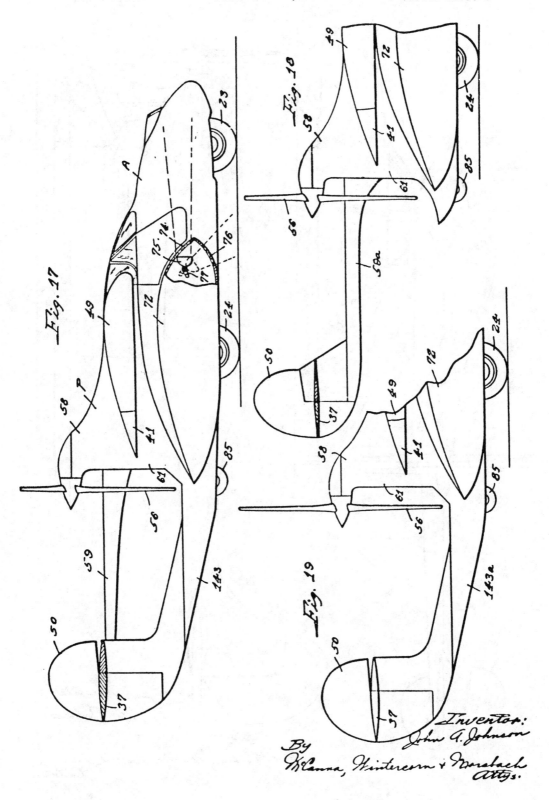

Inventor:
John A. Johnson

By
McKenna, Wintercorn & Marsbach
Attys.

Sept. 17, 1940.

J. A. JOHNSON

2,215,003

AUTOPLANE

Filed June 7, 1938

7 Sheets-Sheet 7

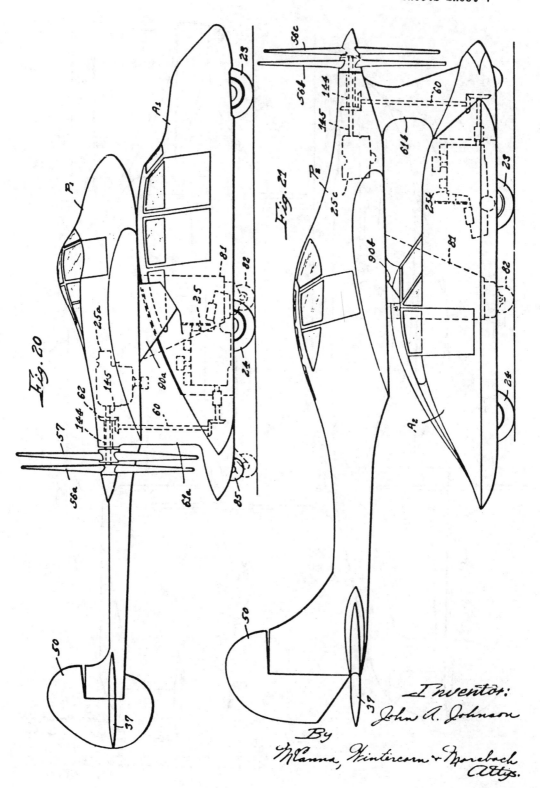

Fig. 20

Fig. 21

Inventor:
John A. Johnson
By
Manna, Wintercorn & Merebach
Attys.

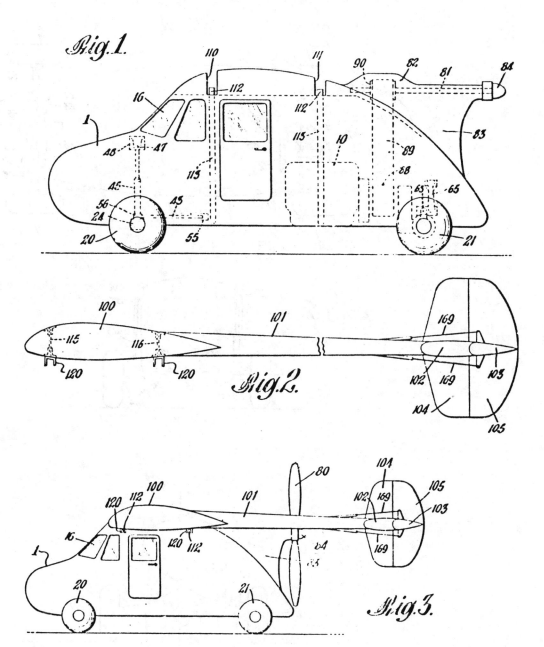

Fig.1.

Fig.2.

Fig.3.

INVENTOR
B. L. Beals Jr.
BY
Morgan Finnegan Durham
ATTORNEYS

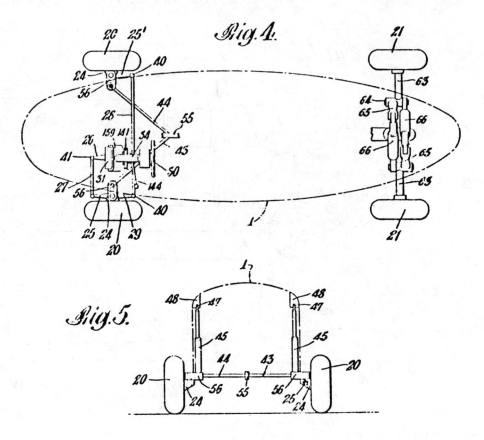

Fig.4.

Fig.5.

Fig.6.

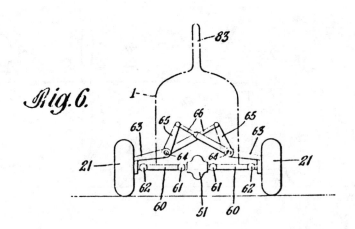

INVENTOR
B. L. Beals, Jr.
BY
Morgan Finnegan Durham
ATTORNEYS

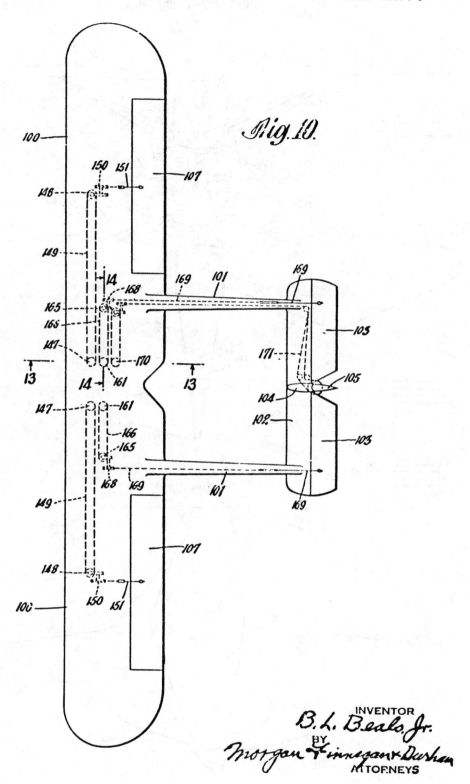

Fig. 10

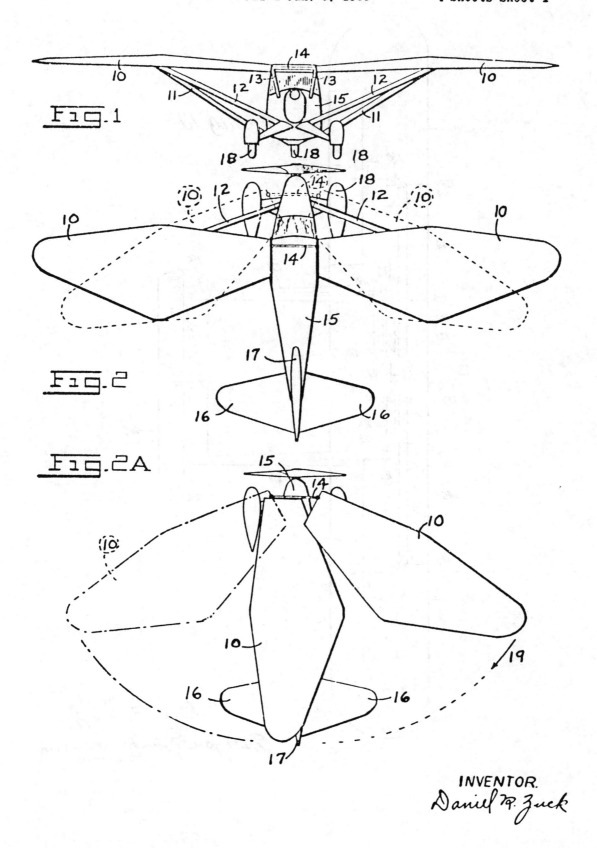

Fig.1

Fig.2

Fig.2A

INVENTOR.
Daniel R. Zuck

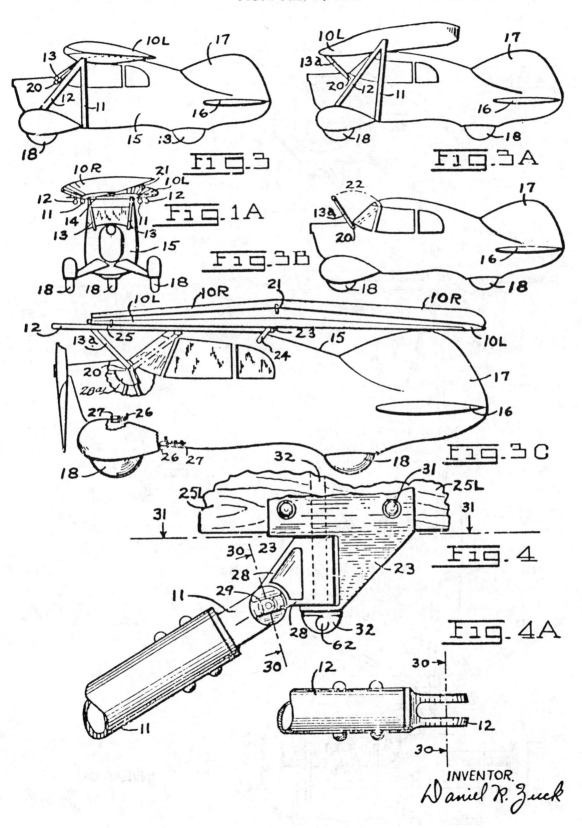

Fig.3

Fig.3A

Fig.1A

Fig.3B

Fig.3C

Fig.4

Fig.4A

INVENTOR.

Daniel R. Zuck

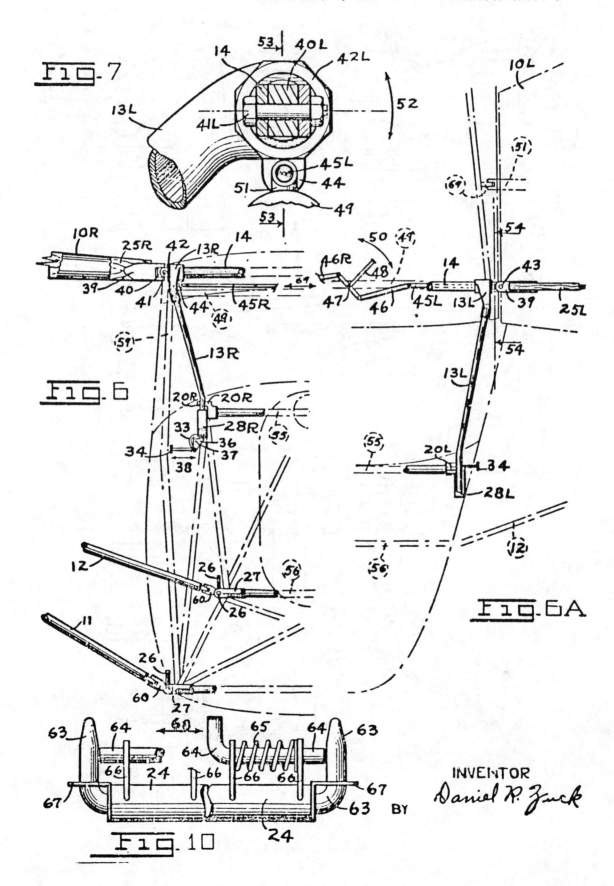

INVENTOR
Daniel R. Zuck
BY

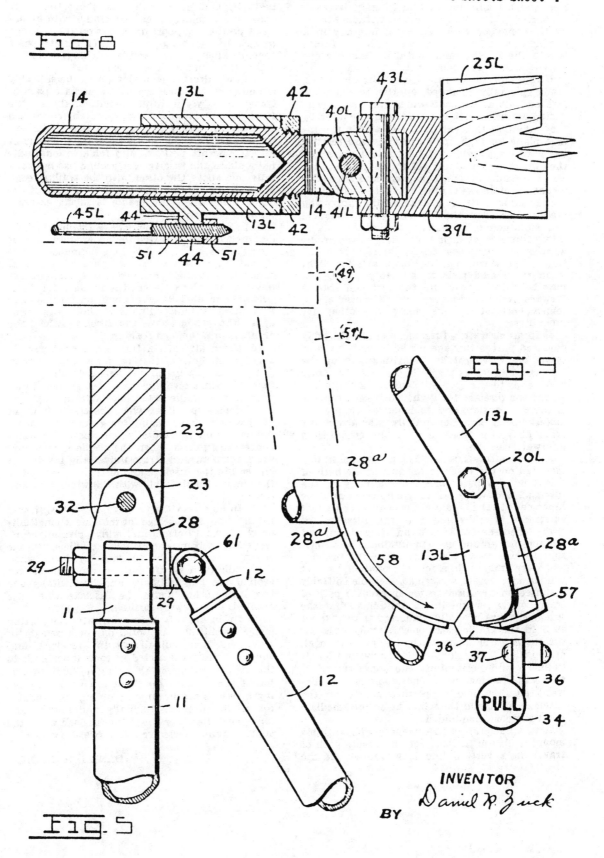

Fig. 8

Fig. 9

Fig. 5

INVENTOR
Daniel R. Zuck
BY

Having thus described my invention, what I claim and desire to protect by Letters Patent is:

1. In an aircraft, a fuselage, a wing supporting cradle pivotally mounted on the fuselage for fore and aft adjustment, and wings universally connected at their inner ends to the cradle whereby they may be either extended laterally in a common plane for flight, or shifted forward relative to the fuselage and folded horizontally one above the other for ground use.

2. In an aircraft, a fuselage, a wing supporting cradle pivotally mounted on the fuselage for fore and aft adjustment, wings universally connected at their inner ends to the cradle whereby they may be either extended laterally in a common plane for flight, or shifted forward relative to the fuselage and folded horizontally one above the other for ground use, releasable means to retain the cradle in its aft position, and releasable means to retain the cradle in its fore position.

3. In an aircraft, a fuselage, a wing supporting cradle mounted on the fuselage for both vertical and longitudinal movement, and wings universally connected at their inner ends to the cradle whereby they may be extended laterally from the fuselage on a common horizontal axis for flight when the cradle rests in an aft position, and may be raised above the fuselage and shifted forward by forward movement of the cradle, and folded horizontally one above the other for ground use.

4. In an aircraft, a fuselage, a cradle shiftably mounted on the fuselage for an arcuate path of travel on a vertical line longitudinally of the fuselage, and wings pivotally connected at their inner ends to the cradle extensible laterally adjacent the fuselage for flight when the cradle is in an aft position, and foldable for ground use longitudinally and horizontally one above the other above the fuselage when the cradle is in a forward position.

5. In an aircraft, a fuselage, a cradle shiftably mounted on the fuselage for an arcuate path of travel on a vertical line longitudinally of the fuselage, and wings pivotally connected at their inner ends to the cradle at opposite sides thereof extensible laterally adjacent the fuselage for flight when the cradle is in an aft position, and foldable for ground use longitudinally and horizontally one above the other above the fuselage when the cradle is in a forward position.

6. In an aircraft, a fuselage, a cradle shiftably mounted on the fuselage for an arcuate path of travel on a vertical line longitudinally of the fuselage, wings pivotally connected at their inner ends to the cradle extensible laterally adjacent the fuselage for flight when the cradle is in an aft position, and foldable for ground use longitudinally and horizontally one above the other above the fuselage when the cradle is in a forward position, and supporting means on the fuselage to sustain the wings at an intermediate point thereof when folded.

7. In an aircraft, a fuselage, a cradle shiftably mounted on the fuselage for an arcuate path of travel on a vertical line longitudinally of the fuselage, wings pivotally connected at their inner ends to the cradle extensible laterally adjacent the fuselage for flight when the cradle is in an aft position, and foldable for ground use longitudinally and horizontally one above the other above the fuselage when the cradle is in a forward position, supporting means on the fuselage to sustain the wings at an intermediate point thereof when folded, and a latching device to secure the wings together when folded.

8. In an aircraft, a fuselage, a cradle shiftably mounted on the fuselage for an arcuate path of travel on a vertical line longitudinally of the fuselage, and cambered wings pivotally connected at their forward inner ends to the cradle extensible laterally for flight when the cradle is in its extreme aft position, and foldable longitudinally above the fuselage for ground use horizontally one above the other with the trailing edge of one wing faired under the leading edge of the other wing when the cradle is in its extreme forward position.

9. In an aircraft, a fuselage, a cradle shiftably mounted on the fuselage for an arcuate path of travel on a vertical line longitudinally of the fuselage, and wings having a universal pivotal connection at their inner ends to the cradle extensible laterally adjacent the fuselage for flight when the cradle is in an aft position, and foldable for ground use longitudinally and horizontally one above the other above the fuselage when the cradle is in a forward position.

10. In an aircraft, a fuselage, a cradle shiftably mounted on the fuselage for an arcuate path of travel on a vertical line longitudinally of the fuselage, wings pivotally connected at their inner ends to the cradle extensible laterally adjacent the fuselage for flight when the cradle is in an aft position, and foldable for ground use longitudinally and horizontally one above the other above the fuselage when the cradle is in a forward position, and struts universally pivoted at one end to the fuselage and at their other end to the wings and shiftable with the wings fore and aft.

11. In an aircraft, a fuselage, a cradle shiftably mounted on the fuselage for movement longitudinally of the fuselage, and wings pivotally connected at their inner ends to the cradle extensible laterally adjacent the fuselage for flight when the cradle is in an aft position, and foldable for ground use longitudinally and horizontally one above the other above the fuselage when the cradle is in a forward position.

12. In an aircraft, a fuselage, wing supporting members shiftably mounted on the fuselage for movement longitudinally of the fuselage, and wings pivotally connected at their inner ends to the supporting members extensible laterally adjacent the fuselage for flight when the supporting members are in an aft position, and foldable for ground use longitudinally and horizontally one above the other above the fuselage when the supporting members are in a forward position.

DANIEL R. ZUCK.

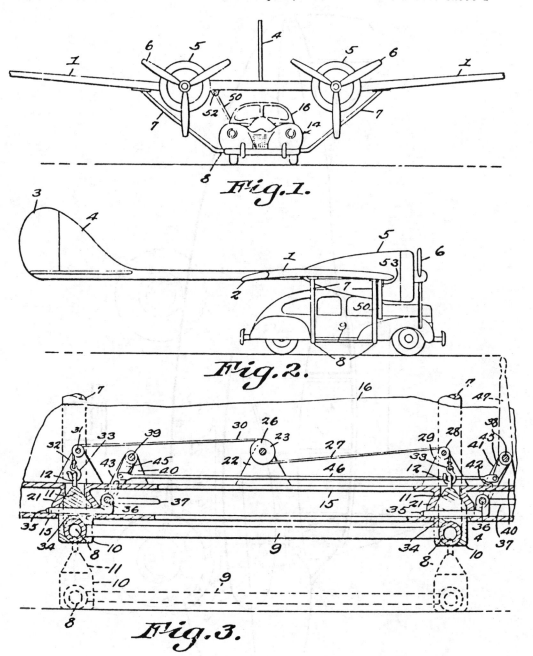

Fig.1.

Fig.2.

Fig.3.

F. F. Frakes

INVENTOR.

BY

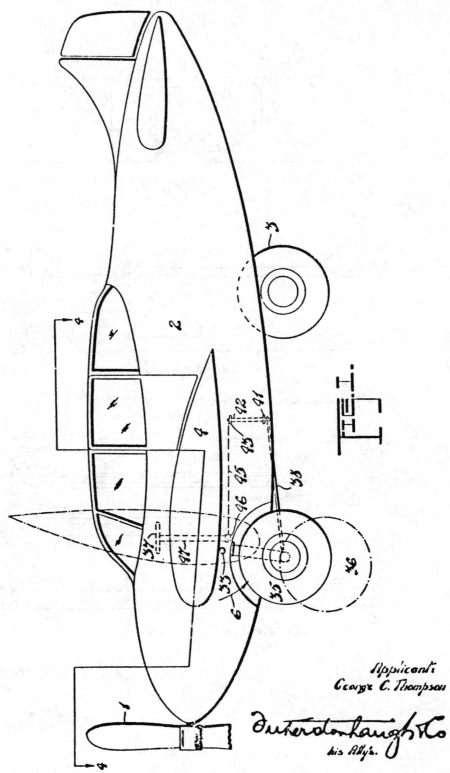

Applicant:
George C. Thompson

Thurstonhaught&Co
his Atty's.

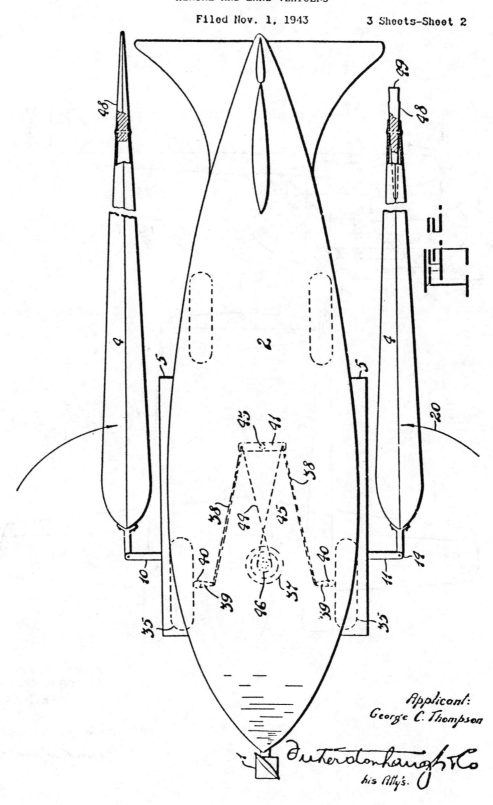

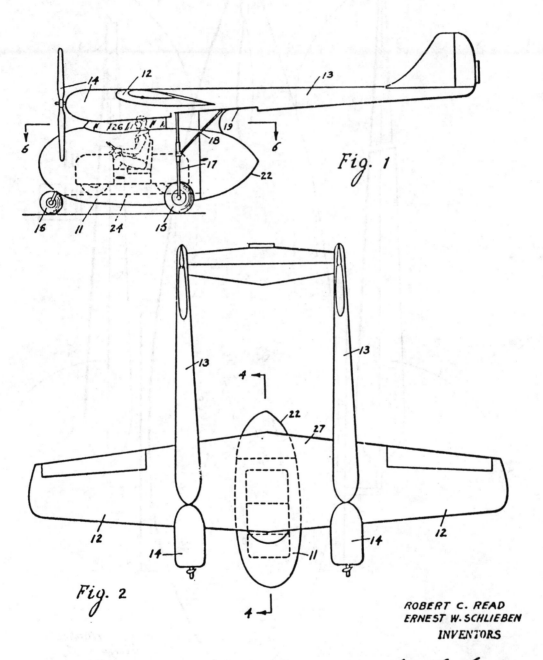

Fig. 1

Fig. 2

ROBERT C. READ
ERNEST W. SCHLIEBEN
INVENTORS

BY

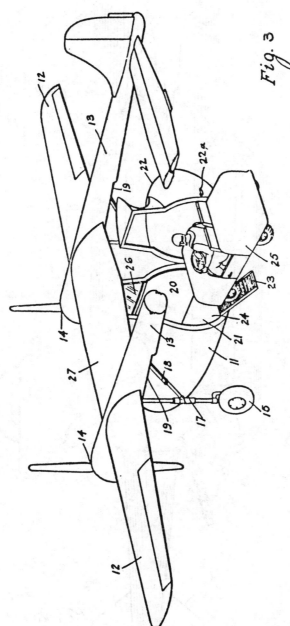

Fig. 3

ROBERT C. READ
ERNEST W. SCHLIEBEN
INVENTOR.

BY

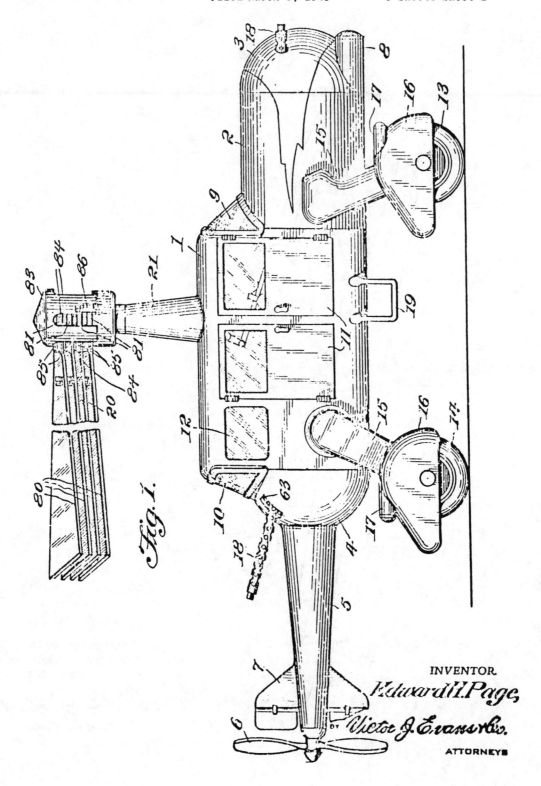

Fig. 1.

INVENTOR

Edward H. Page,

BY Victor J. Evans & Co.

ATTORNEYS

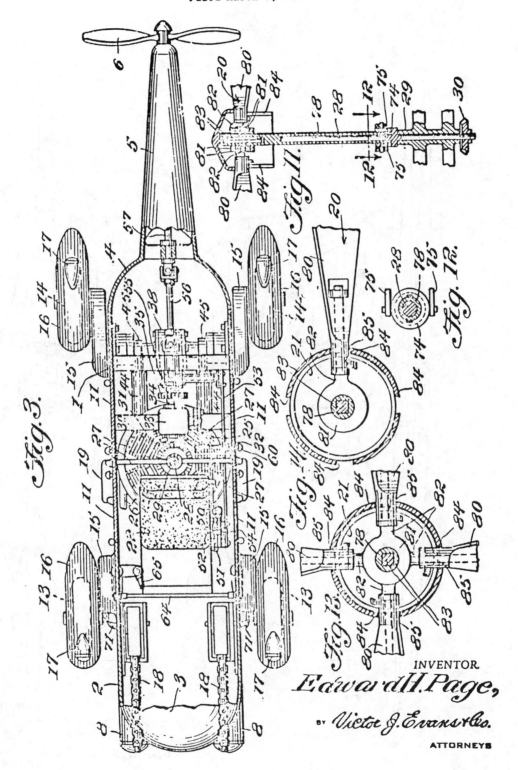

Fig. 3. *Fig. 11.* *Fig. 12.* *Fig. 13.* *Fig. 14.*

INVENTOR.
Edward H. Page,
BY *Victor J. Evans & Co.*
ATTORNEYS

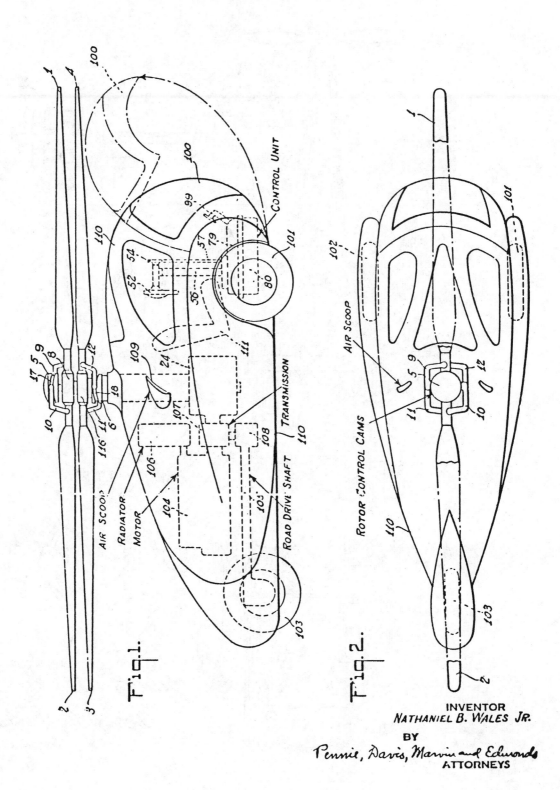

Fig. 1.

Fig. 2.

INVENTOR
NATHANIEL B. WALES JR.
BY
Pennie, Davis, Marvin and Edmonds
ATTORNEYS

Sept. 23, 1947.   N. B. WALES, JR   2,427,936
CONTROL MECHANISM FOR HELICOPTERS HAVING
CO-AXIAL COUNTER-ROTATING ROTORS
Filed Sept. 18, 1943   4 Sheets—Sheet 2

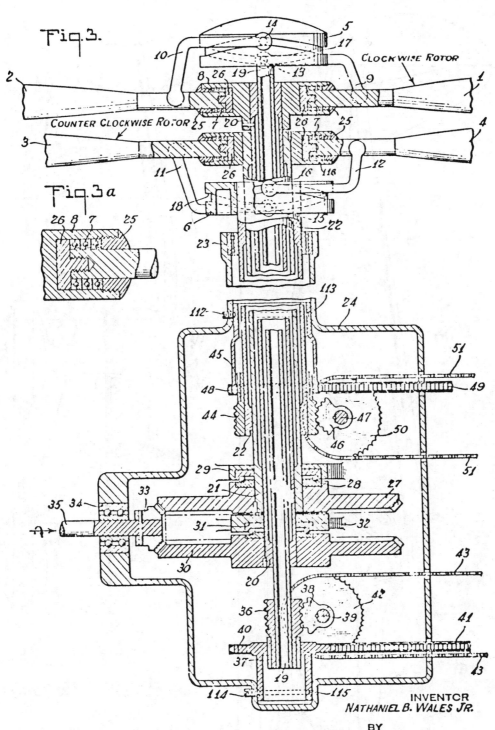

Fig.3.

Fig.3a.

CLOCKWISE ROTOR

COUNTER CLOCKWISE ROTOR

INVENTOR
NATHANIEL B. WALES JR.
BY
Pennie, Davis, Marvin and Edmonds
ATTORNEYS

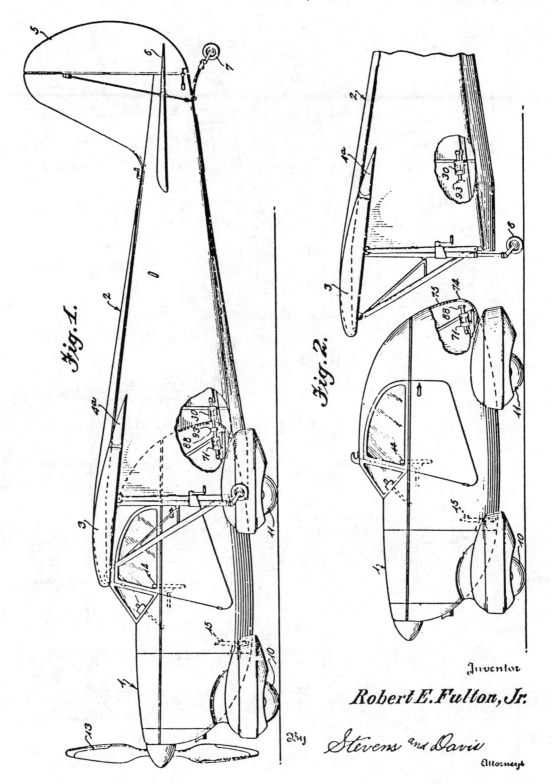

Fig.1.

Fig.2.

Inventor

Robert E. Fulton, Jr.

By

Stevens and Davis

Attorneys

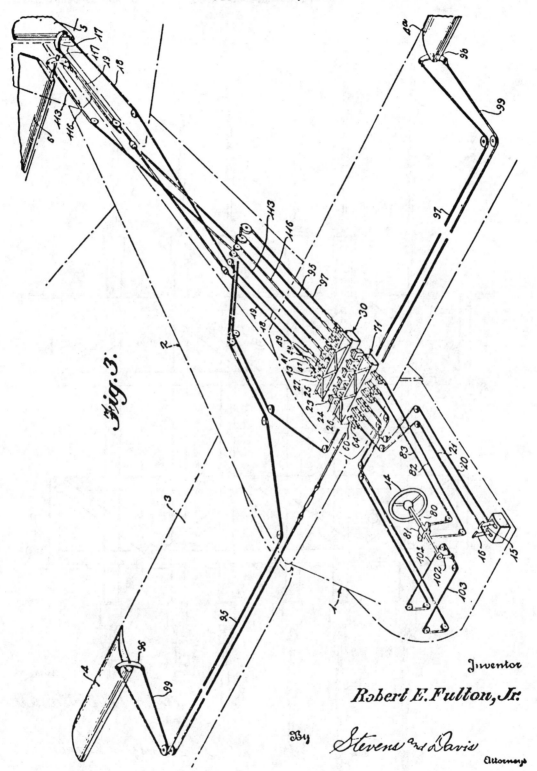

Fig. 3.

Inventor

Robert E. Fulton, Jr.

By   Stevens and Davis
                        Attorneys

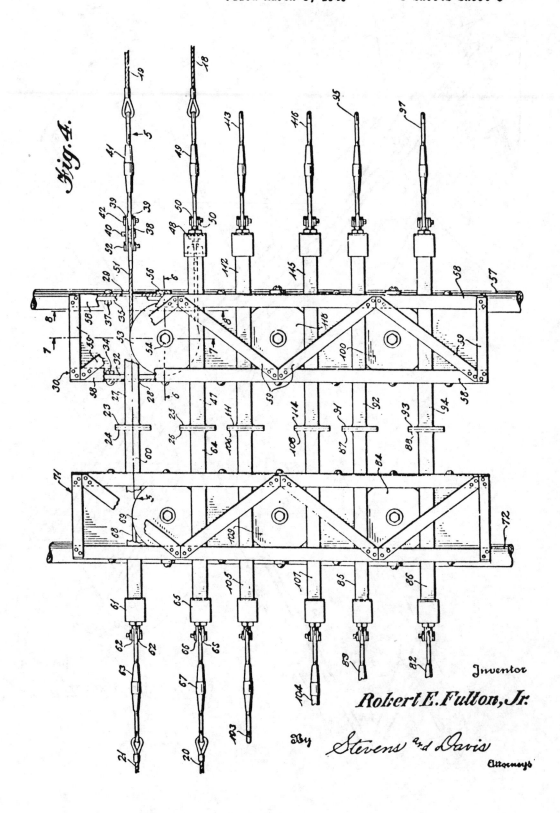

Inventor

Robert E. Fulton, Jr.

By Stevens and Davis

Attorneys

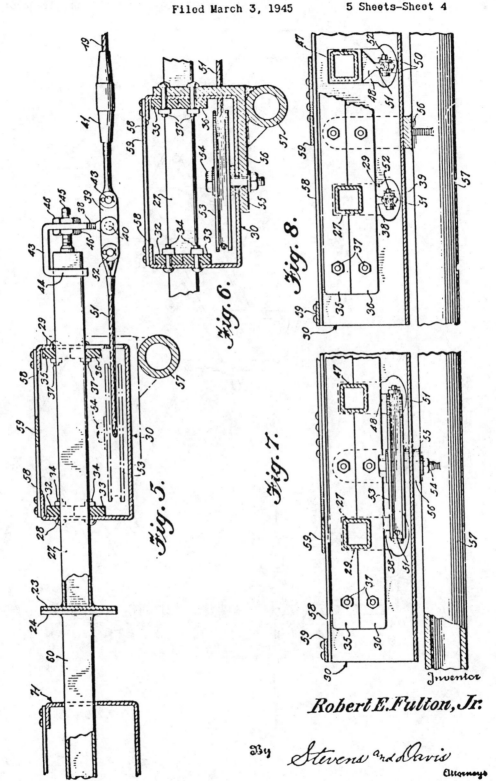

Fig. 5.

Fig. 6.

Fig. 7.

Fig. 8.

Inventor

Robert E. Fulton, Jr.

By Stevens and Davis
Attorneys

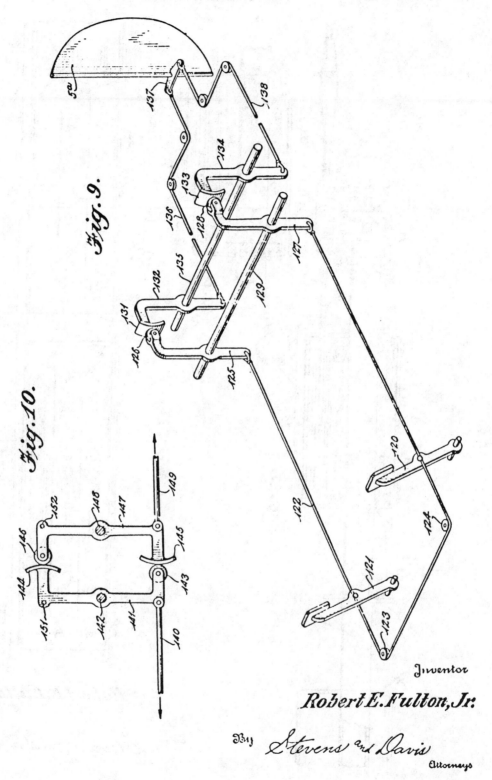

Fig. 9.

Fig. 10.

Inventor
Robert E. Fulton, Jr:

By Stevens and Davis
Attorneys

UNITED STATES PATENT OFFICE

2,430,869

ROADABLE AIRPLANE

Robert E. Fulton, Jr., Washington, D. C., assignor
to Continental, Incorporated, Washington,
D. C., a corporation of Connecticut

Application March 3, 1945, Serial No. 580,842

2 Claims.   (Cl. 244—2)

1

This invention relates to a vehicle primarily intended for use as an airplane in which a section containing the lower unit and the operator's controls may be separately used as an automobile.

The history of the airplane is almost as old as that of the automobile. Both appeared at approximately the turn of the century. Yet today, almost a half a century later, there are a very large number of automobiles in this country to every one privately owned airplane.

Such a condition is the result of certain basic shortcomings in the airplane. Airplanes require airports to operate. Airports are of necessity located on the outskirts of communities, not infrequently at considerable distance. Thus the time saved by the speed of aerial transportation is more frequently than not consumed by the ground-travel time required to get from the airport to the flier's final destination.

Furthermore, the expense of travel between the airport and the community, usually involving taxis, is not inconsiderable. When to this is added the initial cost and upkeep of the airplane plus that of an automobile which the flier undoubtedly owns as well, it is obvious why few can afford to own an aircraft.

The average automobile ride from point of origin to destination is not over five miles. For every automobile trip of several hundred miles, the average man makes as many as a hundred short local trips. Since he can afford only an automobile or an airplane, his choice is obvious.

This has been the basic factor in retarding widespread public adoption of the airplane in the past and, unless remedied, will have a serious effect on its future. Various endeavors have been made to circumvent the situation. Closer-to-town airports, locally available cars for rent, and other expedients have been offered but they fail to solve the basic practical and economic problems.

While the real cure has been much discussed, little or nothing of a practical nature has been executed to carry it into effect. Obviously there is much in common between an automobile and an airplane. Both have wheels, a body, a cab or cabin, a motor, and controls for starting, guiding and stopping. When a pilot leaves his aircraft at an airport and takes a cab to town he is leaving behind 90% of the basic elements of an automobile—an expensive and unnecessary procedure which has done more than any other thing to stifle aviation.

Others have recognized this fundamental

2

problem and have made efforts to solve it by accomplishing a transition from airplane to car and back. But the problem has many aspects—mechanical, aerodynamic, practical, safety, economy, comfort, service and maintenance, public reaction and acceptance. Of the several suggested solutions which have been offered to date, all have failed due to neglect of one or more of the above features. Most have been so radical in conception and based on such untried principles that they have failed to hold public interest. Others have made contributions which, unless supplemented by many additional features, were of little practical value.

It is an object of this invention to produce a roadable airplane by making a practical combination of already accepted forms and styles of automobile and aircraft designs, thereby making the final unit one of greater public value by virtue of its ready acceptance resulting from its being basically a combination of already familiar elements.

The present invention therefore is concerned with an airplane having a removable section which may be used as an automobile for road travel, and an airplane section comprised of wings, fuselage, and control surfaces. Cooperating interlocking means are provided on the airplane and automobile sections by which the sections may be firmly held together to establish a complete airplane for air travel. When these interlocking means are disengaged the automobile section may be driven upon a road, the airplane section being left behind.

The airplane section includes a number of movable flight control surfaces which are moved by force transmitting connections leading from them to a position adjacent to the pilot where he can operate these connections. As the pilot is in a cabin of the automobile section it is apparent that these connections must be broken when the automobile section is removed from the airplane section and must be re-established when the sections are re-united. The present invention provides a means for rapidly breaking and re-establishing these connections.

The control surfaces which should be upon the airplane section include a rudder for determining the forward lateral direction of flight, elevators for determining the vertical direction of flight, and ailerons for determining the level lateral position of the airplane or its banking movement. These control surfaces are customarily operated by manually movable means accessible to the pilot and intermediate force transmitting connec-

3

tions as, for example, cables. Thus the rudder is moved by two foot pedals, the elevators are moved by a back and forth movement of a steering wheel, and the ailerons are moved by rotation of the steering wheel.

It is intended that this steering wheel should be the same one which is utilized to guide the front wheels of the automobile section and that the foot pedals should be the same ones provided to control automobile movement as to apply the clutch and brake when the automobile section is being driven upon a road. However, the invention is not limited in this respect as the steering wheel and foot pedals may be ones especially provided to move the flight control surfaces. It is intended, however, that this steering wheel and pedals should be in the cab of the automobile section and that this cab should constitute the pilot's cabin of the completed airplane. Moreover, the invention is not limited to manipulation of the ailerons, rudder and elevators as it may be applied as well to other movable members as flaps, slots, spoilers, stabilizers and trimtabs. The mechanism of the invention may also be used to transmit forces between the automobile and airplane sections to move other elements as to retract and lower wheels, and to operate lights.

It has been stated that since the airplane flight control surfaces are upon the airplane section, and the manually operable elements for moving them are in the removable automobile section, some means must be provided to break the force transmitting connections between the control surfaces and the manually operable elements when these sections are separated from each other. The present invention provides means by which these connections are rapidly broken when the sections are separated from each other, or are re-established when the sections are interlocked to each other.

As an important feature of the invention, this means for establishing the force transmitting connections between the automobile and airplane sections is such that the connections are established merely upon the act of bringing the sections together so that no actual manual attachment within the connections themselves is necessary.

With the force transmitting means of the invention, the interconnecting of the automobile and airplane sections causes an automatic alignment of the separate elements of this means so that it is assured that the force applied in the airplane section will be properly transmitted to the automobile section.

Inasmuch as the force transmitting connections between the airplane section and the automobile section are established by the mere act of bringing the sections together, an important safety benefit is obtained since it is certain that when the sections are rigidly interlocked the force transmitting connections from the manually operable means to the airplane control surfaces will be established.

Moreover, the invention lends itself to any degree of duplication so that additional manually movable elements within the automobile section will operate elements in the airplane section when the sections are brought together, and all of the force transmitting connections between the sections will be established irrespective of their number when the automobile and airplane sections are interlocked.

Other features of the invention will be evident

4

from the following description and from the drawings which disclose a preferred structural embodiment of the invention.

In the drawings:

Figure 1 is a side elevation of the airplane as it appears when the automobile and airplane sections are assembled for flight, the covering material being broken away to show certain structural elements of the invention;

Fig. 2 shows the automobile section removed from the airplane section and the airplane section in its self-sustaining position;

Figure 3 is a perspective of the airplane, the covering material and supporting structure being removed to show the cable interconnections;

Figure 4 is a plan of the separable force transmitting mechanism of the invention;

Figure 5 is a section on the line 5—5 of Figure 4, on an enlarged scale;

Figure 6 is a section on the line 6—6 of Figure 4, on an enlarged scale;

Figure 7 is a section on the line 7—7 of Figure 4, on an enlarged scale;

Figure 8 is a section on the line 8—8 of Figure 4, on an enlarged scale;

Figure 9 is a schematic representation of a modified form of separable force transmitting mechanism; and

Figure 10 illustrates a further modification of the invention.

Referring first to Figure 1, the automobile section 1 of the airplane appears at the left of the vehicle, and the airplane section 2 appears at the right of the vehicle. In Figure 1, these two sections are combined for flight, and in Figure 2 they are separated from each other so that the automobile section may be driven independently as a unit for road travel. When the automobile section is used as a unit the airplane section 2 is left behind.

The airplane section 2 includes lifting wings 3 at its forward portion and at the trailing edges of these wings are the usual ailerons 4 and 4a. At the rear of the airplane section are the usual control surfaces, and these include the rudder 5 and the elevators 6. Beneath these tail surfaces is a tail wheel 7.

When the airplane section is attached to the automobile section, as shown in Figure 1, the airplane section is supported as a cantilever as shown in Figure 1. The means for attaching these sections together and by which the sections may be released from each other constitute no part of the present invention, and consequently are not shown in detail. A suitable interconnecting means is disclosed in application Serial No. 580,844, filed herewith. When this interconnecting means is released and the sections are separated from each other, the airplane section must be self-supporting, and to accomplish this it is provided with wheels 8 beneath the forward wings.

Just prior to the time that the airplane section is separated from the automobile section, the wheels 8 and the tail wheel 7 are moved downwardly into contact with the ground. The means by which the wheels 7 and 8 are moved downwardly are not a part of the present invention, and therefore are not here described in detail, but suitable means is disclosed in application Serial No. 580,843, filed herewith. These wheels 7 and 8 support the airplane section in the same position which it would occupy if it were attached to the automobile section so that separation of the sections and their reconnection is facilitated.

5

The automobile section 1 includes the front wheels 10 and the rear wheels 11. It also includes a motor to which the propeller 13 may be attached for air travel, as shown in Figure 1, or from which it may be removed for road travel, as shown in Figure 2. A steering wheel 14 within the cab portion of the automobile section is provided so that the front wheels 10 may be turned to guide the automobile during road travel, or so that the ailerons 4 and 4a of the airplane section may be moved during air travel. This steering wheel 14 is movable back and forth in an axial direction, and this movement is intended to move the elevators 6 to control flight of the airplane. The details of construction of a suitable steering mechanism and the means by which the operation of the steering wheel may be changed, if such a change is desired, from control for road travel or to control for air travel is disclosed in application Serial No. 580,845, filed herewith.

Within the cab and accessible to the operator are foot pedals 15 and 16. During air travel these pedals are operated to move the rudder 5 at the rear end of the airplane section, and during road travel one or more of them may be utilized to control the automobile section movement, as to operate the clutch and brake. The details of construction of a suitable pedal mechanism and the means by which this action of the foot pedals may be modified for road travel or for air travel if this is desired, is disclosed in application Serial No. 580,846, filed herewith.

As has been pointed out, since the steering wheel 14 and the pedals 15 and 16 are in the automobile section, and the control surfaces 4, 5 and 6 to be moved thereby are in the airplane section, and inasmuch as the force transmitting connections between these manually operable elements and the control surfaces must be broken when the sections are separated, it is important that means be provided for permitting such a break in the connections. As here shown, this break occurs at the meeting zone between the sections.

Considering first the force transmitting connections between the rudder 5 at the tail end of the airplane section and the foot pedals 15 and 16, the rudder 5 is directly moved by cables 18 and 19 connected to the opposite arms of a double bracket 17 extending on opposite sides of the rudder 5. In an airplane that did not have separable airplane and automobile sections the cables 18 and 19 ordinarily would be directly connected to the pedals 15 and 16 respectively. Thus the cables 20 and 21 which are connected to the pedals 15 and 16 might, in fact, be forward integral parts of cables 18 and 19 respectively. However, in accordance with the invention there is no direct interconnection between cables 18 and 20 on the one hand, and 19 and 21 on the other hand, but movement of cables 20 and 21 under the action of foot pedals 15 and 16 is caused to correspondingly operate cables 18 and 19 by the pressure or force transmitting means of the invention.

This force transmitting means includes a pressure plate 23 which, as will be explained in detail, is connected to cable 19, a pressure plate 24 which is connected to cable 21, a pressure plate 25 which is connected to cable 18, and a pressure plate 26 which is connected to cable 20. As appears from Figures 1 and 2, pressure plates 24 and 26 are carried at the rear portion of the automobile section and pressure plates 23 and 25 are carried at the forward portion of the airplane section. When the automobile and airplane sections are interlocked together, the plates 23 and 24 are in face-to-face contact with each other and serve to transmit forces directly from cable 21 to the cable 19. In like manner plates 25 and 26 are in face-to-face contact with each other when the airplane and automobile sections are interlocked together and serve to transmit forces directly between cables 20 and 18.

As the plates 23 and 25 may separate from plates 24 and 26, respectively, without in any way impairing the attachment of each of these plates to its particular cable, the separation of the automobile and airplane sections may be accomplished without attention being given to these force transmitting elements. After separation of the sections the plates 23, 24, 25 and 26 remain attached to their cables as prior to separation of the sections.

The means by which the plates 23 and 25 are attached to and operated by the cables 19 and 18 is best shown in Figures 4 and 5. Plate 23 is connected to the end of a square push shaft 27 so that it is perpendicular to the axis of this shaft. For lightness, this shaft is made hollow. Shaft 27 is guided in its back and forth movement by passing through aligned openings 28 and 29 on opposite sides of a box-like support 30.

The openings 28 and 29 are larger than the square shaft 27 and a bearing support for the shaft 27 is provided by means of strips 32 and 33 which are affixed by bolts 34 to the wall having therein the openings 28. Similar strips 35 and 36 are attached by bolts 37 to the wall of support 30 having the opening 29 therein. The strips 32, 33, 35 and 36 have square notches to receive the push shaft 27, and when the strips of each pair are brought together around shaft 27, as best shown in Figure 7, they constitute a bearing support on all four sides of the shaft 27.

The push shaft 27 therefore bears upon these broad bearing strips 32, 33, 35 and 36 in its endwise movement, and not upon the thin wall section of the support 30. As the shaft 27 is square and the openings in the bearing strips constitute a square, the shaft 27 cannot rotate but can only move endwise. These bearing strips are preferably made of a low friction material as "Bakelite."

At the end of the push shaft 27 opposite from the plate 23 is a depending arm 38. Connecting links 39 are on opposite sides of the lower end of the depending arm 38 and are pivoted to it by a pin 40. One end of a turnbuckle 41 is between the links 39 and pivoted to them by a pin 42, and this turnbuckle 41 at its other end is connected to the cable 19. A pull upon the cable 19 will therefore draw the presser plate 23 toward the box-like support 30.

The depending cable-attaching arm 38 is adjustable endwise relative to the square shaft 27. To accomplish this the arm 38 is made a part of a bracket 43 of inverted U-shape. The arm 44 of bracket 43 has a square opening therein to receive the square shaft 27 and prevent rotation of bracket 43. A bolt 45 affixed to the end of shaft 27 passes through an opening in arm 38 and nuts 46 are threaded on the bolt 45 on opposite sides of arm 38. By adjusting nuts 46 the arm 38 will be shifted endwise of the square shaft 27.

The cable 18 is connected to the presser plate 25 by a construction similar to that which has been described. This includes a square push shaft 47 at the rearward end of which is attached a bracket 48 similar to bracket 43. Cable 18 is connected to the bracket 48 through a turnbuckle 49 and links 50.

In order to maintain the cables 18 and 19 taut so that movement of one will cause movement of the other, an interconnecting link is located between the cables 18 and 19. In accordance with the present invention this includes a cable 51 one end of which is attached by pin 52 to the ends of the connecting links 39 opposite from turnbuckles 41. The other end of cable 51 is attached by a pin to the connecting links 50. Between its ends the cable 51 passes over a pulley 53 which is rotatably mounted upon a bolt 54 supported in the bottom wall of the box-like support 30. A washer 55 upon the bolt 54 spaces the pulley 53 away from this bottom wall of the support 30. As appears from Figure 8, opening 29 for shaft 27 extends low enough to permit the passage of one end of cable 51 and the opening for shaft 47 also accommodates the other end of cable 51.

The bolt 54 also passes through a bracket 56 which is located along the box-like support 30 at this point. This bracket 56 affords an additional support for bolt 54 and also serves as a means of attaching the support 30 to a frame bar 57 of the fixed framework. Bolts 37 pass through bracket 56, as is shown in Figure 6.

As appears from Figures 5 and 6, the box-like support 30 is made from sheet metal material formed into a channel shape. The bolt 54 passes through the bottom wall of this channel and the openings 28 and 29 are in the opposite walls of the channel. The upper ends 58 of this material are turned inwardly to provide an attachment portion for the cross-ties 59. This channel-shaped support 30 is long enough to accommodate a large number of push shafts as appears from Figure 4. A plurality of brackets similar to bracket 56 are spaced along the support 30 to attach it to frame bar 57.

From Figure 4 it is apparent that the cable 19, links 39, cable 51, links 50, and the cable 18 constitute a direct looped connection to the opposite arms of the lever 17 of the rudder 5. The turnbuckles 41 and 49 may be drawn tight so that the cables 18, 19 and 51 are taut at all times and movement of the one will cause movement of the others and also movement of rudder 5. The square push shaft 27, by means of its bracket 43, is connected to a forward extension of cable 19 to provide a force transmitting take-off from cable 19. A similar relationship is true of pusher plate 25 and push shaft 47 as they constitute the force take-off means with respect to the cable 18.

If the pressure plate 23 is pushed upon by plate 24 toward support 30, cable 51 will thereby be drawn around the pulley 53 by links 39 in such a manner as to pull upon the connecting links 50, the turnbuckle 49 and the cable 18 to thereby move the rudder. Such movement of the connecting links 50 carries with it the push shaft 47 and pressure plate 25 so that the pressure plate 25 moves forwardly against plate 26 in an opposite direction from the direction in which pressure plate 23 is moving. The movement of rudder 5 under the pull of cable 18 will cause a pull upon cable 19 so that cable 19 will follow along with the movement of links 39.

A movement of pressure plate 25 in an opposite direction, that is, towards the support 30, will cause a pull upon the cable 19 through the action of the connecting cable 51 to thereby move the rudder 5 in the opposite direction. Simul-

taneously therewith the pressure plate 23 will be moved in an opposite direction from that in which the pressure plate 25 moves. The rudder 5 will pull upon the cable 18 so that it will follow the motion of links 50.

Pressure plate 24 is connected to cable 21 by means similar to that by which cable 19 is connected to plate 23, except for a reversal of their positions. This connection includes a push shaft 60, adjusting bracket 61, connecting links 62 and a turnbuckle 63. Pressure plate 26 is in like manner connected to cable 20 through a push shaft 64, adjusting bracket 65, connecting plate 66, and a turnbuckle 67. A cable 68 (Figure 4) is connected to the links 62 and 66 and passes around a pulley 69. Cable 66 therefore serves to tie together the cables 20 and 21 and causes movement of one of the plates 24 or 26 to move in the opposite direction from the movement which is imparted to the other one of these pressure plates 24 and 26.

The push shafts 60 and 64 and the pulley 69 are mounted in a box-like support 71 which is similar in construction to support 30. This support 71 is attached to a bar 72 of the automobile fixed framework. As appears from Figures 1 and 2, the supports 30 and 71 are so located in the automobile section 1 and airplane section 2 that when the sections are interconnected the pressure plates in the airplane section will just contact the cooperating pressure plates in the automobile section. In neutral position, the automobile pressure plates lie just inside an opening 74 (Figure 2) in the rear wall 75 of the automobile body. If desired a thin flexible sheet, as of rubber, may be affixed to wall 75 over opening 74 to prevent entry of dirt and this sheet should be flexible enough so that it may remain in place at all times without resisting movement of the pressure plates. The turnbuckles 42, 49, 63 and 67 and the adjustable brackets 43, 48, 61 and 65 permit the movement of the rudder 5, foot pedals 15 and 16, and the pressure plates 23, 24, 25 and 26 to a neutral position with the pressure plates in light contact with each other.

When the airplane and automobile sections are assembled, therefore, a pressure, for example, upon the pedal 16 will exert a pull on the cable 21 and will draw the pressure plate 24 towards the support 71. This will cause a movement of pressure plate 26 away from the support 71 due to the interconnection established by cable 68. Pressure plate 26 will therefore bear upon the pressure plate 25 to exert a pull upon cable 51 which, in turn, will exert a pull upon the cable 19. This pull upon the cable 19 will carry with it the push shaft 27 so that the pressure plate 23 attached thereto will follow along with the pressure plate 24 as though there were, in fact, a connection between the pressure plates 23 and 24 by which plate 23 is drawn along with plate 24. Downward pressure upon the pedal 16 will therefore pull upon the cable 19 to turn the rudder 5 in the desired direction in the same manner that this would be performed if cables 19 and 21 were one cable.

Pressure upon the pedal 15 causes movement of rudder 5 in the opposite direction in a manner similar to that which has been described. Also, the forces exerted in either direction upon the rudder 5 by air pressure will be transmitted forwardly to the foot pedals, through the force transmitting means which have been described. Because of this the pilot can feel the effect of pressure on the rudder 5 in the same manner

Fig.1.

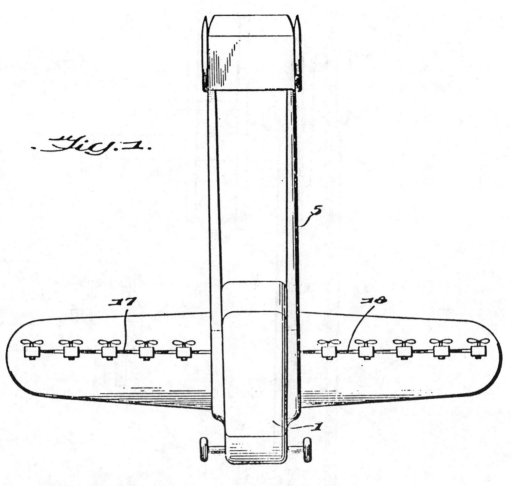

Fig.2.

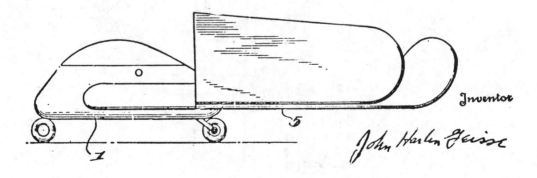

Inventor

John Harlen Geisse

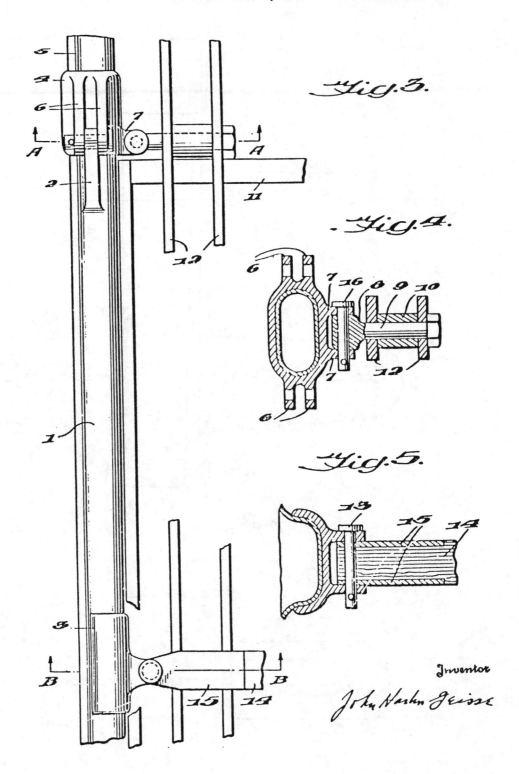

Fig.3.

Fig.4.

Fig.5.

Inventor

John Harkn Geisse

UNITED STATES PATENT OFFICE

2,434,068

ROADABLE AIRPLANE WITH FOLDING AND
DETACHABLE WINGS

John Harlin Geisse, Madison, Wis.

Application October 5, 1944, Serial No. 557,335

2 Claims. (Cl. 244—2)

1

My invention relates to airplane design and has for its object the provision of a simple construction which will permit the operator to use it either as a roadable airplane or a flying automobile. As used herein, the term flying automobile denotes an airplane which can shed its wings and tail surfaces for the purpose of using the body or fuselage as an automobile. The term roadable airplane denotes an airplane whose wings can be folded in such a way that the airplane may then be operated on the highway. Both types have been proposed heretofore and each has its advantages and disadvantages. My invention retains the advantage of both and eliminates their disadvantages.

I attain the object of my invention by providing a design in which the wings may be folded back over the tail booms and when in this position permit the airplane to be operated on the highway. However, if the operator elects to do so, provision is made whereby after folding the wings back over the tail booms, the wings and tail assembly can be readily removed as a unit.

One form of the invention is illustrated in the accompanying drawings, in which Figure I is a plan view of the entire airplane; Figure II is a side view with the wings folded; Figure III is a detail showing the method of attachment of the wings and tail booms; Figure IV is a section taken on the line AA of Figure III; and Figure V is a section taken on the line BB of Figure III.

In Figure III, 1 is the body to which are rigidly attached mounting brackets 2 and 3, 2 being mounted in the rear and 3 in the front.

Removably fastened to bracket 2 is the dual purpose bracket 4 which is in turn rigidly attached to the boom 5. Bracket 4 has in addition to the ears 6 for attachment to bracket 2, ears 7 for holding the rear part of the wing. Rotatably attached to bracket 4 through the ears 7 is part 8. The shank 9 of part 8 is in turn rotatably mounted in the bearing 10 which is rigidly attached to the rear spar 11 between the wing ribs 12.

Removably attached to bracket 3 by means of pin 13 is the front spar 14 of the wing which is equipped with reinforcing plates 15.

From the above description it will be apparent that when pin 13 is removed the wing can be rotated back around pin 16 sufficiently to clear

2

bracket 3. It may then be rotated around the shank 9 and then again rotated around pin 16 until it can be fastened to the tail boom. After both wings have been rotated back along the booms the wings and the tail assembly can be removed as a unit by removing the pins fastening bracket 4 to mounting bracket 2.

In Figure I, 17 and 18 are power shafts driven by an engine mounted within the body. These shafts transmit the power to the 5 propellers mounted on and above each wing. This arrangement of propellers is used not only to facilitate conversion for highway use but also to accomplish the purposes set forth in my pending application for a patent on this propeller arrangement.

The method of transmitting the power from the engine to one or more of the wheels is not germane to this application and hence no details are shown although such a drive would be included.

What I claim is:

1. In combination in an airplane, a body, a tail assembly, means detachably connecting said tail assembly to said body, wings, means detachably connecting each of said wings to said body and other means pivotally mounting each of said wings on said tail assembly.

2. In combination in an airplane, a body, tail surfaces, two booms supporting said tail surfaces, means detachably connecting said booms to said body, wings, means detachably connecting each of said wings to said body and other means pivotally mounting each of said wings on said booms.

JOHN HARLIN GEISSE.

REFERENCES CITED

The following references are of record in the file of this patent:

UNITED STATES PATENTS

Number	Name	Date
2,215,003	Johnson	Sept. 17, 1940
2,368,288	Couse et al.	Jan. 30, 1945
1,757,109	Boyd	May 6, 1930
2,156,288	Holliday	May 2, 1939
2,241,577	Beals	May 13, 1941

FOREIGN PATENTS

Number	Country	Date
275,720	Great Britain	Aug. 11, 1927

Aug. 10, 1948.

E. A. CLARK

2,446,528

AIRCRAFT HAVING POWER-DRIVEN, ADJUSTABLE,
RETRACTABLE AND STEERABLE FRONT WHEELS

Filed Dec. 23, 1944

7 Sheets—Sheet 1

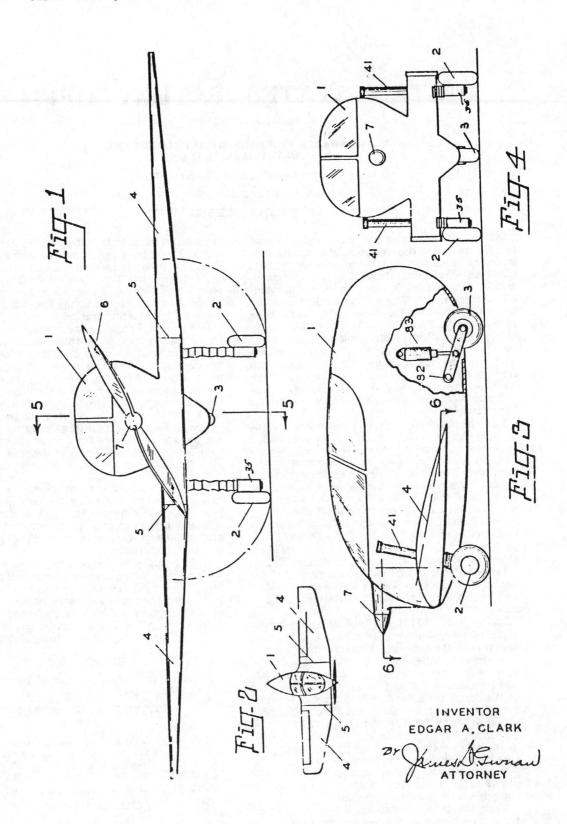

Fig-1

Fig-2

Fig-3

Fig-4

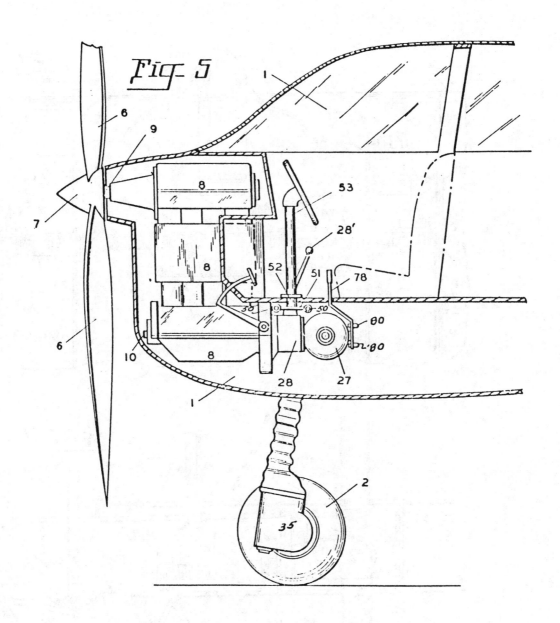

Fig- 5

INVENTOR
EDGAR A. CLARK

By James S. Guinan
ATTORNEY

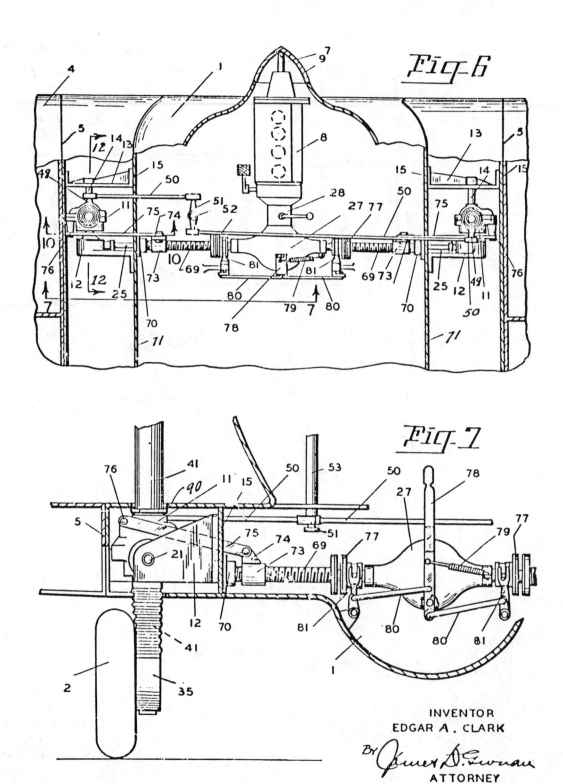

Fig-6

Fig-7

INVENTOR
EDGAR A. CLARK

By *James D. Gorman*
ATTORNEY

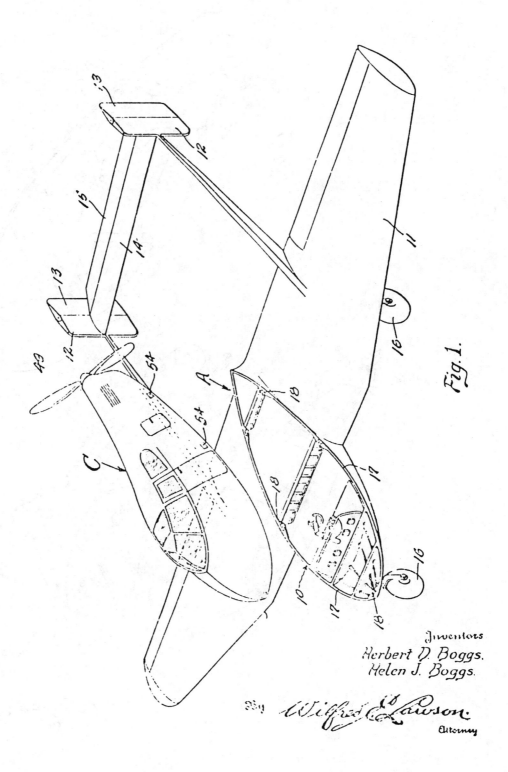

Fig. 1.

Inventors
Herbert D. Boggs.
Helen J. Boggs.

By Wilfred E. Lawson.
                    Attorney

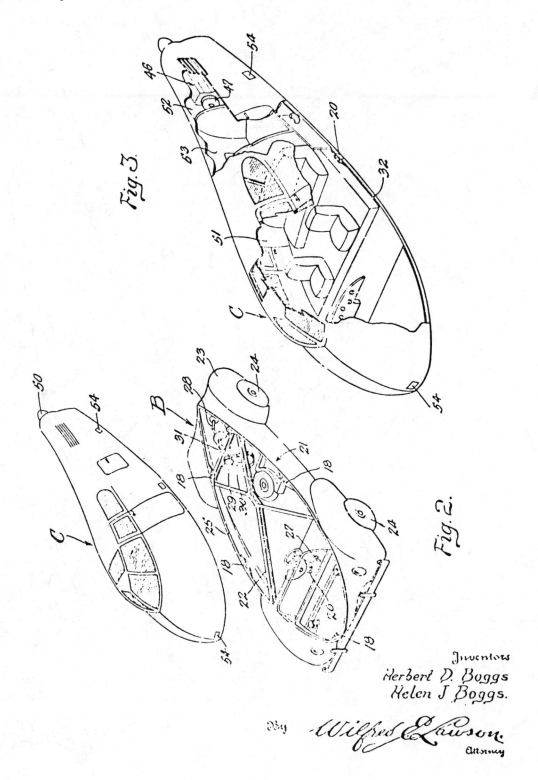

Fig. 3

Fig. 2

Inventors
Herbert D. Boggs
Helen J. Boggs.

By Wilfred E. Lawson
Attorney

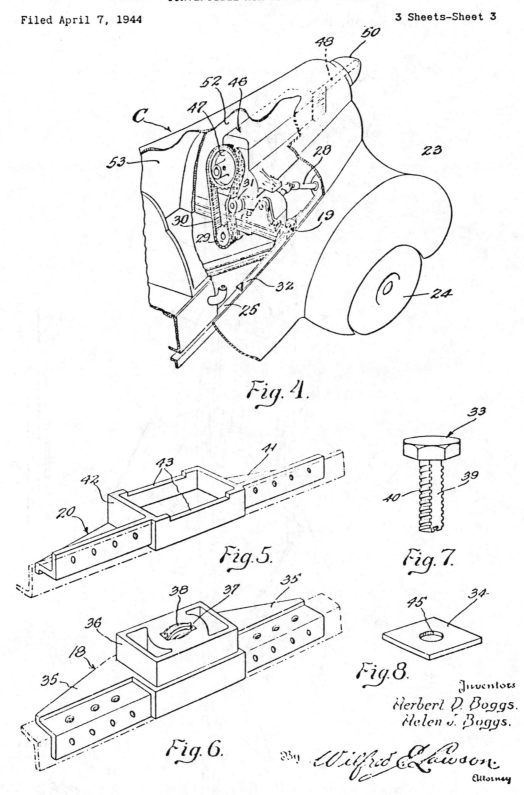

Fig. 4.

Fig. 5.

Fig. 6.

Fig. 7.

Fig. 8.

Inventors
Herbert D. Boggs.
Helen J. Boggs.

By Wilfred E. Lawson.
Attorney

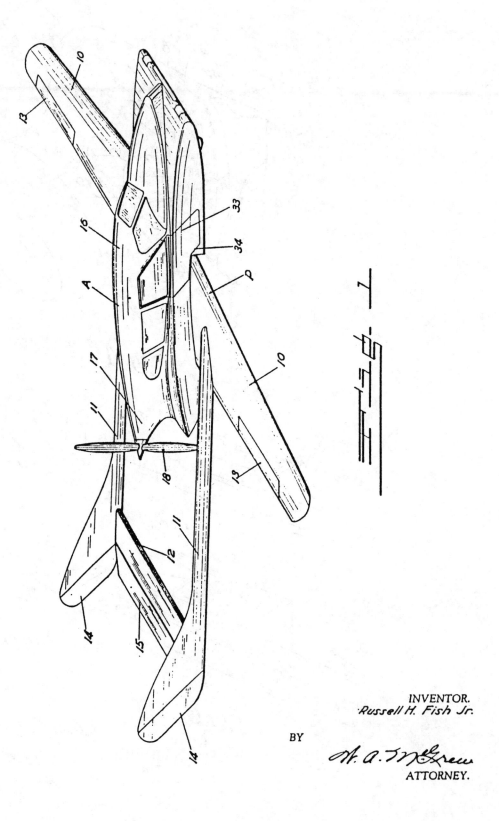

Fig. 1

INVENTOR.
Russell H. Fish Jr.

BY

H. A. McGrew
ATTORNEY.

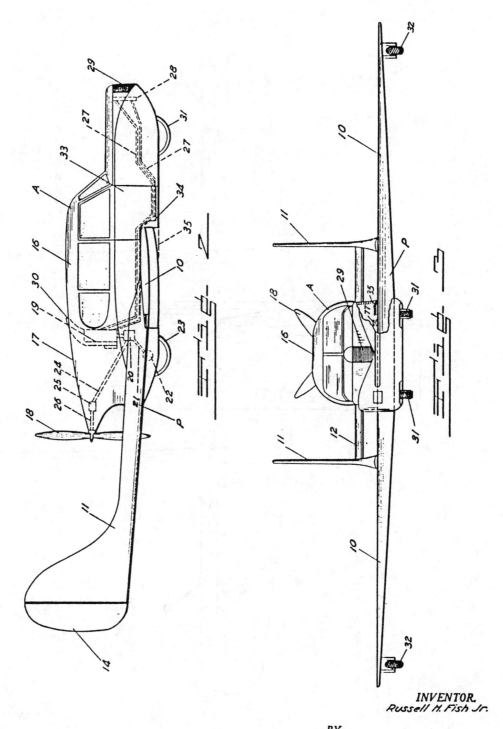

INVENTOR.

Russell H. Fish Jr.

BY

H. A. McGrew

ATTORNEY

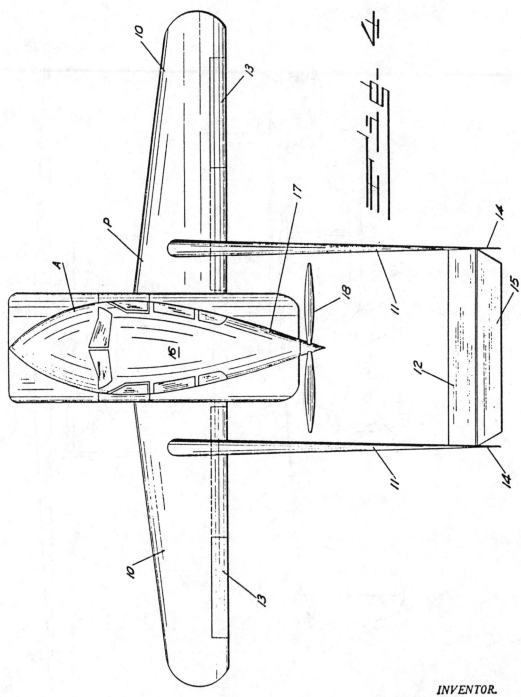

INVENTOR.

Russell H. Fish Jr.

BY

ATTORNEY

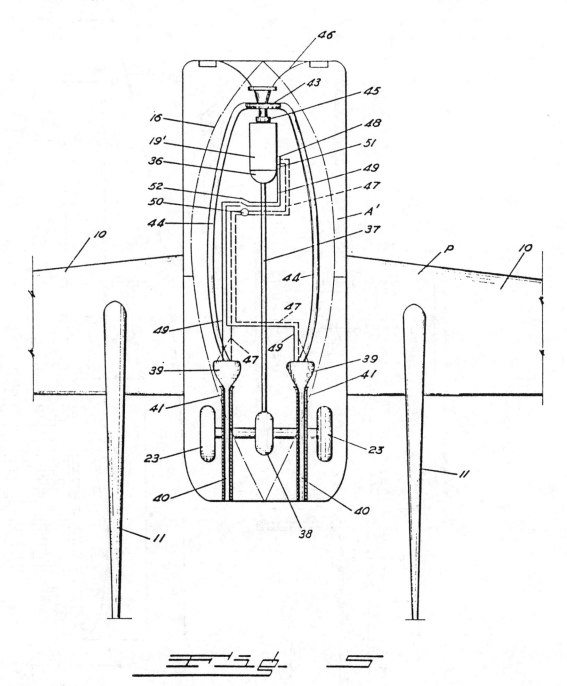

Fig. 5

INVENTOR.
Russell H. Fish Jr.

BY

W. A. McGrew

ATTORNEY

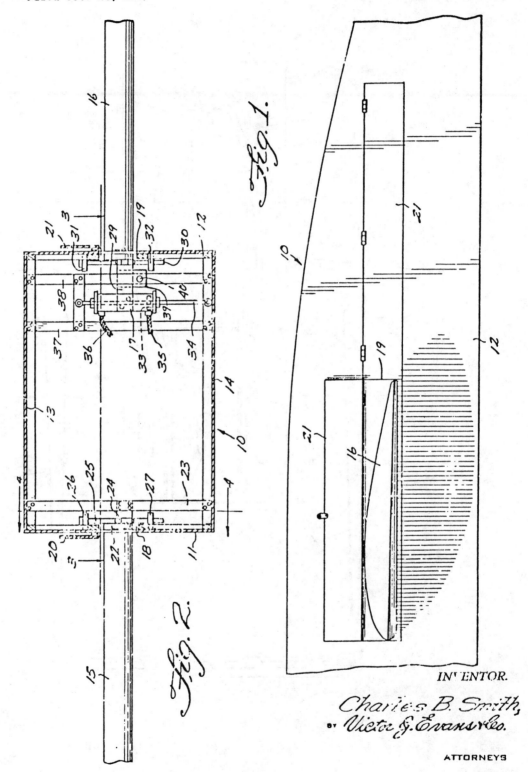

Fig. 1.

Fig. 2.

INVENTOR.

Charles B. Smith,

BY Victor J. Evans & Co.

ATTORNEYS

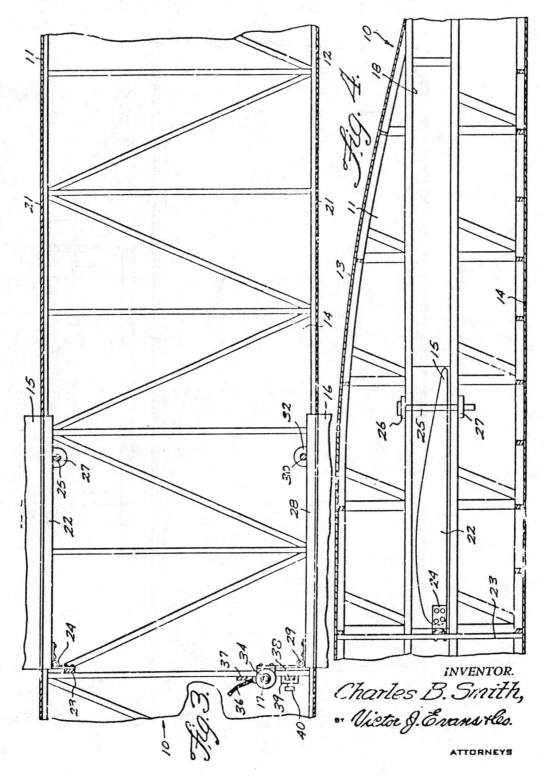

Fig. 4.

Fig. 3.

INVENTOR.

Charles B. Smith,

BY *Victor J. Evans & Co.*

ATTORNEYS

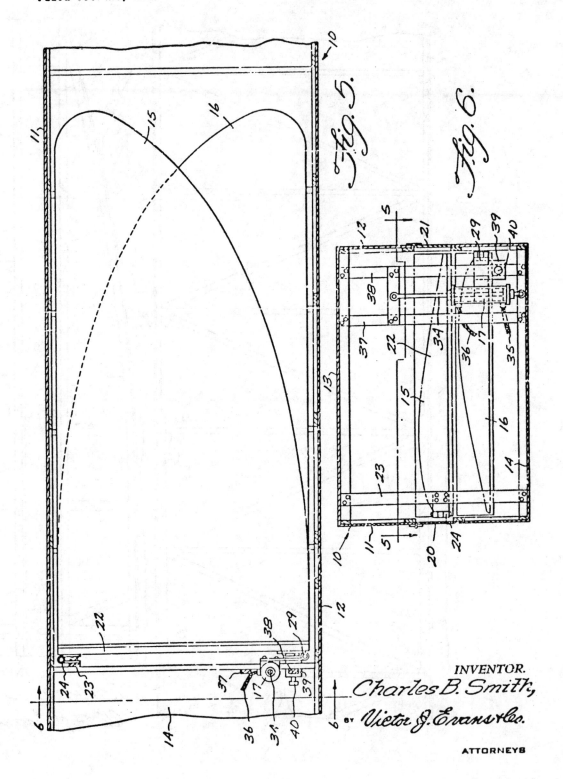

Fig. 5.

Fig. 6.

INVENTOR.

Charles B. Smith,

BY *Victor J. Evans & Co.*

ATTORNEYS

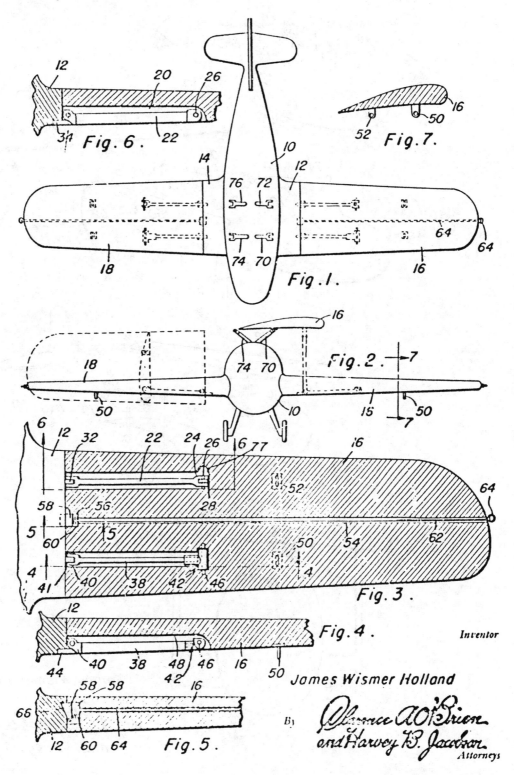

Fig. 6.

Fig. 7.

Fig. 1.

Fig. 2.

Fig. 3.

Fig. 4.

Fig. 5.

Inventor

James Wismer Holland

By

Oliver A. O'Brien
and Harvey B. Jacobson
Attorneys

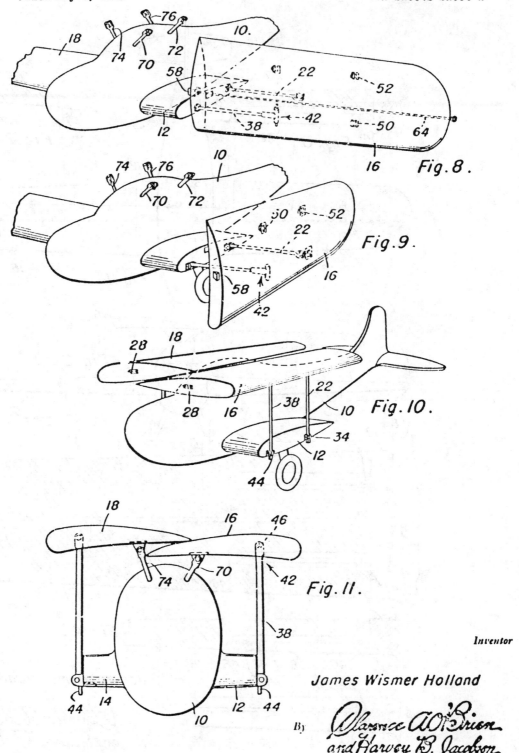

Fig.8.

Fig.9.

Fig.10.

Fig.11.

Inventor

James Wismer Holland

By Clarence A. O'Brien
and Harvey B. Jacobson
                              Attorneys

UNITED STATES PATENT OFFICE

2,544,021

FOLDING WING DEVICE

James Wismer Holland, Valdosta, Ga.

Application May 3, 1948, Serial No. 24,750

7 Claims.   (Cl. 244—49)

1

This invention relates to novel and useful improvements in devices for folding wings of an aircraft to a position substantially parallel to the fuselage of the aircraft and to a position overlying the top portion of the fuselage.

An object of this invention is to fold the wings of an aircraft in order to make the craft roadable.

Another object of this invention is to partially overlie one of the wings over the other or more specifically, partially overlie one half of the wing of the aircraft over the other half.

Another object of this invention is to swivelly connect each of the wings (one half of the wing of the aircraft considered as an entire wing) in such a manner as to permit the wings to first be rotated then hingedly swung to a position substantially parallel to the axis of the fuselage of the craft.

Another object of this invention is to supply a latch within the wings of the craft operable from the wing tips for maintaining the wings in the extended position.

Another object of this invention is to provide a simplified device of the nature to be described which is both practical and safe in operation.

Ancillary objects and features of novelty will become apparent to those skilled in the art, in following the description of the preferred form of the invention, illustrated in the accompanying drawings, wherein:

Figure 1 is a plan view of an aircraft having the invention associated therewith;

Figure 2 is a front view of the invention shown in Figure 1, showing the device in various operational forms and steps;

Figure 3 is a sectional view of a wing section having the invention applied thereto;

Figure 4 is a sectional view taken substantially on the line 4—4 of Figure 3;

Figure 5 is a sectional view taken on the line 5—5 of Figure 3;

Figure 6 is a sectional view taken substantially on the line 6—6 of Figure 3;

Figure 7 is a sectional view taken substantially on the line 7—7 of Figure 2 and in the direction of the arrows;

Figure 8 is a perspective view showing operational positions of the preferred form of the invention;

Figure 9 is a perspective view showing a second stage in the operation of the invention while folding;

Figure 10 is a perspective view of the invention illustrating the wings in the folded position, and;

Figure 11 is a front view of the invention shown in Figure 10, the wheel assembly or landing gear being removed.

The utility of the present invention permits the operator of the craft to actuate the same down a highway or the like without restricting the

2

operator's vision, without changing materially the aircraft center of gravity and without setting up objectionable frontal area which might be effected by wind. Of course, by utility of the present invention the craft may be utilized in a conventional garage instead of a hanger, whether the invention be used solely for air transportation, or air and road transportation.

The present invention may be folded and unfolded quickly by a single individual and does not materially offset the aerodynamic characteristic of the air foil.

The preferred field of utility of the present invention is in small and light aircraft however, it is within the purview of the present invention to utilize various adaptations of the same for military craft particularly that utilized in carriers or the like.

A substantially conventional fuselage 10 is illustrated with projections 12 and 14 respectively which are actually the root of wings or air foil. As is known in the art both halves or portions of the wings are generally considered as a "wing" however, for descriptive purposes either of the sections 16 or 18 which cooperate to form a single wing will be termed a wing.

The fuselage 10 is of course, supplied with various appurtenances contiguous to aircraft such as the landing gear, empennage and the like. Further, the projections 12 and 14 may be faired.

Each of the wings 16 and 18 are identical in structure therefore, a description of one will lead to a clear understanding of the other. Taking the wing 16 for illustrative purposes and as is seen in Figure 6 a recess 20 is supplied in the lower surface thereof. This recess has a stay rod 22 supplied therein, which stay rod is provided with bifurcated terminals. The bifurcated end 24 is adapted to receive a pin 26 therethrough, which pin also extends through a bracket 28. This bracket 28 is received entirely within the recess 20. The opposite end of the stay rod 22 has its bifurcated end hingedly secured to a plate 32 which is secured to the projection 12. The end 34 of the stay rod 22 is engageable with the projection 12 in order to form limiting means for restricting the travel of the stay rod 22 and consequently the wing 16. This construction prevents the wing 16 from falling downward to a degree which is undesirable in order that the proper dihedral may be maintained.

A rod (see Figure 4) 38 is provided with bifurcations 40 at one end thereof and a sleeve-type universal joint generally indicated at 42 at the opposite end thereof. The said bifurcations 40 are attached to a plate 41 which is rigidly secured to the said projection 12. By this means it is quite apparent that the rod 38 is pivotally associated with the projection 12. Also, the end 44 of the said rod 38 clampingly engages the projection 12 for preventing undesired pivotal movement of the wing 16. The said universal joint 42 is associated with the wing 16 through the medium of a conventional pivot pin 46. The entire arm 38 and its associated mechanism is received completely within a recess 48 formed on the under surface of the wing 16.

Also supplied on the under surface of the said wing 16 is a pair of spaced hook members 50 and 52 respectively for a purpose to be described subsequently.

A central aperture 54 is supplied longitudinally of the wing 16 and has an enlargement 56 at one end thereof. A latch assembly is provided in the enlargement 56 and includes a tongue 58 which is backed by means of a spring 60 or other suitable resilient biasing means. A cable 62, rod or the like is supplied in the bore 54 and attaches at one end to the latch plate 58. The opposite end of the said cable 62 may have a ring 64 or other suitable grasping means secured thereto. However, the ring is in such a position as to be accessible from the wing tip.

A latch keeper, preferably in the form of an appropriately configured recess 66 is supplied in the extension 12 for accommodation of the latch plate 58. It is readily appreciated from an inspection of Figure 5 that the spring 60 normally biases the latch plate 58 within the recess 66 to maintain the wing 16 in the closed or latched position.

Referring to Figure 9 it will be seen that a plurality of brackets or posts are provided on the fuselage. These posts are actually two pairs, each of the posts forming a pair 70, 72 and 74, 76 are at opposite sides of the fuselage and one pair of posts is relatively shorter than the other pair. By this means the wings 16 and 18 may be folded over the top of each other as is seen in this figure.

In operation the pin 26 is removed from its position by being slid in the recess 77 and the extensions 44 and 34 prevent either of the wings from dipping or falling. The operator then walks to the wing tip and pulls the ring 64 which releases the latch assembly. Then, the trailing edge of the wing is rotated upward until the wing is in substantially a vertical position (see Figure 8).

The wing tip is then swung on the pin 46 until it is substantially parallel to the axis of the fuselage 10. The next step is to replace the pin 26 fastening the rod 22 to the wing and then raise the wing to the position shown in Figure 10, using the brackets 50 and 52 respectively which attach in the bifurcated end of the small posts 70, 72 to hold the wing as shown in Figure 10. Conventional pins or the like may be used in this connection. The small posts 74 and 76 are employed in holding the other wing section after it has been similarly operated.

Having described the invention, what is claimed as new is:

1. An aircraft including a fuselage having attached projections, each of said projections having a wing disposed in a first position and means for hingedly and swivelly attaching the wing thereto, said means for one wing and projection including a rod pivoted at one end to the projection, a universal joint connecting the opposite end of the rod and the wing, and clamping means spaced from the universal joint secured on said wing and on the fuselage to releasably hold the wing in a second position, a latch in said wing, a latch keeper in said projection, said latch being removably disposed in said keeper to retain the

wing in the first position, and means at the wing tip for actuating said latch.

2. An aircraft including a fuselage having attached projections, each of said projections having a wing disposed in a first position with respect to the fuselage and means for hingedly and swivelly attaching the wing thereto, said means for one wing and projection including a rod pivoted at one end to the projection, a universal joint connecting the opposite end of the rod and the wing, clamping means spaced from the universal joint and secured on said wing and on the fuselage to releasably hold the wing in a second position, a stay rod pivoted to said projection, and means for detachably securing said stay rod to said wing.

3. An aircraft including a fuselage having attached projections, each of said projections having a wing and means for hingedly and swivelly attaching the wings to the projections, said means including rods pivoted to the projections, a universal joint connecting each rod and wing, and clamping means spaced from the universal joint secured to said wings and to the fuselage, and said clamping means including spaced pairs of posts of unequal length secured to the fuselage for accommodation of each wing in spaced relation relative to each other on the fuselage.

4. An aircraft including a fuselage having attached projections, each of said projections having a wing and means for hingedly and swivelly attaching the wings to the projections, said means including rods pivoted to the projections, a universal joint connecting each rod and wing, and clamping means spaced from the universal joint secured to said wings and to the fuselage, said clamping means including spaced pairs of posts of unequal length secured to the fuselage for accommodation of each wing in spaced relation relative to each other on the fuselage, a stay rod pivoted to each of said projections, and means for detachably securing said stay rod to said wing.

5. The combination of claim 4 and recesses in each of said wings for accommodation of said stay rod and said rod.

6. The combination of claim 5 and means forming stops on said rods limiting the pivotal movement of said rods and said stay rod by abutting said projections.

7. The combination of claim 4 and a latch and a latch keeper operatively connected with each wing and each projection, together with means for operating each latch carried by the wings, the latches and latch keepers being employed to releasably clamp the wings to the projections in a predetermined position with respect to the projections.

JAMES WISMER HOLLAND.

REFERENCES CITED

The following references are of record in the file of this patent:

UNITED STATES PATENTS

Number	Name	Date
1,652,618	Fairey	Dec. 13, 1927
1,723,962	Weymouth	Aug. 6, 1929
1,757,109	Boyd	May 6, 1930
1,793,956	Carns	Feb. 17, 1931
1,855,012	Dill	Apr. 19, 1932
2,434,068	Geisse	Jan. 6, 1948

FOREIGN PATENTS

Number	Country	Date
239,971	Great Britain	Sept. 24, 1925

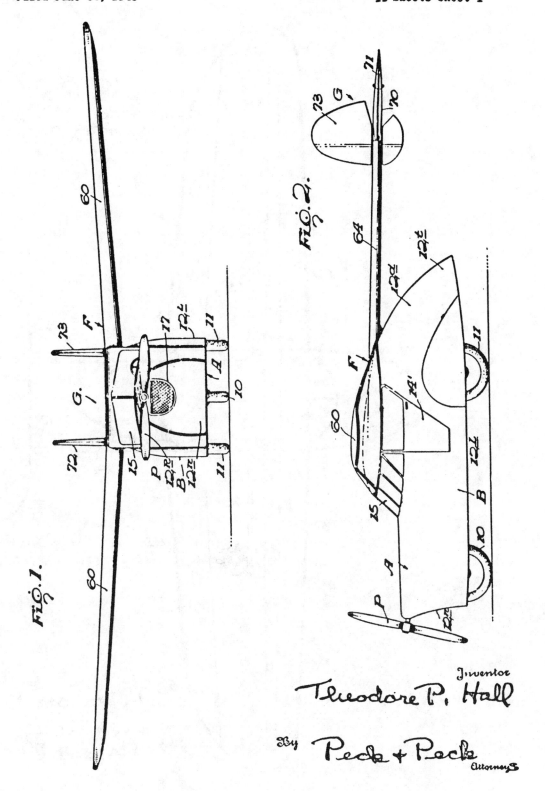

Inventor

Theodore P. Hall

By Peck & Peck

Attorneys

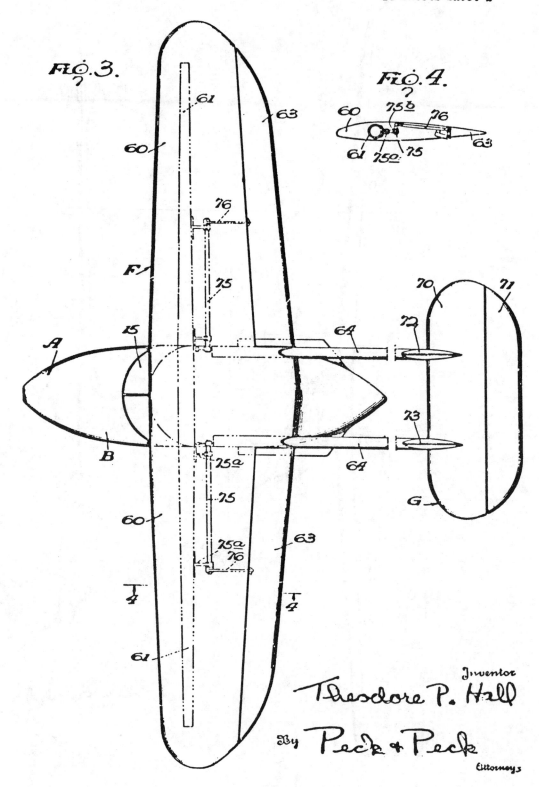

Inventor

Theodore P. Hall

By Peck & Peck

Attorneys

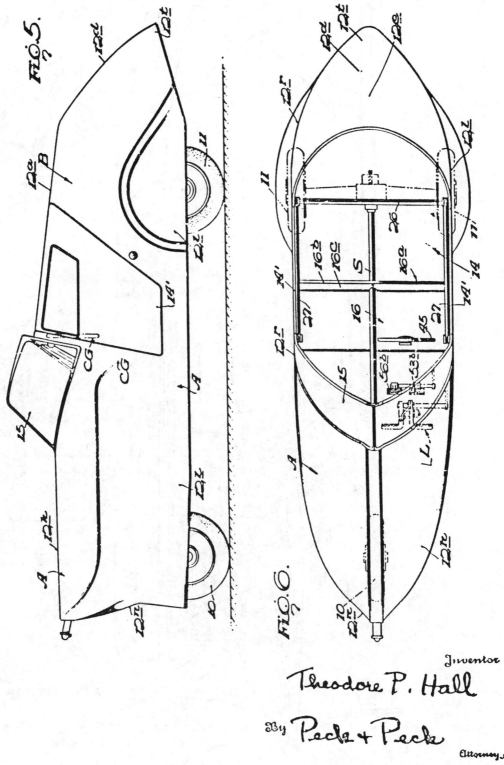

Inventor

Theodore P. Hall

By *Peck + Peck*

Attorneys.

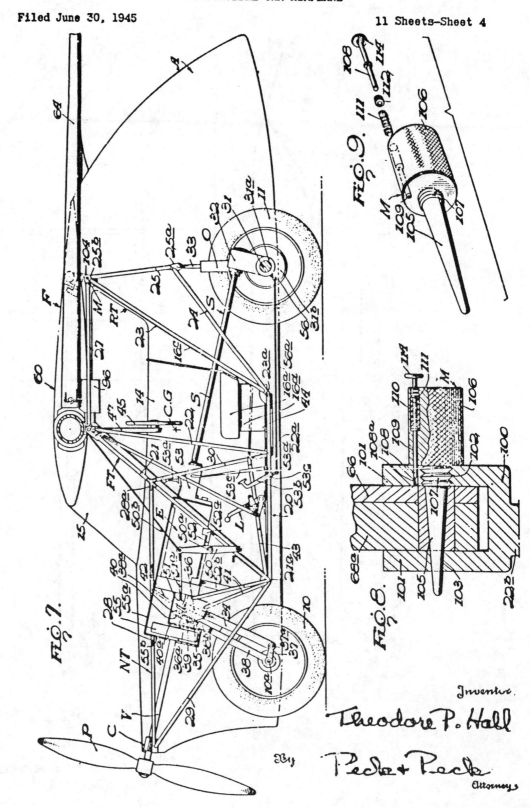

FIG.1.

FIG.8.

FIG.9.

Inventor.
Theodore P. Hall

By
Peck & Peck
Attorneys

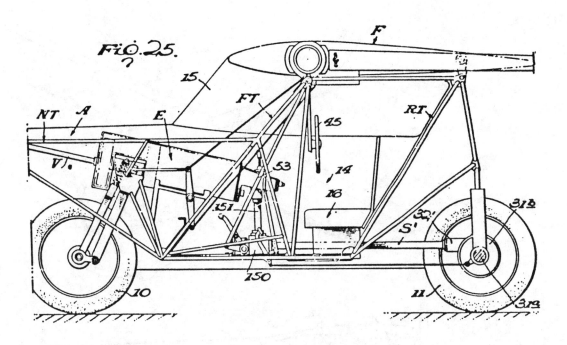

FIG. 25.

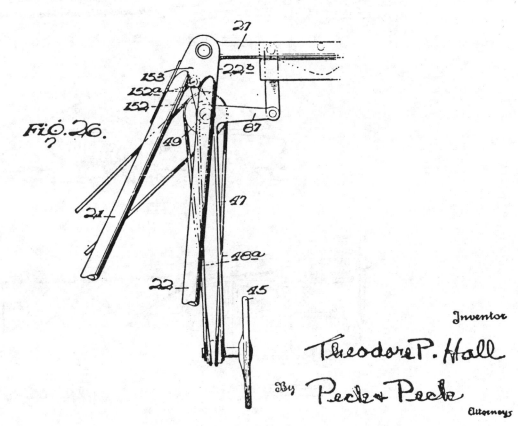

FIG. 26.

Inventor

Theodore P. Hall

By Peck & Peck

Attorneys

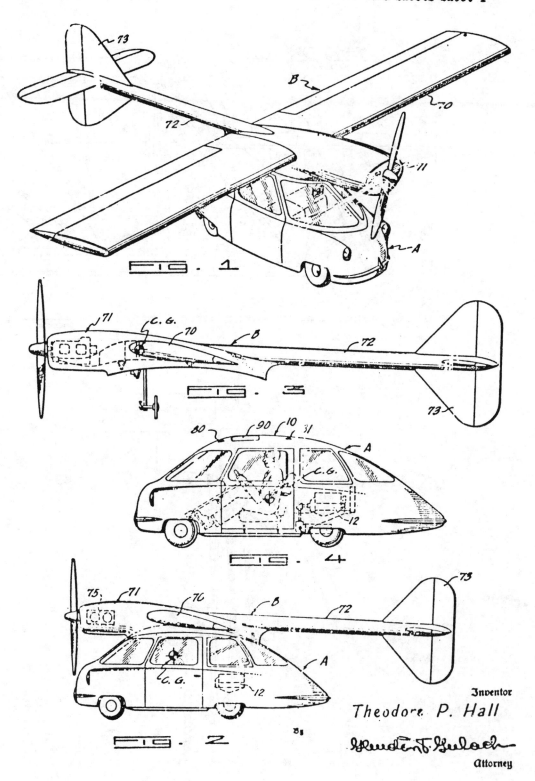

FIG. 1

FIG. 3

FIG. 4

FIG. 2

Inventor
Theodore P. Hall

Attorney

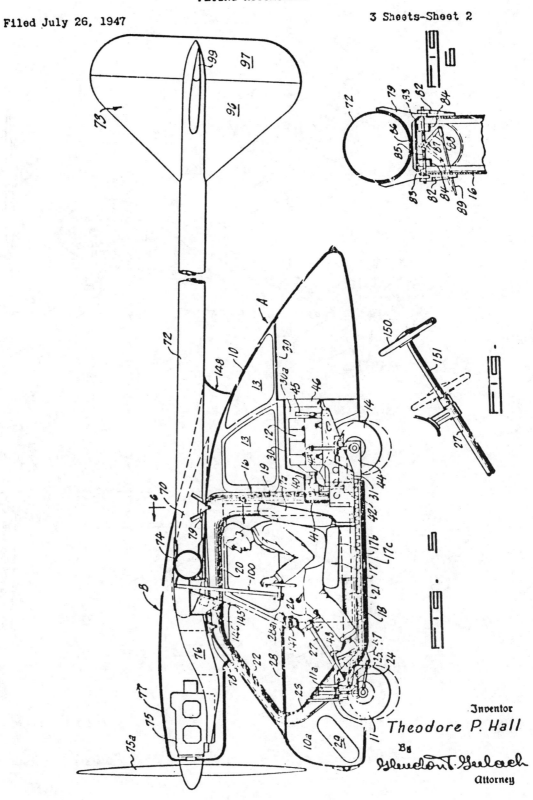

Inventor

Theodore P. Hall

By

Glendon T. Gerlach

Attorney

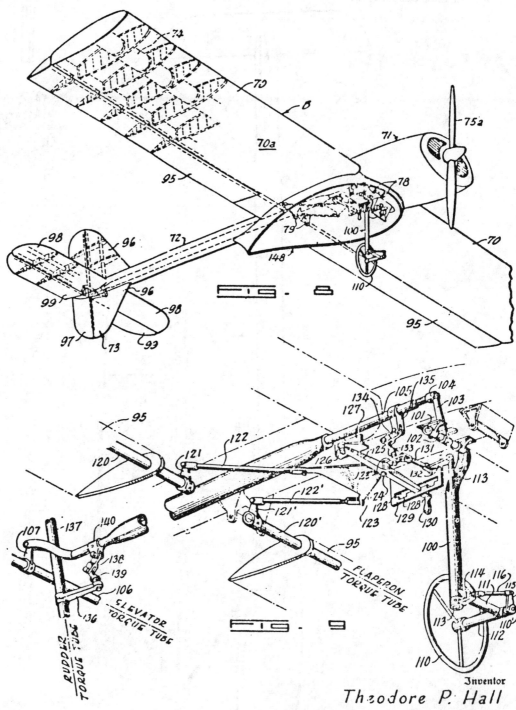

FIG. 8

FIG. 9

RUDDER TORQUE TUBE

ELEVATOR TORQUE TUBE

FLAPERON TORQUE TUBE

Inventor

Theodore P. Hall

Glenadon Gerlach

Attorney

UNITED STATES PATENT OFFICE

2,562,491

FLYING AUTOMOBILE

Theodore P. Hall, San Diego, Calif.

Application July 26, 1947, Serial No. 763,859

1 Claim.　(Cl. 244—2)

1

This invention relates to automotive vehicles adapted to become airborne by the attachment of a novel form of flight component.

The utility of flying automobiles is well recognized and in striving to effect a vehicle of this type having a maximum of efficiency both as an aircraft and as a land vehicle troublesome structural problems are encountered by reason of the fact that the design criteria for aircraft are radically different than for automotive vehicles. In the design or aircraft it is particularly essential to minimize gross weight and reduce overall dimensions in order to obtain optimum performance. It has been found necessary in prior proposals of this type of flying vehicle to compromise the characteristics and design of the automotive vehicle in favor of the airborne unit. The present invention contemplates a combination automobile and aircraft in which the gross weight of the vehicle is kept within practical limits as a useful airplane, and the characteristics of the automotive component meet conventional automobile specifications while being considerably lighter by reason of a novel arrangement of load distribution and structural members.

The present invention also contemplates the complete independency of the flight component and its controls from the automotive unit. Earlier proposals have combined their flight and automotive controls and instruments in such a manner that operation of the vehicle as an automobile or as an airplane has been complicated by the presence of unfamiliar or unnecessary controls when in one situation or another. At the same time, the inter-dependency of the control systems in prior designs complicates the conversion of the vehicle from an airplane to an automobile or vice-versa and obviously increases the possibility of failures and accidents due to improper rigging or mal-functioning of the controls.

The primary object of this invention therefore is to provide a ground vehicle meeting the performance specifications of modern automobiles and adapted to become airborne by the attachment of an independently provided flight component.

Another object of the invention is to provide an automotive vehicle adapted to be airborne and in which stability, comfort, and safety characteristics are held to a maximum while weight is minimized through the arrangement of the structure and the distribution of loads.

A further object of this invention is to provide an improved combination automobile-aircraft

2

comprising a powered unit for ground travel and a readily attachable flight section having its own power plant and controls.

A still further object is the provision of an attachable flight section for an automobile containing all of the elements essential for flight including propeller, power plant, instruments and flight controls.

A still further object of the invention is to provide in a flying automobile comprising an automotive component and a flight component having separate control systems and power plants, an improved arrangement whereby these components may be easily and efficiently joined or disconnected without interconnection of said control systems and power plants.

Other objects of the invention and its various characteristics and advantages will be readily apparent from consideration of the following detailed description and drawings which form a part of this disclosure and in which like numerals of reference denote corresponding parts throughout the several views.

The invention consists in the several novel features which are hereinafter set forth and are more particularly defined by claims at the conclusion thereof.

In the drawings:

Figure 1 is a perspective view of an airborne vehicle constructed in accordance with the present invention;

Figure 2 is a side elevation of the assembled airborne vehicle illustrating the disposition of the major elements and the location of the center of gravity;

Figure 3 is a side elevation of the flight component per se;

Figure 4 is a side elevation of the automotive component per se;

Figure 5 is a section of the vehicle with the flight component in assembled relation, illustrating the major elements and the arrangement of the principal loads and structural members;

Figure 6 is a section on line 6—6 of Figure 5 illustrating a typical form of attachment between the automotive and flight components;

Figure 7 is a detail showing an alternative arrangement of the steering wheel of the automotive component;

Figure 8 is a perspective of the flight component illustrating the general arrangement of the structure and the flight control system; and

Figure 9 is an enlarged perspective of the flight control system with certain portions broken away for the purpose of clarity.

The invention consists essentially of an auto-

3

mobile A as illustrated in the drawings, designed and constructed to perform the conventional functions of such a vehicle, and which in addition may be airborne by the attachment of a flight section B, the combination being shown in Figures 1, 2, and 5.

As illustrated in the drawings, the automotive unit A of the invention is arranged for a driver and passenger in conventional side-by-side relationship, but if desired the principles of this invention may be embodied as advantageously in other seating arrangements accommodating additional passengers or seats other than the pilot's may be omitted and provision made for various dispositions of cargo. The automotive unit A may be designed to serve a number of purposes, for example, as a light delivery vehicle, or as an armored, reconaissance, or ambulance car for military purposes. The principal objective of the invention, however, is to provide a safe, comfortable vehicle having the combined utility of the conventional automobile and airplane. To this end, it is provided with an enclosed body 10, a pair of forward steerable wheels 11, and a rearwardly disposed engine 12 for driving the vehicle through ground engagement of a pair of drive wheels 14. The body portion 10 is of streamlined shape and is provided with front, side and rear windows 13 to permit optimum visibility. The external dimensions of the body 10 are somewhat less than for conventional automobiles of the same general capacity this being made possible without an attendant decrease in the internal dimensions because of the arrangement of the structure and elements as will be explained below. The reduction in overall size and weight of the vehicle improves its maneuverability as an automobile and, of course, reduces drag when airborne.

It is well understood in the automotive art, that the center of gravity of a road vehicle should be as low as possible for stability and as nearly as possible to the mid-point between the wheels to provide optimum riding qualities. In the present embodiment, these conditions are obtained by the disposition of the power plant 12 in the rear of the vehicle, and the arrangement of the occupants, controls, structure, etc., so that the center of gravity approximates the position indicated in Figure 4 by the symbol C. G.

Because of the structural arrangement, the compact arrangement of the elements, and the use of materials having high strength-weight ratios, the gross weight of the automobile as herein described is kept low in comparison to that of comparable automobiles of present design. For example, it has been found that an automobile constructed in accordance with the principles of this invention may be designed to have a gross weight, empty, of approximately 900 pounds as compared to conventional automobiles of comparable characteristics which have a gross weight of approximately 3000 pounds. As a result of this considerable reduction in weight, a smaller power plant is permissible to provide equivalent speed and power performance, and this in itself contributes to weight reduction as well as economy of operation. We have determined that an automobile embodying the present invention and having the above gross weight provides comparable performance when powered with an engine of 25-30 rated horsepower, as against 85-100 horsepower engines used in present conventional automobiles.

4

With particular reference to Figure 5, the automobile A comprises essentially a generally D-shaped tubular steel frame 16, which serves as a central structure to support all of the principal loads including the body 10, the wheels 11 and 14, the engine 12, a floor structure 18, and a seat 17. The frame 16 has a vertical central member 19, upper and lower horizontal members 20 and 21 respectively, and upper and lower inclined members 22 and 23 which complete the frame and form a rigid structure. The wheels 11 are suspended by suitable hydraulic assemblies 11a, which assemblies 11a are supported from the lower end of the member 23. The particular construction of these assemblies forms no part of the present invention. The wheels 11 are controllable to steer the automobile A on the ground by means of a convention tie rod (not shown) which is moved through a steering link 24 and an arm 25, which arm 25 is reciprocally movable in response to rotation of a steering lever 26 supported by a steering column 27.

The body 10 is primarily a shell or sheath which will bear but small loads and which therefore can be built of a minimum weight material such as Duralumin or as an alternative, of a high strength laminate such as, for example, fiber glass cloth impregnated with a thermosetting resin. The body 10 is supported along its fore-and-aft centerline by suitable attachment to the frame 16. The floor structure 18 may be of Duralumin or of high strength laminate and is preferably of a corrugated form, as shown, to promote lateral rigidity. It is attached, in suitable manner, to the lower frame member 21 of frame 16 and to the sides of the body 10 for support transversely and effects an efficient structure. The body 10 is provided with a forward deck 28 having a depending portion 28a at its rearward edge forming an instrument panel and to define the driving compartment. A spare wheel and tire 29 is mounted in the forward space 10a within the body 10 and beneath the deck 28. A rear deck 30 is supported between the sides of the body 10 and the central vertical frame member 19 to define an engine compartment 30a below it, and to serve as a support for luggage.

A seat 17 is provided forward of vertical frame member 19 and consists essentially of upholstered back and seat portions 17a and 17b respectively, supported on a generally box-like frame 17c, which is welded or otherwise attached to the lower frame member 21 and to the floor structure 18 to form a rigid seat structure and to contribute to the transverse strength of the body.

The engine 12 and the drive wheels 14 with their suspension system are supported by a rearwardly extending cantilever structure 31 which is suitably attached by bolts or welding to the lower end of the central vertical frame member 19, in such a manner that the load of the power plant and rear drive system are transmitted to the frame 16. The engine may be of either the air or water cooled types and disposed with its principal axis in either the fore-and-aft direction, or else transversely of the vehicle. In the present instance, a water cooled type is illustrated, mounted with its drive shaft 40 directed towards the front of the vehicle. Power from the engine is transmitted to the drive wheels 14 through upper and lower right angled drive units 41 and 42 respectively, an intermediate shaft 43 and a suitable combined clutch, transmission, and differential gear assembly 44. Whereas the power plant location and manner of support and the drive arrangement may be varied without departing from the spirit of the invention, the method and manner illustrated and herein described provides a particularly compact and efficient arrangement which is well adapted to the overall specifications and characteristics of the present vehicle.

Because of the relatively low power requirements of the automobile of the present invention, ample power range may be obtained for all practical purposes by the use of a transmission 44 having but two speeds forward and one in reverse in distinction to the conventional automotive types in which the gross weights of the vehicle require three speed ratios to obtain comparable performance. The use of a two-speed transmission contributes to weight reduction and simplifies driving control, since the automobile may be started and driven on level or moderate inclines without shifting gears with the second or low speed being used only for unusual power demands.

Water cooling is provided in the present embodiment by a conventional engine driven fan 45 and a radiator 46 which is supported by suitable brackets on the rear end of the cantilever structure 31.

The controls of the present automobile are identical in location, operation and function as in conventional automobiles to eliminate need for additional training in the use of the vehicle as an automobile and to fully utilize the normal reactions of the trained automobile driver. They include in addition to the steering lever 26, a foot accelerator 47, a clutch pedal 48 operatively connected by suitable mechanism to the transmission 44 for response to actuation by the driver's left foot, a hand actuated gear shift (not shown), and a brake pedal located for operation by the right foot of the driver to control a conventional 4-wheeled brake system associated with the forward wheels 11 and power wheels 14. In conformance with the other aspects of the automobile of the present invention wherein power and strength have been pointed out as being primary considerations, therefore because of the general strength-weight efficiency of the whole structural arrangement, the brake system components may be smaller and consequently lighter, even though conventional in function.

The invention as thus far described exemplifies a light, compact automotive type vehicle providing the equivalent characteristics and performance of the modern automobile in respect to strength, safety, comfort, ease of operation, and utility at greatly reduced gross weight and somewhat reduced overall dimensions. It is characterized by the use of a generally D-shaped frame member disposed on the fore-and-aft centerline of the vehicle, from which all of the principal loads are supported including the body, the wheels, the power plant, and the occupants. By reason of the central support of the main loads, an enclosed body which is primarily a shell made of high-strength, low-weight materials, is used in combination with similarly constructed floor and seat sections to form a unitary body and frame assembly of high efficiency.

While the vehicle described is comparable in every way with conventional performance specifications for a light automobile, it also conforms to the practical requirements for the passenger and load carrying portions of a light airplane,

and is suited aerodynamically and from a weight standpoint to become airborne particularly when utilized in conjunction with a flight component B as shown and described hereafter, although it is to be understood that this presents but one form of flight component, and that this may be varied or modified in many respects without departing from the scope of the invention.

Having particular reference to Figures 1, 3, 5 and 8, the flight component B is shown consisting essentially of a pair of wings 70, a cowled tractor-mounted power plant 71, a tail boom 72, and an empennage 73.

The primary structure of the flight component B comprises a tubular wing spar 74 supporting a series of suitable airfoil shaped ribs (as indicated in dotted lines in Figure 8) and a usual skin 70a. The tubular tail boom 72 supports the empennage 73 and its controls. The power plant 71 consists of an engine 75, supported on a pair of cantilever engine bearers 76 from the intersection of the spar 74 and tail boom 72, a propeller 75a and a streamlined cowl 77.

It is to be noted that the principal loads of the flight component are transmitted through the tubular wing spar 74 and the tubular tail boom 72 and concentrated at their intersection, the arrangement being particularly advantageous for the attachment at the same location to the automobile component A. This is accomplished through a pair of laterally spaced forward attachment fittings 78, and a pair of rear laterally spaced attachment fittings 79, both pairs of which are rigidly attached to the fore-and-aft structure of the flight component B. These fittings effect a positive connection between the automobile component A and the flight component B and serve also to locate positively the one with respect to the other.

With the flight component B assembled to the automobile component A, a vehicle is formed which may be characterized generally as a high-wing tractor monoplane, a type of aircraft which is particularly adapted for moderate performance passenger travel because of its stability, visibility, and advantageous landing and take-off characteristics. In aircraft of this type, it is essential to good stability and flight performance that the center of gravity be located as low and as near to the center of pressure of the wing as possible. In available airfoil sections applicable to the present invention the center of pressure of the wing occurs at or near 30% of the mean aerodynamic chord. We have found that with the arrangement described herein, the center of gravity of the combined automobile-airplane is located at about 27% mean aerodynamic chord when the vehicle is fully loaded and is sufficiently low as illustrated in Figure 2 to provide optimum flight characteristics. The rearward location of the motor 12 in the automobile component A to oppose the forward location of the flight engine 75 advantageously positions two of the principal loads and tends to effect a desirable location of the center of gravity therebetween. Location of the seating means 17 forwardly of motor 12 and disposal of the wings 70 substantially directly over seat 17 locates two other principal load sources favorable to the maintenance of a low C. G.

A further requirement of weight distribution is that the center of gravity location of the aircraft does not vary considerably in the event of different arrangements or change in the disposable load, i. e., passengers, baggage, and fuel. In the present arrangement, since these elements are located at or near the center of pressure of the wing, we have found it possible to limit the horizontal movement of the center of gravity to within the limits of good aircraft design.

Figure 6 illustrates a preferred form of mechanism for quickly and positively latching or connecting the automotive component A to the flight component B. In the connecting operation, the flight component B is suspended on jacks or by means of a hoist (not shown), and the automobile A is driven or positioned under it so that the forward and rear attachment fittings 78 and 79 are located over attachment openings 80 and 81 (Figure 4) provided in the top of the body 10. The flight component B is then lowered so that the attachment fittings 78 and 79 engage pairs of lugs, as indicated at 82, attached to the upper horizontally disposed frame member 20. As shown in Figure 6, to service the rear attachment fittings 79, a pair of pins 83, journaled in suitable bearing members 84 within the upper frame member 20, are retractable through aligned holes in the lugs 82 and upper frame member 20 to engage holes in the attachment fittings 79 to form a positive lock therewith. The pins 83 are attached through horizontally movable links 85 to a toggle 86. A similar locking arrangement is provided at the forward attachment fittings 78. The toggles 86 at the front and rear attachment locations are fixed to a common shaft 87, suitably supported for rotation on the inside wall of upper frame member 20. A bell crank 88 is fixed to the shaft 87 so that rotation thereof by a manually operable control rod 89 retracts or extends the pins 83 to lock or unlock the automobile and flight components through the attachment fittings 78 and 79.

An important feature of the present invention which is here particularly stressed is the independence of the control system of the flight component B from that of the automobile component A. To effect this independence a two-control system is employed in place of the more conventional three-control system wherein aileron, rudder and elevator surfaces are provided under the control of independent actuating systems. In the latter case, it is usual to actuate the ailerons and elevators for horizontal and longitudinal control by differential movement of a control stick or wheel, and to actuate the rudder for directional control by foot pedals. Since the foot pedal positions of the present invention are utilized for clutch and brake control of the automobile unit, we prefer to utilize a flight control system in which the rudder and ailerons are coordinated in such a manner that horizontal and directional controls are combined and actuated through a single system. By so providing, complete flight control of the vehicle can be provided from a single overhead type control column 100 which depends from and is supported by the structure of the flight component B, in such a manner that when the flight component B is in assembled relation to the automotive unit A, the control column 100 projects through a normally covered opening 90 in the body 10 and will be positioned in proper relation to the driver to permit complete and effective flight control of the vehicle.

The operation and function of two-control flight systems are well understood in the art, and the specific form thereof shown and described herein exemplifies an embodiment which provides advantages which are particularly evident in

combination with other features of this invention. However, it is not to be understood that the invention is limited to the particular flight control system shown since there are many forms of combined flight control systems which may be used and are contemplated as within the scope of this invention.

With particular reference to Figure 8, the wings 70 are shown provided with control surfaces 95 pivotally connected at the trailing edge thereof, serving to provide horizontal control of the airborne vehicle when moved differentially or as ailerons. To eliminate the necessity of flaps or other high lift devices, provision is made in the present embodiment to "droop" the surfaces 95, i. e., to depress them simultaneously, while at the same time permitting differential action. As is well understood and accepted in the art, control surfaces so characterized are known as "flaperons."

The empennage 73 consists essentially of a fixed vertical fin 96, to which a rudder 97 is pivotally attached at its trailing edge, and a fixed horizontal stabilizer 98 supporting a pair of elevators 99 which are adapted for simultaneous vertical movement for controlling the longitudinal direction of the airborne vehicle.

The details of the system for actuating the flight control surfaces are most clearly illustrated in Figure 9. As shown, the control column 100 is suspended from bearings 101, provided on the flight component structure, for fore and aft movement about a cross-shaft 102. A lever 103 affixed to the cross-shaft 102 for rotation therewith is pivotally attached at its upper end through a clevis 104 to the elevator control tube 105. Rotation of the link 103 in response to the fore-and-aft movement of the control column 100 moves the elevator control tube 105 longitudinally or in a fore-and-aft direction to rotate the elevator torque tube 106, through a bell crank 107. The elevator torque tube 106 is connected to the elevators 99 to deflect them upwards when the control column 100 is moved aft, and downwards when the control column is moved forward, to effect longitudinal control of the airborne vehicle. Tube 105 is suitably mounted for rotative movement for operation of the rudder 97; the interconnection of tube 105 and rudder 97 will be hereinafter described.

Coordinated control of the flaperons 95 and the rudder 97 is provided through a control wheel 110, which is supported to one side of the lower end of the control column 100, as best shown in Figure 9, by a transverse support tube 111 and a horizontal fore-and-aft extension 112, which houses the control wheel axle 110'. A shaft 113 supported axially of the control column 100 is adapted for rotation in response to rotation of the control wheel 110, through a pair of bell cranks 114 and 115, pinned respectively to the lower end of the shaft 113 and the control wheel axle 110', and interconnected by a link 116.

The flaperons 95 are adapted to be pivotally moved by the torque tubes 120 and 120', which tubes are operatively connected to the rearwardly projecting corners of a generally triangular plate member 123 through adjustable links 122 and 122'. The plate member 123 is pivotally supported at 124 on a transverse arm 125, one end of which arm is supported on a pivot 126, in a rigidly fixed bracket 127 and is swingable horizontally about the pivot 126. The free end of the arm 125 extends through a slot 128 in a depending fixed support bracket 129, and is provided with a control handle 130. By means of the handle 130,

9

the arm 125 may be moved about its pivot 126 in a fore-and-aft direction, and may be restrained in any of a plurality of positions by dropping the arm into one or another of a series of notches 128' associated with the slot 120. By this means, the position of the triangular plate member 123 relative to the other elements of the control system may be manually adjusted.

Movement of the plate member 123 in response to manual operation of the handle 130 simultaneously depresses or elevates each of the flaperons 95, through interconnecting links 122 and 122' the same amount to change the effective camber of both wings 70 to vary their lift characteristics, as is well understood in the art; and thus this portion of the control system by the simultaneous control of the flaperons 95 provides the function of conventional flaps or other high lift devices.

To effect differential action of the flaperons 95 for lateral control, a projection 123' of the plate 123 extends forward of the pivot 124 and is pivotally connected to a link 131 which in turn is pivotally connected to a bell crank 132 carried by and rotatable with the shaft 113. Thus rotation of the link 131 in response to manual actuation of the control wheel 110, rotates the triangular plate member 123 about its pivot 124 and moves the flaperons differentially, that is, one will move up as the other moves down and vice versa. The differential control of the flaperons 95 for lateral control is obtained in this system regardless of the relative neutral position of the flaperons 95 with respect to the wing 70, as established by the position of the lever handle 130, so that lateral control of the vehicle is obtained even when the flaperons 95 are in the fully depressed or "drooped" position.

The lateral and directional control systems are coordinated so that flaperons 95 and rudder 97 are simultaneously operated by rotation of the control wheel 110 in such a manner that the rudder is deflected to produce a given amount of yawing or directional movement to the vehicle for any lateral moment produced by the flaperons 95, and in the proper direction. This coordination of controls is accomplished by means of a link 133 which is universally pivoted at its lower end to the projection 123' of plate 123, between the pivot point 124 and the attachment point to the link 131, and at its other end to a link 134 which in turn rotates a bell crank 135 pinned to the elevator control tube 105. The geometry of the system comprising the bell crank 135 and the links 133 and 134 is such that fore-and-aft movement of the control tube 105, which occurs when the elevators 99 are to be operated, merely displaces the links 133 and 134 in the same direction without affecting the position of the triangular plate member 123, while rotation of the plate member 123, which occurs when the flaperons are differentially actuated, rotates the control tube 105 without affecting the relative longitudinal position of the control tube 105, or the setting of the elevators 99.

The rudder 97 is adapted to be rotated about its vertical axis in response to rotation of the control tube 105. An operative connection is had between the rudder 97 and control tube 105 through a rudder horn 136 pinned to a rudder torque tube 137, an attachment fitting 140 fastened to the rear end of the control tube 105 and a pair of links 138 and 139 interconnecting the tube 137 and the fitting 140. The geometry of this system is such that longitudinal movement

10

of the control tube 105 to actuate the elevators 99 displaces the links 138 and 139 without rotation of the rudder horn 136 (or the rudder 97 controlled thereby) while rotation of the control tube 105 effects rotation of the rudder horn 136 and the rudder 97 without affecting the position of elevators 99.

It will be apparent from the foregoing description that the flight control system comprises three distinct components: (a) a longitudinal control operable by fore-and-aft movement of the control column 100, (b) a combined lateral and directional control operable by rotation of the control wheel 110, and (c) a control for changing lift characteristics operable in response to movement of the handle 130. The arrangement may be further characterized as a two control system employing a conventional elevator for longitudinal control and a combined rudder and aileron system to produce coordinated lateral and directional movement, in which the ailerons are capable of being "drooped" to provide high-lift characteristics for take-off and landing, thus serving as "flaperons."

It is to be particularly noted that the entire flight control system is supported by the flight component B and is completely independent of the control system of the automotive component A, thus facilitating the assembly and dis-assembly of the vehicle, and eliminating the mechanical complications inherent in inter-connected systems.

This invention also provides that the engine controls for the engine 75 and the flight instruments are supported as part of the flight component B and are independent of the automotive component A or its controls. A flight control panel 145 is supported by the primary structure of flight component B, in suitable manner, and is adapted to extend through opening 90 in the roof of body 10, along with control column 100, when the major components are assembled. The control panel 145 will carry the usual flight instruments, indicated generally at 146, and will position these instruments above the head of the pilot but in a readily readable position, as is best shown in Figure 5.

The controls for the engine 75 are conventional and their particular construction form no part of this invention and they are not shown in the drawings. These controls will be operated from the flight control panel 145.

The controls for the motor 12 carried by the automotive unit A are not shown and are likewise of conventional design and construction and form no part of this invention, and are located within easy access of the driver upon the automobile instrument panel 28a, which panel 28a carries the usual automotive instruments indicated generally at 147.

As best seen in Figure 8, a fairing 148, generally cap-like or oval in shape, depends from the flight component B and is adapted to fit over and snugly enclose substantially the entire roof portion of the body 10 of the automotive component A. The shape of the fairing 148 tends to reduce drag, and hides the attachment points between the two major components A and B and generally adds to the appearance of the combination, continuing the streamline effect of the automotive unit A.

In Figure 5 there is illustrated a form of steering mechanism which is best utilized when the vehicle of the present invention is engaged in taxiing operations. It may readily be actuated by one hand of the operator while with the other he controls the movable control surfaces provided on the flight unit B. Steering lever 26 is pivotally connected to steering column 27 so that it may be moved to stowed position (as shown in dotted outline in Figure 5) when the device is serving as an airborne vehicle. When the autoplane of the present invention is to serve as a ground vehicle, with the portable flight unit B removed, another form of steering device is better utilized. This latter form is shown in Figure 7 and comprises a conventional steering wheel 150 carried by a shaft 151 which shaft 151 is adapted to have a telescoping engagement with column 27. If the driver desires, this latter form of steering apparatus may be maintained at all times in the ship, being telescoped into a stowed position, as shown in dotted outline, to be out of the way when in flight.

Figures 2, 3, and 4 illustrate the positions of the various centers of gravity of the flight unit B, of the automobile unit A, and of the combination of these two units. As has been pointed out hereinbefore the location of two principal loads, the motors 76 and 12 on opposite sides of the center of gravity of the assembled units, the positioning of the seating arrangement 17 between the motors, and the disposal of the wing section substantially directly over the seat 17, assists in locating the center of gravity in a desirable position for satisfactory performance of the vehicle.

An airplane-automobile combination has been herein described which incorporates desirable aerodynamical and mechanical operating efficiency and maintains passenger comfort. A novel design is utilized providing low weight but advantageously possessing high strength. The design and construction employed in the present invention provides a vehicle which satisfactorily performs both as a ground device and as an airborne vehicle and performs with safety and ease.

While certain preferred embodiments of the invention have been specifically disclosed, it is understood that the invention is not limited thereto as many variations will be readily apparent to those skilled in the art and the invention is to be given its broadest possible interpretation within the terms of the following claim.

I claim:

In an autoplane comprising in combination an automotive unit and a flight unit, said automotive unit comprising a central load bearing tubular frame, a body of generally shell-like construction supported by said frame, steering and drive ground-engaging wheels carried by said body, a motor mounted in said body rearwardly of said frame and being operatively connected to said drive wheels, means for supporting said motor on said load bearing frame, seating means within said body disposed forwardly of said motor and supported upon said frame, said flight unit comprising a transverse tubular wing spar and a tubular tail boom connected to said wing spar substantially centrally thereof, wings provided on said wing spar, an empennage supported by said tail boom, means connecting said flight unit to said load bearing frame with the wing disposed substantially directly over the seating means, a motor for driving a propeller carried by said flight unit, means mounting said motor forwardly of said wings, said motor on said automotive unit being located rearwardly of the center of gravity of the autoplane and said motor carried by said flight unit being located forwardly of said center of gravity.

THEODORE P. HALL.

REFERENCES CITED

The following references are of record in the file of this patent:

UNITED STATES PATENTS

Number	Name	Date
1,348,548	Dominicis et al.	Aug. 13, 1920
2,156,288	Holliday	May 2, 1939
2,410,234	Read et al.	Oct. 20, 1946

FOREIGN PATENTS

Number	Country	Date
559,819	Great Britain	Mar. 7, 1944
820,336	France	July 26, 1937

OTHER REFERENCES

Warner: "Airplane Design," 1st edition, 1927, pp. 242 and 243.

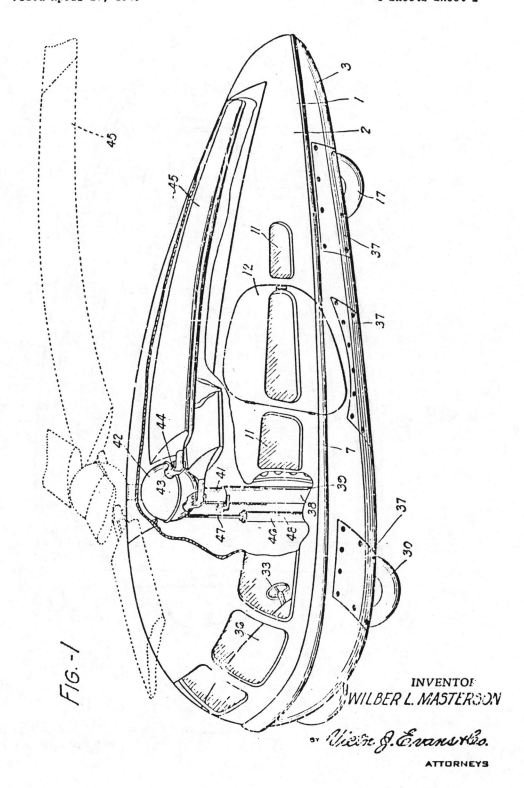

FIG. -1

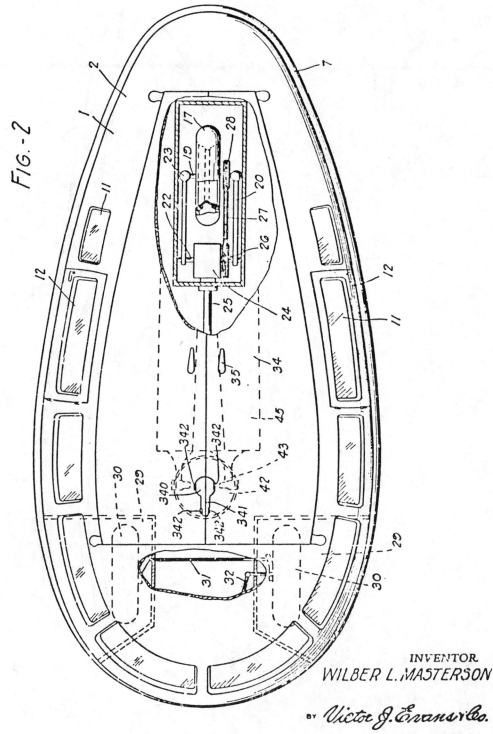

FIG.-2

INVENTOR.
WILBER L. MASTERSON

BY *Victor J. Evans & Co.*

ATTORNEYS

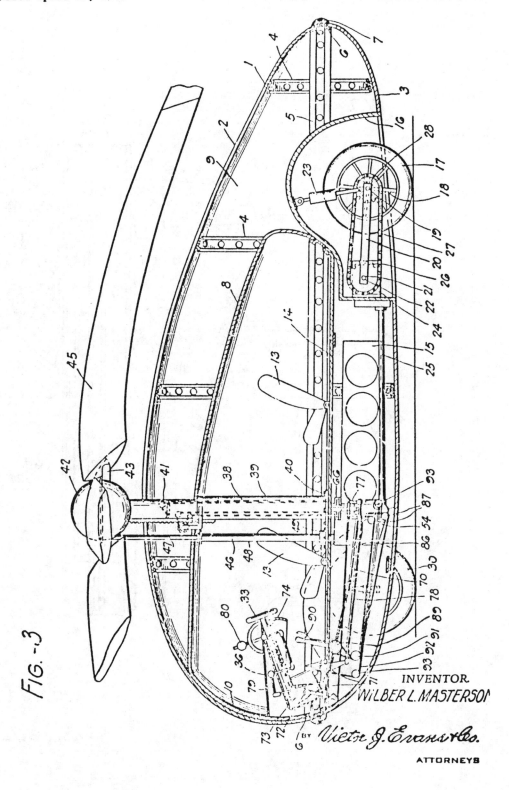

FIG. -3

INVENTOR.
WiLBER L. MASTERSON

BY Victor J. Evans & Co.

ATTORNEYS

FIG.-4

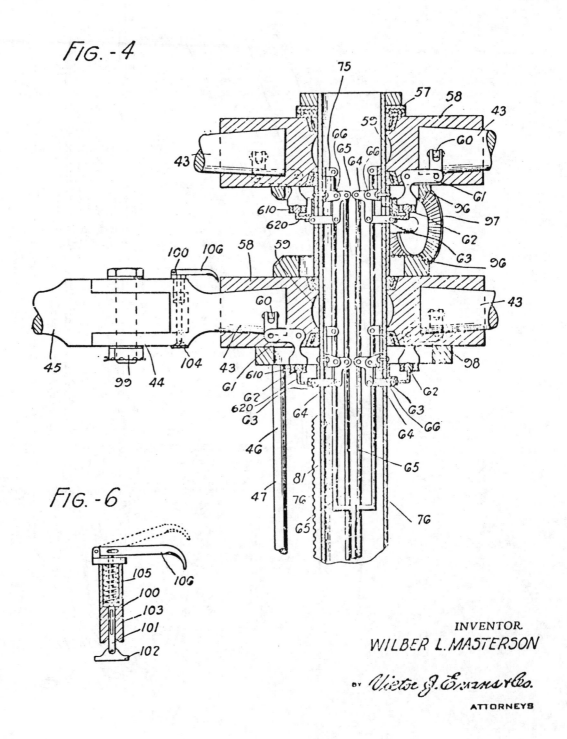

FIG.-6

INVENTOR.
WILBER L. MASTERSON

BY Victor J. Evans & Co.
                    ATTORNEYS

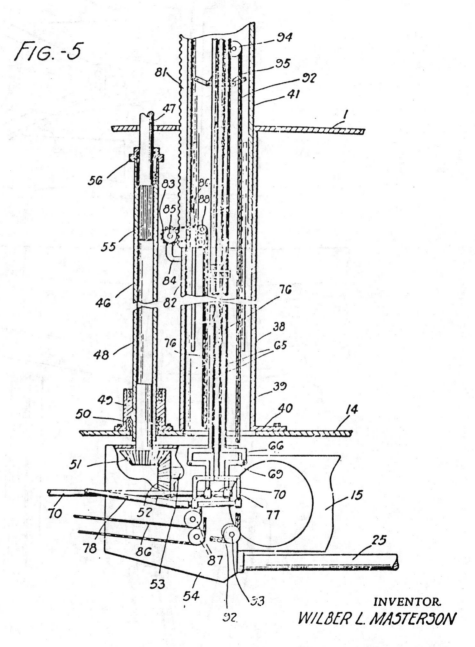

FIG.-5

INVENTOR.
WILBER L. MASTERSON

BY Victor J. Evans & Co.

ATTORNEYS

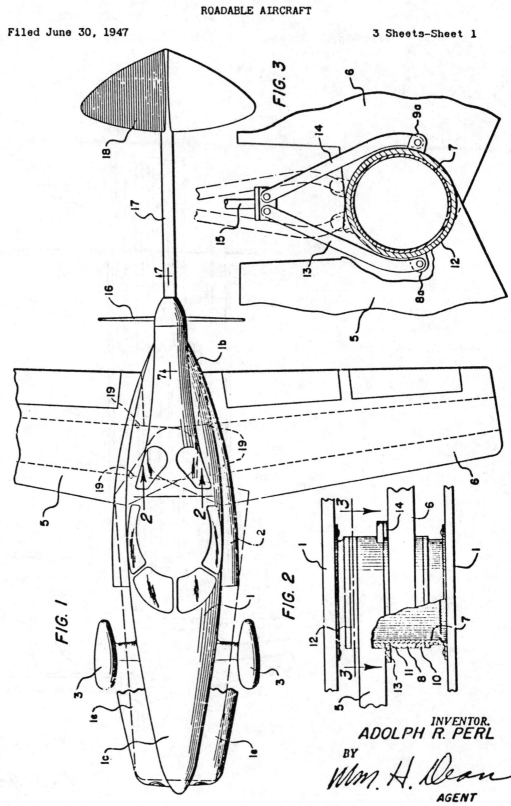

INVENTOR.
ADOLPH R. PERL

BY

Wm. H. Dean

AGENT

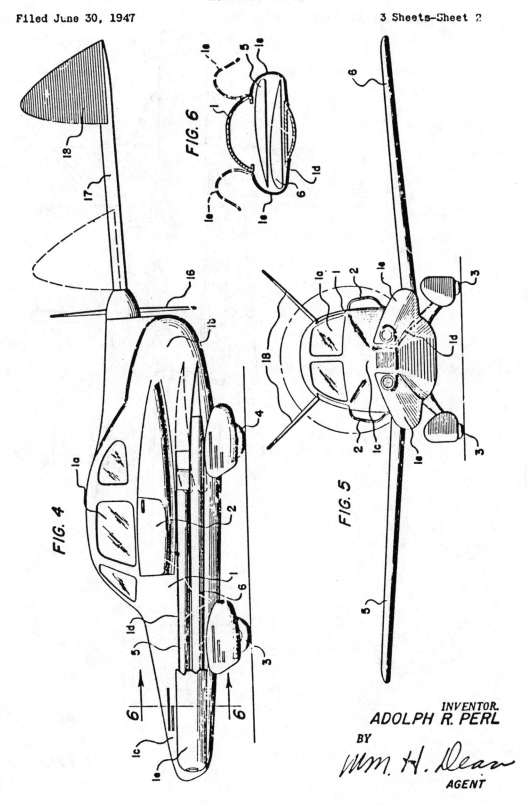

FIG. 6

FIG. 4

FIG. 5

INVENTOR.
ADOLPH R. PERL

BY

WM. H. Dean

AGENT

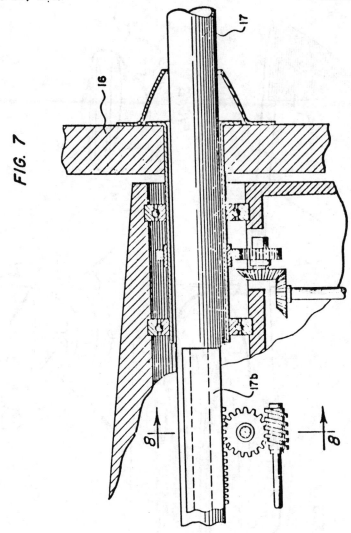

FIG. 7

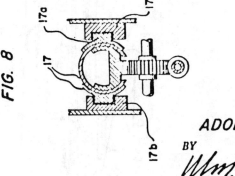

FIG. 8

INVENTOR.
ADOLPH R. PERL

BY

Wm. H. Dean

AGENT

UNITED STATES PATENT OFFICE

2,573,271

ROADABLE AIRCRAFT

Adolph R. Perl, San Diego, Calif.

Application June 30, 1947, Serial No. 758,059

4 Claims. (Cl. 244—2)

1

My invention relates to a roadable aircraft, more particularly to an aircraft having folding multiple wings and retractable tail boom, and the objects of my invention are:

First, to provide an aircraft of this class which can be very readily and very quickly converted from an aircraft to a roadable vehicle;

Second, to provide a roadable aircraft of this class in which the wings are foldable into the body of the fuselage longitudinally thereof, presenting an overall breadth of the roadable aircraft at the fuselage portion thereof substantially equal to the chord of the wings when in folded position;

Third, to provide a roadable aircraft of this class in which the center of gravity thereof is changed by the pivotal movement of the wings when folding whereby forward movement of said center of gravity is changed to the desirable position for roadwork and is proper with respect to the wing when the wings are in extended position for flight;

Fourth, to provide a roadable aircraft of this class having a retractable tail boom which greatly reduces the overall length of the vehicle when operated on the ground;

Fifth, to provide an aircraft having novel folding wings which are retractable into the fuselage of said aircraft;

Sixth, to provide a roadable aircraft of this class having novel air scoop means in connection with the doors of the fuselage thereof for directing air backwardly into the engine at the rear of said fuselage;

Seventh, to provide a roadable aircraft of this class which is properly balanced when in various operating conditions and in which the wings thereof are foldable in superimposed relationship to each other for attaining such balance;

Eighth, to provide a novel means for folding aircraft wings into superimposed parallel relationship with each other whereby a very compact roadable aircraft may be produced;

Ninth, to provide a roadable aircraft of this class having four wheels which operate equally as well on the ground or in connection with the aircraft when taking off or landing; and

Tenth, to provide a roadable aircraft of this class which is very simple and economical of construction in accordance with its utility, efficient in operation and which will not readily deteriorate or get out of order.

With these and other objects in view, as will appear hereinafter, my invention consists of certain novel features of construction, combination

2

and arrangement of parts and portions as will be hereinafter described in detail and particularly set forth in the appended claims, reference being had to the accompanying drawings and to the characters of reference thereon forming a part of this application in which:

Fig. 1 is a fragmentary top or plan view of my roadable aircraft, showing by dash lines varying positions of parts thereof, Fig. 2 is an enlarged fragmentary sectional view taken from the line 2—2 of Fig. 1, showing portions further broken away and in section to amplify the illustration, Fig. 3 is a fragmentary plan sectional view taken from the line 3—3 of Fig. 2 showing by dash lines varying positions of parts thereof, Fig. 4 is a side elevational view of my roadable aircraft showing by dash lines varying positions of parts thereof, Fig. 5 is a front elevational view of my roadable aircraft, Fig. 6 is a transverse sectional view through the fuselage thereof taken from the line 6—6 of Fig. 4. Fig. 7 is an enlarged sectional view, taken from the line 7—7 of Fig. 1; and Fig. 8 is a sectional view, taken from the line 8—8 of Fig. 7.

Similar characters of reference refer to similar parts and portions throughout the several views of the drawings.

The fuselage 1, doors 2, wheels 3 and 4, wings 5 and 6, wing root hub 7, wing root bearings 8 and 9, spacers 10, 11 and 12, links 13 and 14, actuator rod 15, propeller 16, tail boom 17, tail 18 and the drag pins 19 constitute the principal parts and portions of my roadable aircraft.

The fuselage 1 is provided with a passenger compartment 1a having an engine compartment 1b rearwardly thereof and a forwardly projecting portion 1c arranged to receive the wings of the aircraft when in folded position substantially parallel to the axis of said aircraft. The forwardly projecting portion 1c is provided with a slotted portion 1d therein arranged to retain the wings 5 and 6 in superimposed spaced relation to each other and this slotted portion extends rearwardly to a location below the passenger's compartment 1a and terminates forwardly of the engine compartment 1b, all as shown best in Fig. 4 of the drawings. The wings 5 and 6 are hinged on the longitudinal axis of the aircraft and the roots of the wings rotate about the vertical axis of the wing root hub 7 which is interposed between the upper and lower structure about the slotted portion 1d in the fuselage 1. The wing root hub 7 consists of a cylindrical member having a bearing surface at the outer side thereof on which the wing root bearings 8 and 9 are pivot-

3

ally mounted. These bearings 8 and 9 are spaced by means of the spacers 10, 11 and 12 and in connection with each of the bearings 8 and 9 is a projecting lug as shown in Figs. 2 and 3 of the drawings. The bearing 8 is provided with a projecting lug 8a and the bearing 9 is provided with a projecting lug 9a, as shown in Fig. 3 of the drawings, to which the link 14 is pivotally connected. The link 13 is pivotally connected to the projecting lug 8a of the wing root bearing 8 and both of the links 13 and 14 are pivotally connected to the actuator rod 15 which is a rectilinear rod and power operated. The drag pins 19 are shear pins and are projected through the root portion of the wings 5 and 6 when in the extended position, as shown in Fig. 1 of the drawings, to prevent axial movement of the wings about the vertical axis of the wing root hub 7. The propeller 16 is mounted on a hollow shaft through which the tail boom 17 extends and in which it is reciprocally and non-rotatably mounted. The tail boom 17 is provided with runners 17a, which slide in grooves 17b in the aircraft fuselage, as shown best in Fig. 8 of the drawings, which runners and grooves prevent the tail boom 17 from rotating. When in the extended position, as shown in Fig. 4 of the drawings, the tail 18 in connection with the tail boom 17 is arranged for flight operation. The tail 8 consists of two upwardly diverging tail surface members, as shown in Fig. 5 of the drawings. The forward portion 1c of the fuselage 1, at the slotted portions 1d therein, is provided with a pair of pivoted fairing doors 1e which pivot downwardly and inwardly, as indicated by dash lines in Fig. 6 of the drawings, to a flush position with the outer side of the fuselage when the wings are extended ready for flight.

The wheels 3 are stationarily mounted in connection with the fuselage 1 at the lower side thereof and the wheels 4 are mounted rearwardly of the wheels 3 near the engine in the compartment 1b of the fuselage 1 and the wheels 4 are powered while the wheels 3 are steerable and these wheels 3 and 4 provide for land transportation similar to automobile wheels and also serve the roadable aircraft when landing and taking off.

The operation of my roadable aircraft is substantially as follows:

When the wings 5 and 6 are extended, as shown in Figs. 1 and 5 of the drawings, and the tail boom 17 is extended to the solid line position, as shown in Fig. 4 of the drawings, the roadable aircraft is ready to fly, it being noted, however, that the drag pins 19 must be positioned in shear before taking off. In flight, the air scoop portions protruding from the doors 2 conduct air backwardly into the engine compartment 1b which drives the propeller 16. When landing, the wheels 3 and 4 operate to provide stable wheel bearing on the runway and after landing the drag pins 19 are pulled and the wings 5 and 6 are hinged forwardly into superimposed relationship about the axis of the wing root hub 7. This pivotal movement of the wings 5 and 6 is accomplished by the links 13 and 14 in connection with the actuator rod 15 which moves into the dash line position as shown best in Fig. 3 of the drawings. When the wings are in the position as shown in Fig. 6 of the drawings, in parallel relationship to the axis of the fuselage 1 and the tail boom 17 is retracted to the dash line position, as shown in Fig. 4 of the drawings, the engine in the engine compartment 1b operates the rear wheels where-

4

by the roadable aircraft is substantially a conventional motor vehicle similar to automobiles now in operation.

Though I have shown and described a particular construction, combination and arrangement of parts and portions, I do not wish to be limited to this particular construction, combination and arrangement, but desire to include in the scope of my invention the construction, combination and arrangement substantially as set forth in the appended claims.

Having thus described my invention, what I claim as new and desire to secure by Letters Patent is:

1. In an aircraft of the class described the combination of a fuselage having a longitudinally horizontally disposed slotted portion extending through opposite sides thereof, a pair of pivoted wings pivotally mounted on a substantially vertical axis, rearwardly of said slotted portion and movable into said slotted portion in superimposed spaced relation to each other, a propeller at the rear end of said fuselage having a hollow hub and a tail boom extending therethrough and non-rotatably mounted in said fuselage provided with upwardly diverging tail surfaces at the rear end thereof.

2. In an aircraft of the class described, the combination of a fuselage having a longitudinally horizontally disposed slotted portion extending through opposite sides thereof, a pair of pivoted wings pivotally mounted on a substantially vertical axis rearwardly of said slotted portion and movable into said slotted portion in superimposed spaced relation to each other, a propeller at the rear end of said fuselage having a hollow hub, a tail boom extending therethrough and non-rotatably mounted in said fuselage provided with upwardly diverging tail surfaces at the rear end thereof and air scoops at opposite sides of said fuselage communicating with the rear engine compartment of said fuselage.

3. In an aircraft of the class described the combination of an operator's compartment, a forwardly extending fuselage portion, a rearwardly extending fuselage portion having an engine compartment therein, a pair of wings pivotally mounted in connection with said fuselage, said fuselage provided with a slotted portion longitudinally thereof and forwardly of the pivotal axis of said wings into which said wings are pivoted substantially parallel to the axis of said fuselage, said wings pivoted on a substantially vertical axis and foldable into said fuselage in superimposed spaced relation to each other, a propeller at the rear of said fuselage adjacent said engine compartment having a hollow hub and a tail boom extending therethrough and non-rotatably mounted in said fuselage.

4. In an aircraft of the class described the combination of an operator's compartment, a forwardly extending fuselage portion, a rearwardly extending fuselage portion having an engine compartment therein, a pair of wings pivotally mounted in connection with said fuselage, said fuselage provided with a slotted portion longitudinally thereof and forwardly of the pivotal axis of said wings into which said wings are pivoted substantially parallel to the axis of said fuselage, said wings pivoted on a substantially vertical axis and foldable into said fuselage in superimposed relation to each other, a propeller at the rear of said fuselage adjacent said engine compartment having a hollow hub, a tail boom extending therethrough and non-rotatably mounted in said fuse-

5

lage and said tail boom provided with upwardly diverging tail surfaces thereon.

ADOLPH R. PERL.

REFERENCES CITED

The following references are of record in the file of this patent:

UNITED STATES PATENTS

Number	Name	Date
1,731,757	Tubbe	Oct. 15, 1929

6

Number	Name	Date
1,928,336	Kindelberger	Sept. 26, 1933
2,241,577	Beals	May 13, 1941
2,410,239	Roe	Oct. 29, 1946
2,424,889	Holmes	July 29, 1947

FOREIGN PATENTS

Number	Country	Date
256,743	Great Britain	Aug. 19, 1926

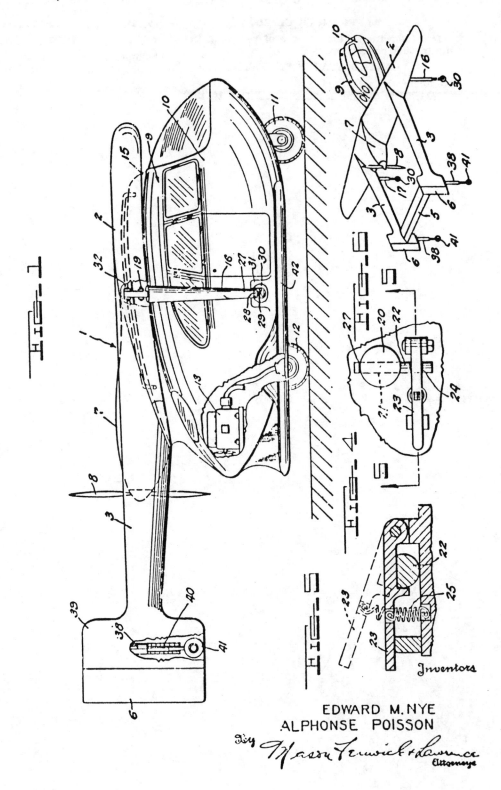

Inventors

EDWARD M. NYE
ALPHONSE POISSON

By Mason Fenwick & Lawrence
Attorneys

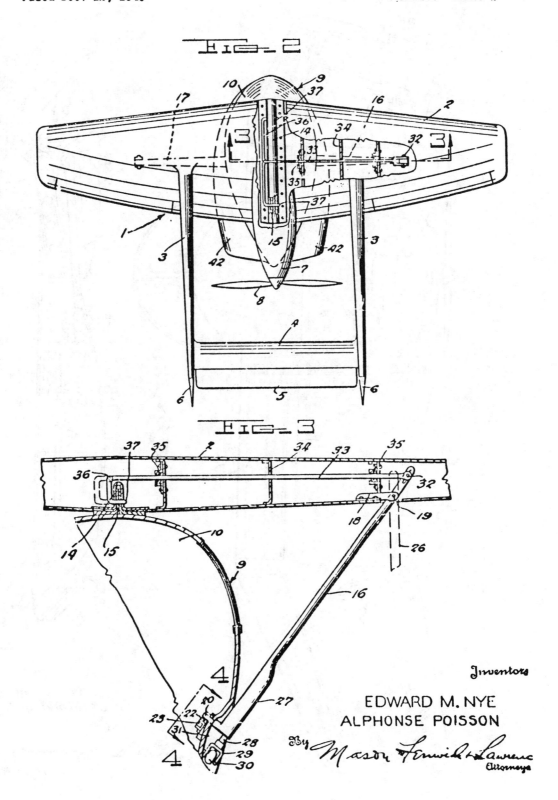

FIG_2

FIG_3

Inventors

EDWARD M. NYE
ALPHONSE POISSON

By Mason Fenwick Lawrence

Attorneys

Sept. 2, 1952 A. J. GERO, JR 2,609,167

TAILLESS CONVERTIBLE AIRPLANE AND ROADMOBILE

Filed Nov. 30, 1948 10 Sheets-Sheet 1

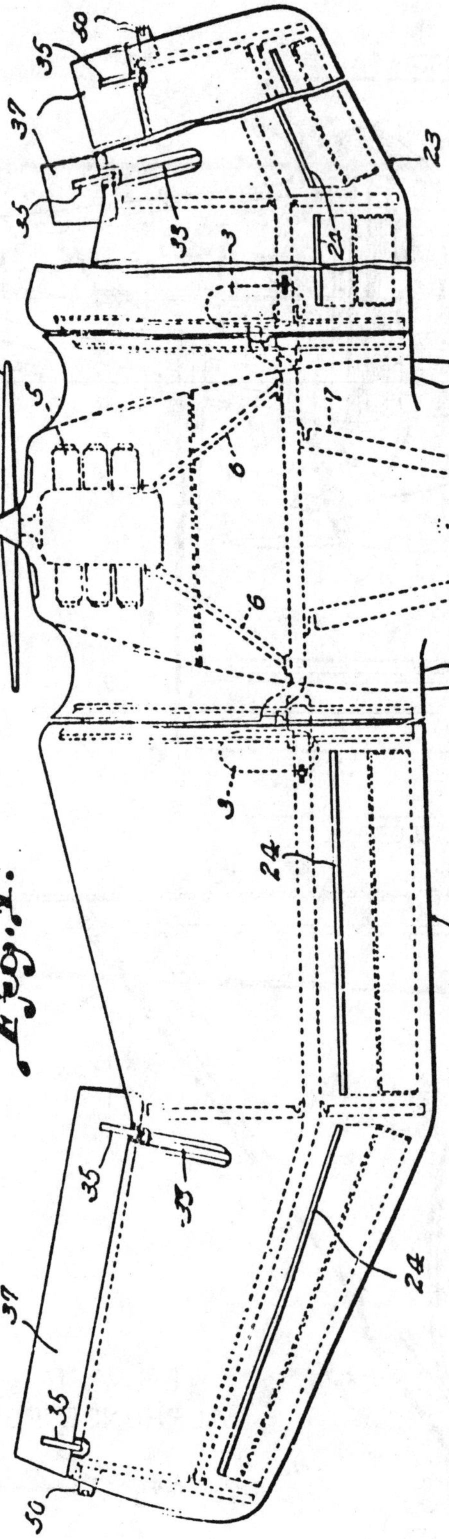

Fig. 1.

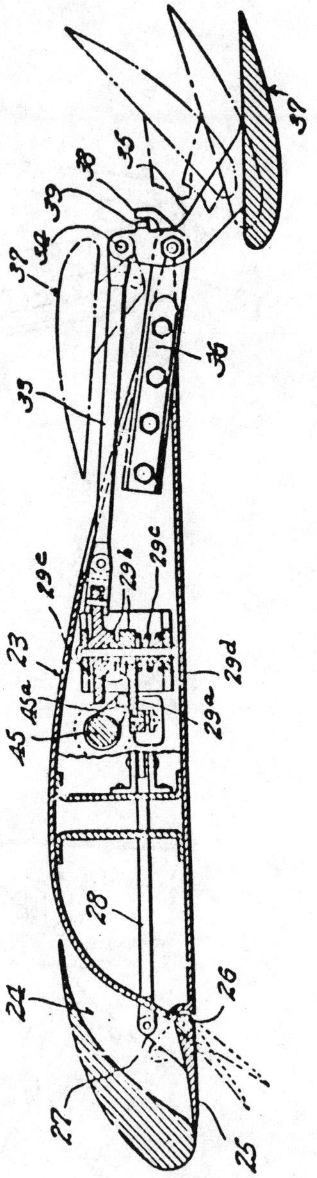

Fig. 12.

INVENTOR,
Adelard J. Gero Jr.

BY

E. E. Vrooman Co.,
ATTORNEYS.

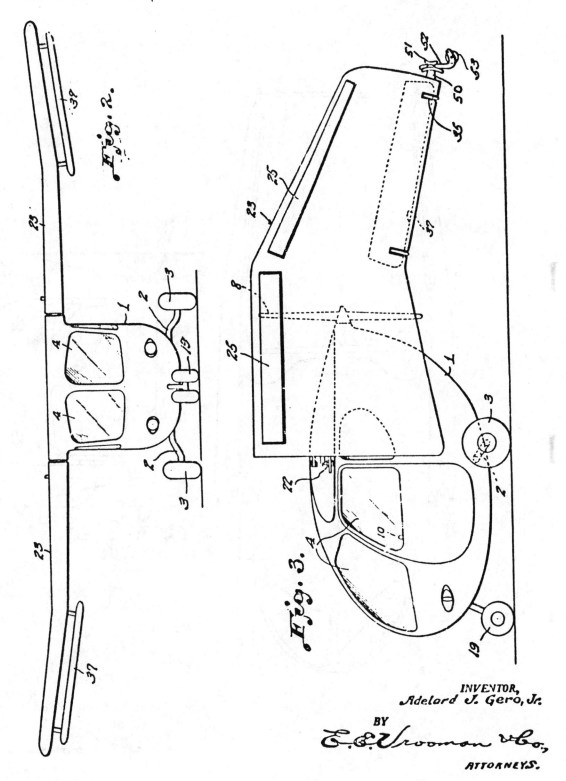

Fig. 2.

Fig. 3.

INVENTOR,
Adelard J. Gero, Jr.

BY

E. E. Vrooman & Co.,

ATTORNEYS.

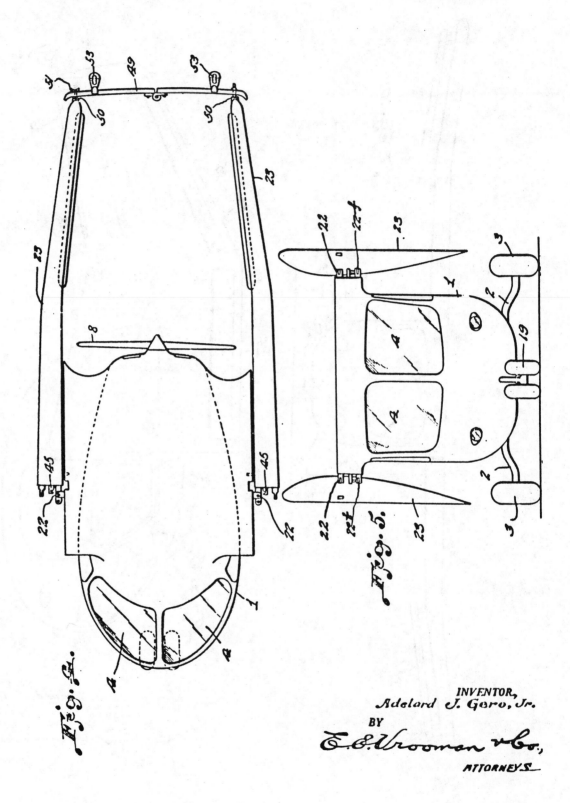

INVENTOR,
Adelard J. Gero, Jr.
BY
E. E. Vrooman & Co.,
ATTORNEYS

FIG. 1

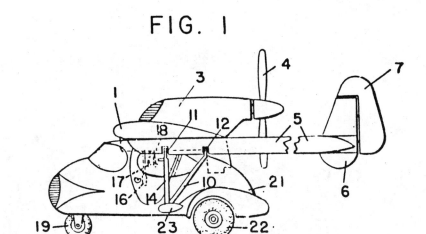

FIG. 2

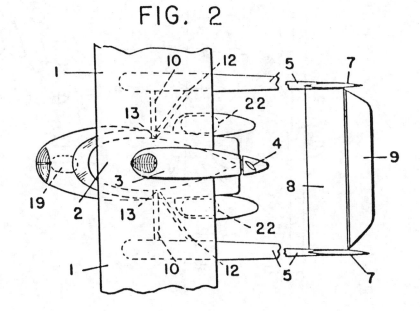

Inventor
JOZEF HENDRIK HANSSEN,

By Wenderolf, Lind & Ponack
Attorneys

FIG. 3

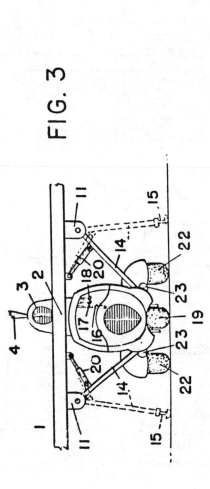

FIG. 4

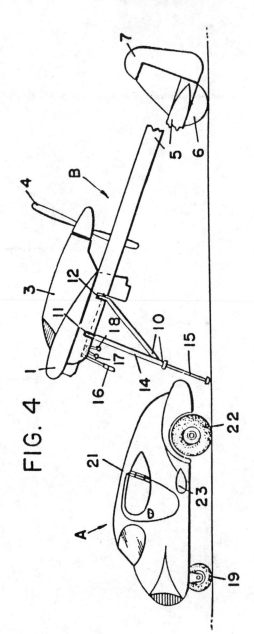

Inventor

JOZEF HENDRIK HANSSEN,

By _Winston D. Lind & Ponach_

Attorneys

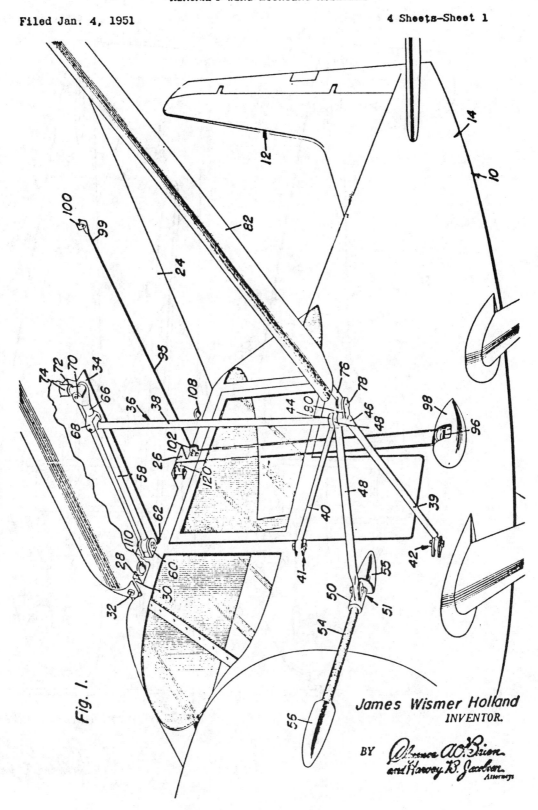

Fig. I.

James Wismer Holland
INVENTOR.

BY
Oliver A. O'Brien
and Harvey B. Jacobson
Attorneys

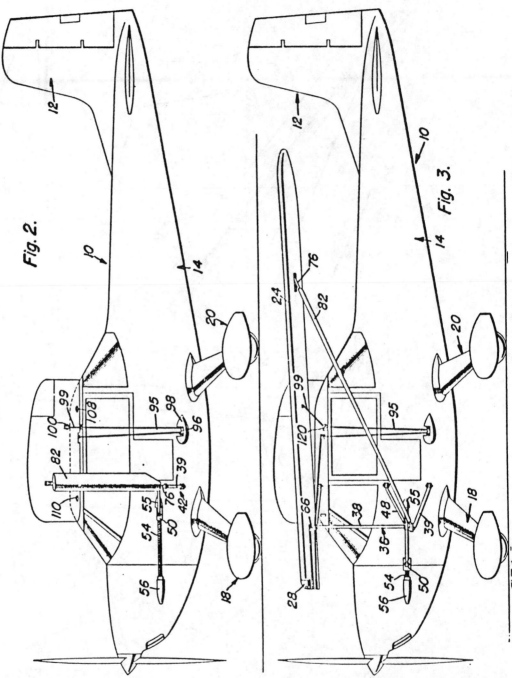

Fig. 2.

Fig. 3.

James Wismer Holland   INVENTOR.

BY

Attorneys

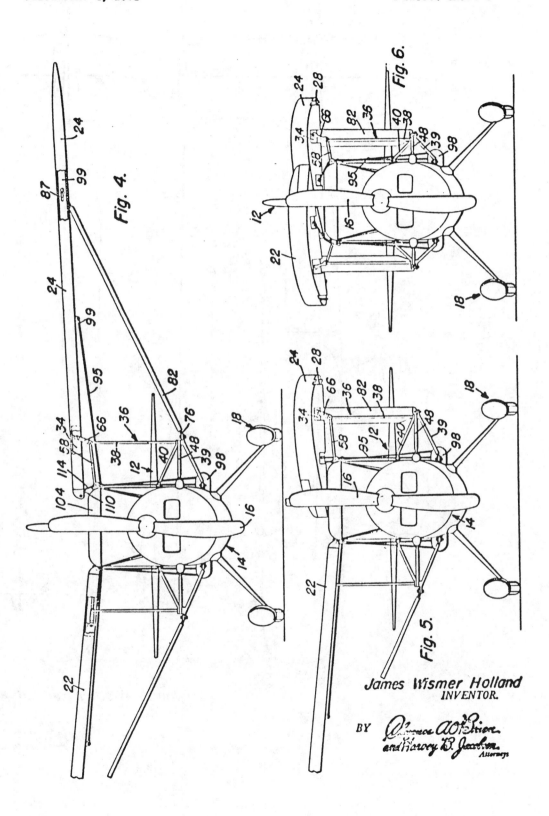

Fig. 4.

Fig. 5.

Fig. 6.

James Wismer Holland
INVENTOR.

BY

Attorneys

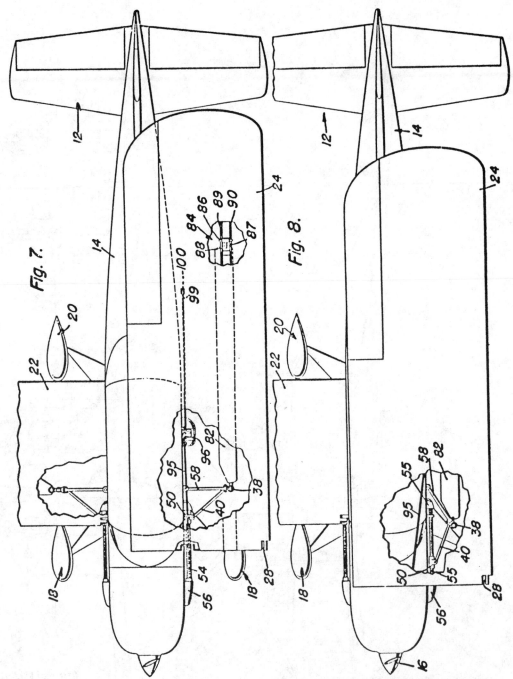

Fig. 7.

Fig. 8.

James Wismer Holland INVENTOR.

BY

Attorneys

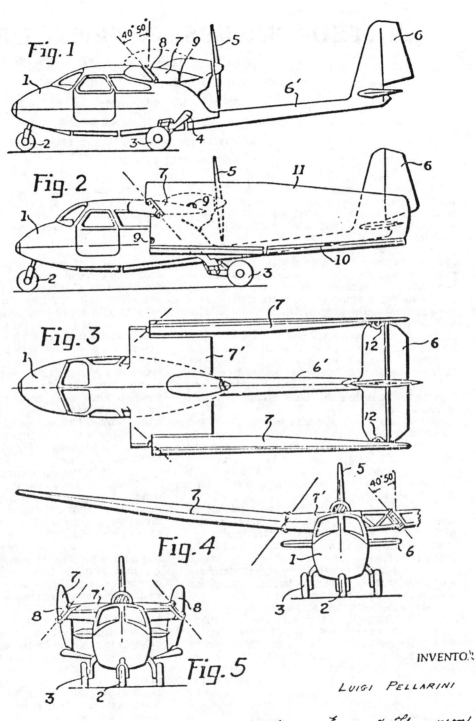

Fig. 1

Fig. 2

Fig. 3

Fig. 4

Fig. 5

INVENTOR

LUIGI PELLARINI

BY Young, Emery & Thompson

ATTORNEYS

UNITED STATES PATENT OFFICE

2,674,422

FOLDING WING FOR ROADABLE AIRCRAFT

Luigi Pellarini, Milan, Italy

Application May 8, 1950, Serial No. 160,596

Claims priority, application Italy May 12, 1949

1 Claim. (Cl. 244—49)

1

The present invention relates to an aircraft which when its half wings are folded at the sides of the frame and with retrocession of the back wheels, can be turned into a screw propelled land vehicle.

According to the invention the half wings are provided at their ends with a main coupling for their connection with the middle trunk of the wing fixed to the frame, which remains permanently hingedly connected with the corresponding coupling on the wing middle trunk, and with at least one secondary coupling easily releasable from its corresponding coupling fixed to the middle trunk, the main hinge coupling having a slanting pivotal axis which guides the half wings in their backward movement so as to place them with their wing plane just about vertical and parallel to the middle surface of symmetry of the aircraft.

In this way the half wings extend along the frame and their ends lie in close proximity to the empennages to which they can be coupled rigidly so as to completely close in the propeller.

The invention will be described with more particulars in connection with the accompanying drawing in which:

Figures 1 and 2 show schematically side elevational views of an aircraft in a flight position and with the wings folded, respectively.

Fig. 3 is a plan view of the aircraft with the wings folded.

Figures 4 and 5 represent two front views respectively with the wings in the flying position and in the folded position.

The aircraft according to the present invention embodies a frame 1, front wheel 2 and the undercarriage 3 fixed on axis 4. The aircraft is driven by a propeller 5 and has a rearwardly extending strut 6' carrying the control and stability surfaces 6. In accordance with this invention the two half wings 7 are fixed on the middle trunk 7' with a main hinged coupling having a slanting axis 8, and secondary releasable coupling 9 behind the main coupling 8. The axis of the hinged coupling is approximately slanting at 45° in regard to the three cartesian axes and in front it is displaced in regard to the center of pressure line of the half wing.

In the flying position the secondary coupling 9 on the half wings 7 is attached to the corresponding fixed coupling on the middle wing trunk 7', and the half wings 7 are therefore stably coupled with the middle wing body 7' and in a position to hold out against all outside stresses in the three orthogonal surfaces.

2

When the aircraft has to be changed into a land vehicle all that has to be done is to release the secondary couplings 9 so that the half wings when thrust backwards turn around the slanting axis at an angle of more than 90°. Rotation takes place in accordance with a trajectory which is the result of the circular trajectories of the half wings around the three projections of the rotation axis in the three orthogonal surfaces. Following this resulting movement each half wing is placed with the wing chords in a practically vertical surface and with its opening rests substantially parallel with the lengthwise plane of symmetry of the vehicle. In this way the trailing edge 10 of the half wing is directed towards the ground and leading edge 11 of the section, upwards. In this position the ends of the half wings 7 can come into contact with the back empennages of the vehicle, with which they can be coupled rigidly with a coupling 12, so as to completely close in the propeller and prevent entrance from the outside to the screw in movement for the purpose of safeguarding persons and things in the surroundings.

Of course the vehicle must be of such measurements that when the wings are folded it does not take up more space than the front and crosswise measurements called for by the vehicle traffic regulations.

To guaranty the stability and manoeuvring of the land vehicle in its movement on roads, seeing that with the half wings folded the center of gravity of the vehicle moves backwards, the wheel 3 can be made movable backwards too, by making the legs of the carriage rotate around the axles 4, so as to ensure, even with the center of gravity displaced, that the front wheel always adheres to the road to the proper extent.

The secondary coupling 9 in the description is provided for at the back of the principal coupling 8 with reference to the direction of movement of the vehicle, but in certain cases it can be advantageously applied in front or there can also be two, releasable either separately or at the same time, arranged at the two sides of the hinge coupling 8.

The other constructional particulars of the vehicle with reference to the couplings, movability of the carriage etc. can vary to be suitable for the different types of aircraft, etc. without departing from the scope of this invention.

What I claim is:

An aircraft of the character described comprising a cabin, a propeller at the rear of the cabin, a short stub sustaining wing extending

3

laterally outwardly from each side of the upper rear portion of the cabin forwardly of the propeller, the span of said stub wings being greater than the diameter of the propeller, a tail structure at the rear of the aircraft, means extending rearwardly from the cabin and supporting said tail structure, an extension sustaining wing for each stub wing, and hinge means positioned closer to the leading edge of the wings than to the trailing edge for mounting each extension wing on its stub wing, each hinge means having its hinge axis fixedly inclined at an angle of about 45° with respect to the three cartesian axes of the aircraft with the upper portion of each hinge axis lying more forward and nearer the longitudinal central plane of the aircraft than the lower portion thereof to cause the chords of the extension wings to swing from a general hori-

4

zontal to a vertical position upon swinging the extension wings rearwardly about the hinges to lie against the tail structure and thereby form an enclosure on each side of the propeller.

References Cited in the file of this patent

UNITED STATES PATENTS

Number	Name	Date
1,556,414	Bumpus	Oct. 6 ,1925
1,793,056	Carns	Feb. 17, 1931
2,434,068	Geisse	Jan. 6, 1948

FOREIGN PATENTS

Number	Country	Date
274,151	Great Britain	July 11, 1927
447,577	Great Britain	May 21, 1936
506,528	Great Britain	May 30, 1939
559,819	Great Britain	Mar. 7, 1944

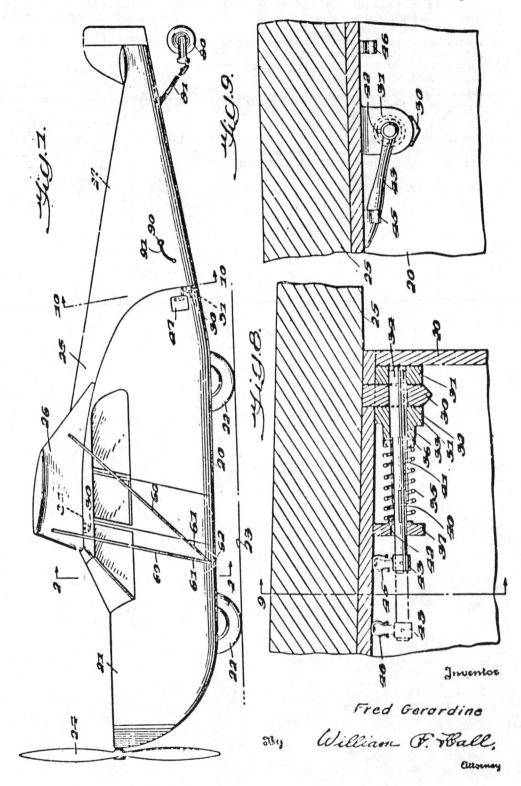

Inventor

Fred Gerardine

By   William F. Ball,

Attorney

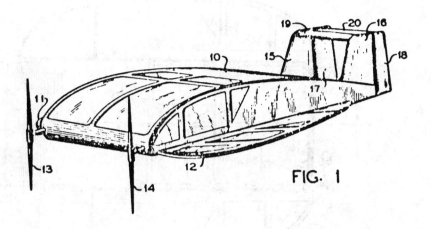

FIG. 1

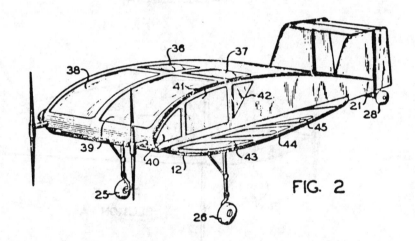

FIG. 2

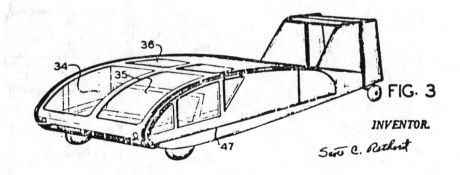

FIG. 3

INVENTOR.

Scott C. Rethorst

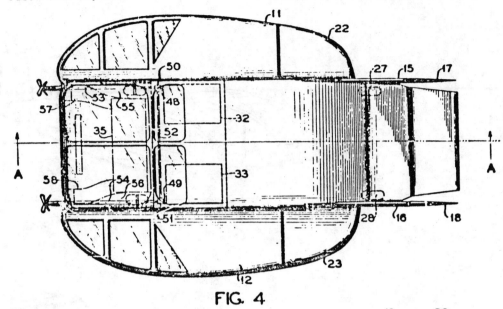

FIG. 4

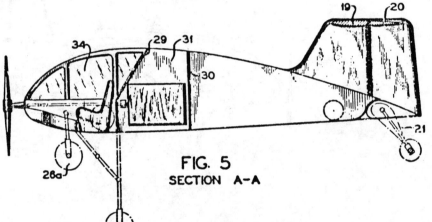

FIG. 5
SECTION A-A

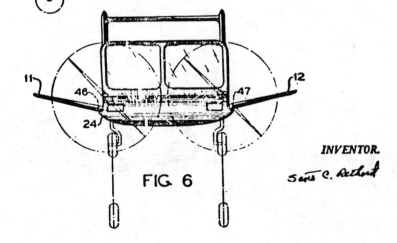

FIG. 6

INVENTOR.

Sam C. Rethorst

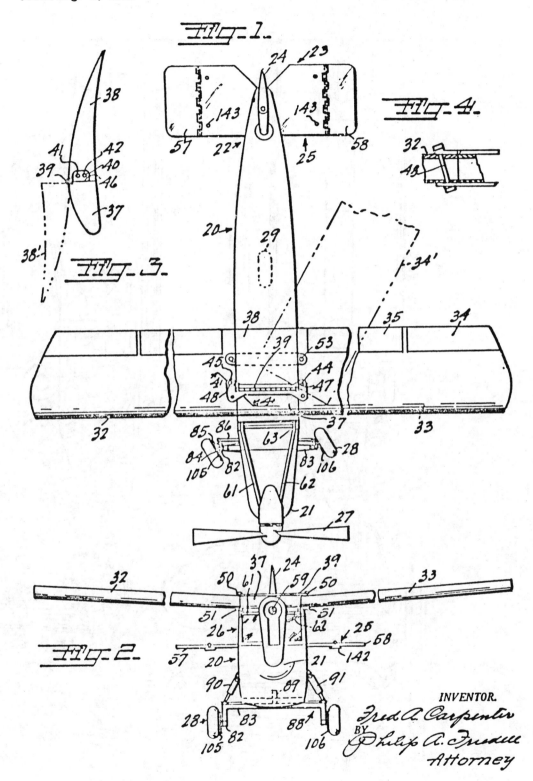

INVENTOR.
Fred A. Carpenter
BY
Philip A. Tredell
Attorney

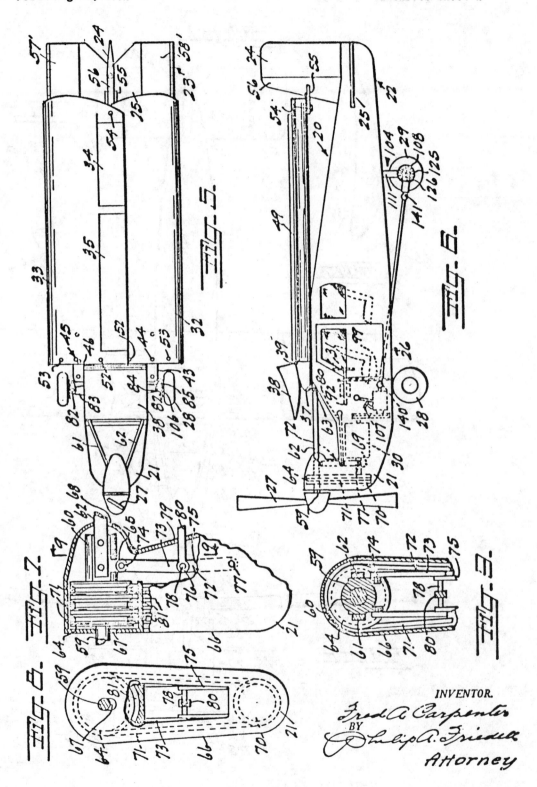

INVENTOR.

Fred A. Carpenter

BY Philip A. Friedell

Attorney

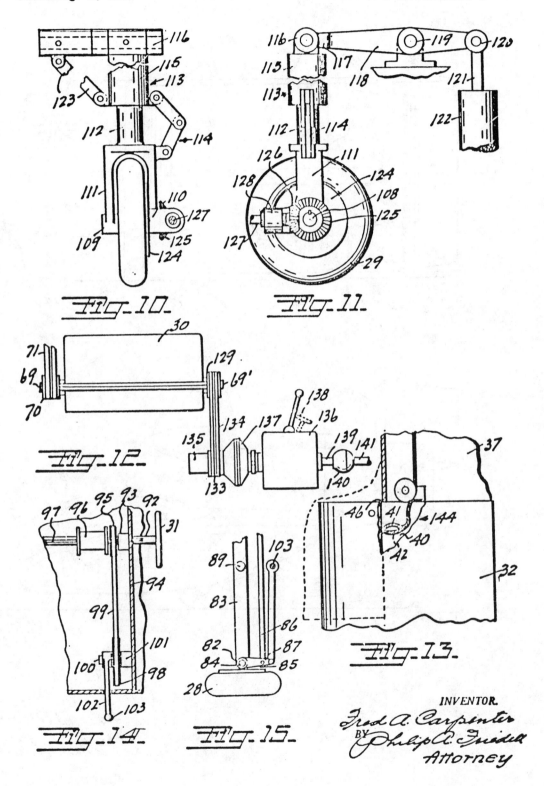

Fig-10.

Fig-11.

Fig-12.

Fig-13.

Fig-14.

Fig-15.

INVENTOR.

Fred A. Carpenter
BY Philip A. Fridell
Attorney

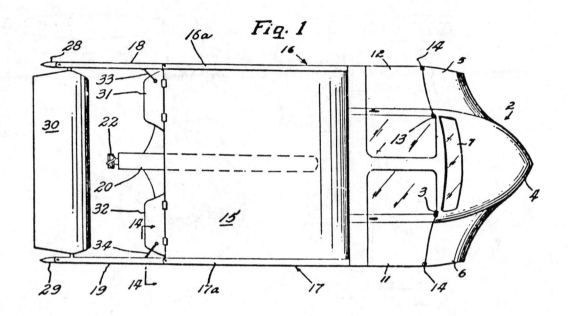

Fig. 1

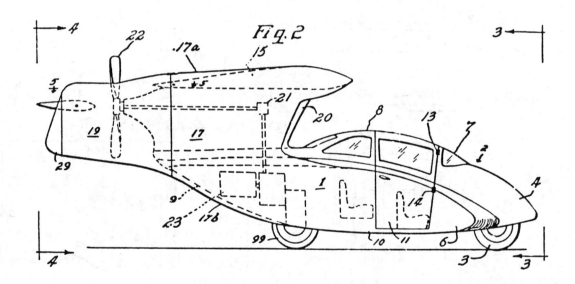

Fig. 2

INVENTOR.

Harry E. Novinger

BY

Fred Wells

Atty.

Fig. 3

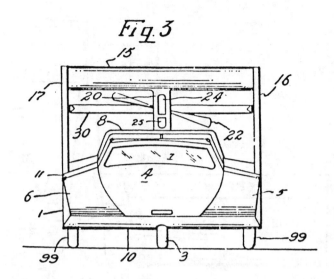

Fig. 4

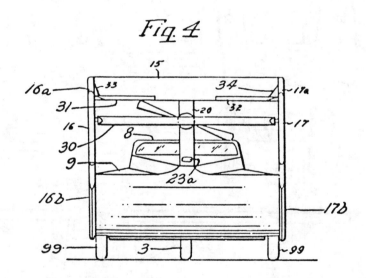

INVENTOR.

Harry E. Novinger

BY

GrukWells

atty.

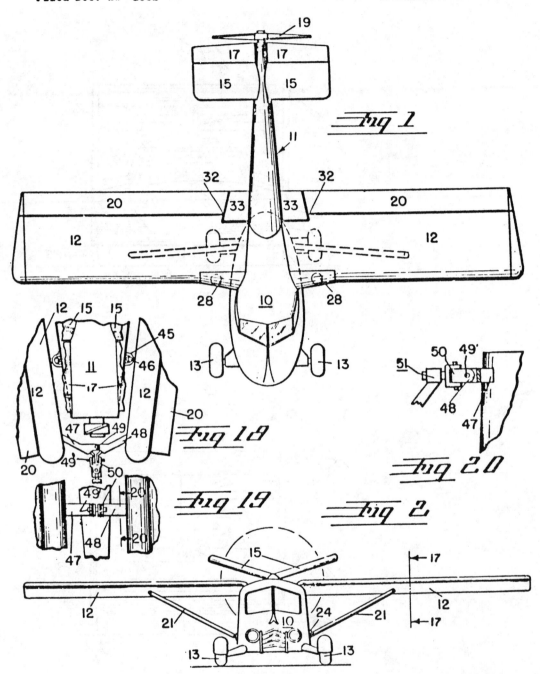

INVENTOR.

MOULTON B. TAYLOR

BY

ATTORNEY

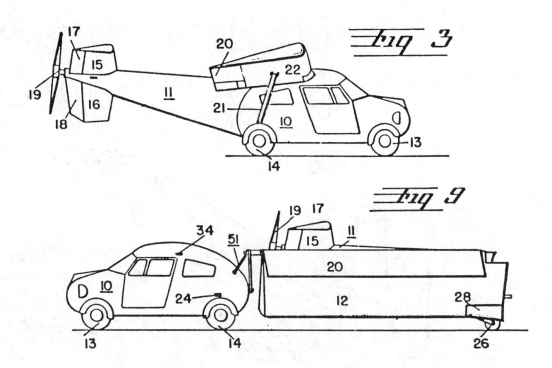

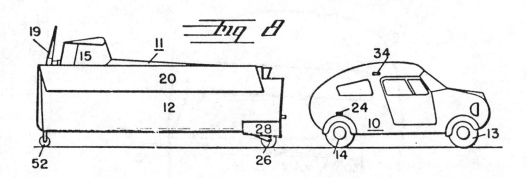

INVENTOR.

MOULTON B TAYLOR
BY

ATTORNEY

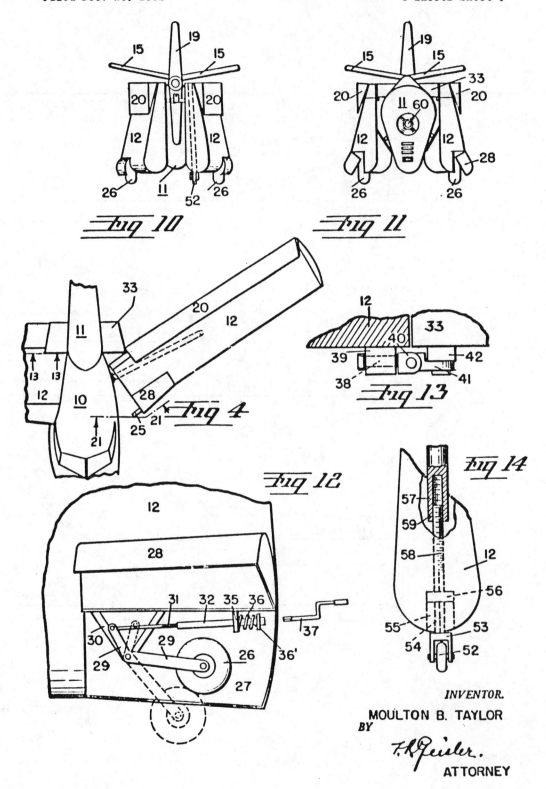

Fig 10

Fig 11

Fig 4

Fig 13

Fig 12

Fig 14

INVENTOR.

MOULTON B. TAYLOR
BY

F. L. Geisler.

ATTORNEY

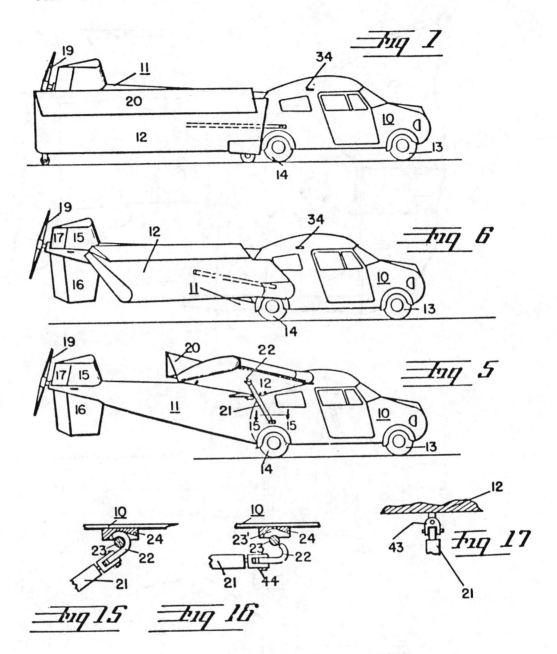

INVENTOR.

MOULTON B. TAYLOR
BY

F. L. Geisler.

ATTORNEY.

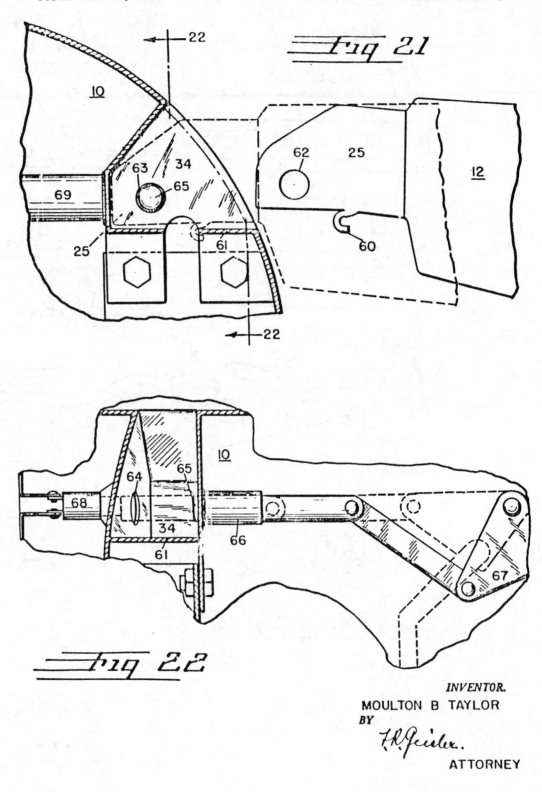

Fig 21

Fig 22

INVENTOR.
MOULTON B TAYLOR
BY

ATTORNEY

1

2,767,939
FLYING AUTOMOTIVE VEHICLE ASSEMBLY
Moulton B. Taylor, Longview, Wash., assignor to Aerocar, Inc., Longview, Wash., a corporation of Washington

Application December 26, 1952, Serial No. 328,043

9 Claims. (Cl. 244—2)

This invention relates in general to an automotive vehicle assembly equally suitable either for air travel or
for land travel and capable of being converted quickly
and easily from a highway automobile to an aeroplane
and vice versa.

More specifically this invention relates to a convertible
assembly, one arrangement of which results in a complete
aeroplane and the other arrangement of which results in
a highway automobile having a detachable trailer, which
assembly is completely mobile without recourse to other
transport means.

While various attempts have heretofore been made to
produce vehicles adapted for both land and air travel,
the necessity of removing or folding at least the wings
from an aeroplane, or similar vehicle adapted for air
travel, before the same can be operated on a highway as
a land vehicle, has heretofore presented two main difficulties.

One of these difficulties is the problem of folding or
removing or demounting the external members necessary for air travel, in particular the wings, when the
vehicle is to be used for land travel, and remounting such
members again for air travel. Thus when the folding,
demounting or remounting of the wings involves considerable effort, labor, time or encumbrance, the convertible feature of the vehicle is largely negatived.

In the situation of demounting the wings, the other
difficulty is the problem of temporarily disposing of the
wings, transporting them and handling the demounted
members while the vehicle is used for land travel. If
such removed members are stored at the landing field
then it is necessary, after the vehicle has been used for
land travel, to return to the same landing field for the
remounting of such members for air travel. This defeats
a main objective which would be to enable the vehicle
to proceed by land when conditions are temporarily un-
suited for air travel and then subsequently again to continue on the course by air.

One of the objects of the present invention is to provide
an improved convertible flying automotive assembly in
which the wings and other members, which are required
only for air travel, can be easily and quickly demounted
and again remounted by a single operator with very little
physical effort and only a minimum expenditure of time.

Another principal object of the invention is to provide
an improved convertible assembly of the character described wherein the demountable members, not used in
land travel, will combine of themselves to form a separate
trailer vehicle complete in itself, so as to be capable of
being towed along the highway by the land automobile
portion of the assembly, instead of necessitating the leaving of such members at the spot where their demounting
takes place, or instead of requiring the temporary em-
ployment of another vehicle or other additional equip-
ment to provide mobility for conveying the demounted
members, or even requiring the demounted members to
be awkwardly carried by such land automobile portion
of the assembly.

A related object of the invention is to provide such an
assembly in which the demounted members will constitute a trailer vehicle which can be easily unhitched entirely from the land automobile portion of the assembly

2

and thus, at the option of the operator or driver, either
be towed along the highway or temporarily parked at any
convenient spot along the highway, stored in a conventional auto garage instead of hangar, in the same manner
as any ordinary automobile trailer, and at the same time
meeting existing vehicle codes and highway regulations.

A further object of this present invention is to provide
such an assembly in which that portion of the assembly
which remains after the demountable members required
for air travel are removed will constitute not merely a
vehicle capable of some degree of travel on land, but
actually a land automobile capable of, and suitable for,
extensive highway travel and embodying all features required to meet existing codes and regulations for highway
vehicles.

An additional object is to provide a so-called flying
automobile which will be complete, self contained, practical, of suitable design and construction for air or highway travel, and inexpensive enough to appeal to a po-
tentially large market.

The manner in which and the means by which these
objects and other advantages are attained through my
invention will be briefly described with reference to the
accompanying drawings.

In the drawings, which are more or less diagrammatic:

Fig. 1 is a top plan view of the vehicle assembly as
arranged for air travel and thus in the form simulating
an aeroplane;

Fig. 2 is a corresponding front elevation;

Fig. 3 is a corresponding side elevation;

Fig. 4 (Sheet 4) is a fragmentary top plan view illustrating one of the wings in the process of being folded so
as to be demounted from the automobile portion of the
assembly;

Fig. 5 (Sheet 2) is a side elevation also showing the
wings in the process of being demounted;

Figs. 6 and 7 (Sheet 2) are side elevations illustrating
the successive stages in the demounting of the wings;

Fig. 8 (Sheet 3) is a side elevation illustrating the entire separation of the automobile portion of the assembly
from the wings and tail portion of the assembly and
showing the wings and tail portion forming an entirely
separate trailer vehicle;

Fig. 9 (Sheet 3) is a side elevation of the same trailer
vehicle and automobile portion, illustrating the trailer
vehicle attached to the automobile for the purpose of
being towed by the latter;

Fig. 10 (Sheet 4) is an end view of the trailer vehicle
taken from the left of Fig. 8;

Fig. 11 (Sheet 4) is an opposite end view of the trailer
vehicle taken from the right of Fig. 9;

Fig. 12 (Sheet 4) is a fragmentary side elevation, on
an enlarged scale, of an end of a demounted wing with
the cover of a wheel housing chamber raised to show the
wing-wheel, a lowered position of such wing-wheel being
indicated by broken line;

Fig. 13 (Sheet 4) is an enlarged fragmentary section
taken on line 13—13 of Fig. 4 showing the universal-
pivotal joint by which each wing is secured to its mounting block on the tail portion of the entire assembly;

Fig. 14 (Sheet 4) is a fragmentary end view, on an enlarged scale, of the outer end of one of the wings showing
an additional wheel for temporarily supporting the end
of the wing and therewith the corresponding ends of the
tail section end and the other wing when the wings are
demounted from the automobile portion, and indicating
in broken lines the adjustable screw jack mounting for
the wheel;

Fig. 15 (Sheet 2) is an enlarged fragmentary plan section taken on line 15—15 of Fig. 5 looking downwardly
on the strut when the wing is in the process of being
swung back before the strut is detached from the auto-

mobile portion showing the detachable, pivotal and swivel mounting at the bottom end of one of the wing struts;

Fig. 16 (Sheet 2) illustrates the same strut detached from its mounting on the automobile when the wing has been swung further back;

Fig. 17 (Sheet 2) is an enlarged fragmentary sectional elevation showing the upper end of one of the wing struts and its connection with the wing, the section being taken on line 17—17 of Figure 2;

Fig. 18 (Sheet 1) is a fragmentary plan view, on an enlarged scale, showing the end of the tail portion and the corresponding ends of the two wings when the wings are in folded position and placed adjacent the opposite sides of the tail portion, and illustrating the means by which the ends of the wings are attached together in such position;

Fig. 19 (Sheet 1) is a fragmentary end elevation of the means connecting the wing ends shown in Fig. 18;

Fig. 20 (Sheet 1) is a fragmentary sectional elevation taken in part on line 20—20 of Fig. 19 showing the same wing-end connecting means and also showing a portion of the trailer coupling attached to the connecting means whereby the separate trailer is connected to the automobile for towing;

Fig. 21 (Sheet 5) is an enlarged elevation of the latch element on the front edge of one of the wings and a fragmentary sectional elevation of the adjacent portion of the automobile showing the aperture into which the latch element is received, this composite figure being taken on the line indicated at 21—21 in Fig. 4; and

Fig. 22 (Sheet 5) is a fragmentary sectional elevation of the same portion of the automobile taken on line 22—22 of Fig. 21.

In the drawings the reference character 10 indicates in general the automobile portion of the assembly, 11 indicates the tail portion and 12, 12 indicate the wings.

The automobile 10 has a pair of front steering wheels 13, 13 which are driven by the motor (not shown) located in the automobile in a more or less conventional manner. However, the motor in the automobile is located near the rear of the automobile instead of in the front. The automobile also has a pair of rear wheels 14, 14 which are not driven and thus are free to rotate except for the customary brake controls. The horizontal stabilizers 15, 15 are mounted on the tail portion 11 together with the vertical stabilizer 16 and rudder 18. The horizontal stabilizers 15, 15 preferably extend slightly obliquely upwardly, as shown in Fig. 2, instead of extending in the same horizontal plane, to facilitate wing folding and improve aerodynamic characteristics. The usual elevators 17 (Fig. 1) are hinged to the stabilizers 15 and the usual rudder 18 (Fig. 3) is hinged to the vertical stabilizer 16. The usual ailerons 20 (Fig. 1) are hinged to the wings 12.

The aeroplane propeller 19 is mounted on the end of the tail portion 11 and, as will be noted from Fig. 3, the axis of rotation of the propeller 19 is oblique to the horizontal plane of the four wheels of the automobile, the reason for which will be apparent later. Similarly the tail portion 11 is inclined slightly upwardly with respect to the horizontal plane of the wheels, the longitudinal bottom line of the tail portion sloping upwardly to a greater degree than the longitudinal top line, as apparent from Fig. 3, inasmuch as the tail portion 11 decreases constantly in cross sectional size from the front to the rear, as is generally customary.

When the tail section of the assembly is connected to the automobile (as illustrated in Figs. 1–7), the propeller shaft (the end of which is indicated at 60 in Fig. 11) is joined to the automobile drive shaft through the medium of a splined sleeve connection (not shown), the rear end of the drive shaft being exposed at the rear of the automobile portion when a cover door (not shown) on the rear of the automobile is opened preparatory to the securing of the tail section to the automobile. The various controls for the ailerons, elevators and rudder are not illustrated. However it will suffice for the present application to explain merely that the controls, as well as the motor control and clutch control, are located in the automobile in close proximity to the driver's seat. The tail portion is secured to the rear of the automobile by a suitable three-point locking connection. These various connecting and control means are not illustrated in the drawings since they do not form any part of the invention claimed in this present application.

The center of gravity of the entire assembly, when the assembly is arranged for air travel, is slightly forward of the rear wheels 14. This is an important feature in the invention and this feature combines with the upwardly sloping tail portion and inclined propeller and thrust axis to enable the free rear wheels of the automobile to serve as landing wheels for the aeroplane with only a light weight at any time imposed on the front wheels when the assembly is arranged for air travel. This facilitates control and balance of the machine as an aircraft to permit takeoff and landings. On the other hand, when the tail portion and wings are disconnected from the automobile, the center of gravity for the automobile is shifted forward sufficiently to provide the desired weight on the front wheels for suitable road traction and for proper steering.

The tail portion 11 includes a pair of wing mount supports 33 (Fig. 1) at the forward end of the tail section and on opposite sides respectively. Each of the wings 12 is permanently connected to one of these wing mount supports by a flexible joint assembly comprising a universal-pivotal joint as shown in detail in Fig. 13.

A strut 21 (Fig. 2) extends from the under side of each wing downwardly and inwardly to the respective side of the automobile. The upper end of each strut is permanently connected to its wing by a pivotal connection shown in detail in Fig. 17. The lower end of each strut 21 carries a swivelly and pivotally-mounted hook 22 (Fig. 16) adapted for engagement with a loop 23 and recess slot 23' in a strut mounting support 24 secured on the automobile. Each wing 12 also has a latch element 25 (Fig. 4) secured to the inner end of the front or leading edge spar of the wing, which latch element is adapted to extend into an aperture 34 in the side of the automobile and to be engaged inside the automobile by a locking pin when the wing is in position for flying. Referring to Fig. 21, the latch element 25 of the wing 12 (being the wing on the right as viewed in Fig. 4) is shown in the act of being inserted into the corresponding aperture 34 in the side of the automobile 10. A hook 60 on the latch element is adapted to engage a lip 61 provided in the aperture 34 for temporarily holding the latch element 25 in place in the automobile during the locking of the latch element. The latch element 25 has an opening 62, which, when the latch element is in place in the automobile, registers with a pair of locking pin holes 63 and 64 (Fig. 22) in the side walls of the aperture 34 respectively. A locking pin 65, slidably supported in a stationary sleeve 66 (Fig. 22), is connected by suitable linkage with a manually operated lever, a portion of which is shown at 67 in Fig. 22, which is operated from inside the automobile, so that when the lever 67 is pulled forwardly to the broken line position indicated in Fig. 22, the locking pin 65 will be moved into the opening 62 in the latch element 25 and extend a slight distance into the hole 64 in the opposite wall of the aperture 34. A stationary rest (not shown) on the inside of the automobile holds the lever 67 against inadvertent movement when the locking pin 65 has been set in locking position. A switch 68 in the starter circuit of the automobile engine is so arranged as to be closed by the locking pin 65 when the pin is in locking position. The switch 68 and the corresponding switch (not shown) on the opposite side of the automobile are so arranged that the automobile engine cannot be started if either of the locking pins for the two wings should not be in locking position. Thus when each wing 12 is mounted for flying it is secured at its leading edge to the automobile portion of the assembly and secured to its mount support on the tail portion of the assembly and is also supported on its strut which extends from the automobile portion up against the under side of the wing.

The flexible joint assembly (Fig. 13) by which each wing 12 is secured to its mount support 33 on the tail portion, comprises a stub shaft 38 rotatably held in a bearing 39 secured under the wing 12. One end of the shaft 38 is formed into a ring 40 in which a bearing block 41 is pivotally mounted. A boss 42, secured to the wing support 33 is pivotally held on the block 41. The three axes of rotation of the members of the joint assembly are thus perpendicular to each other.

The connection (Fig. 17) by which the upper end of each strut 21 is connected to the under side of its respective wing, includes a double yoke member 43, pivotally secured to the wing, in which the strut 21 is pivotally held.

The lower end of each strut 21 (Figs. 15 and 16) carries a swively-mounted member 44 to which is pivotally connected the hook 22 which is adapted to fit into the recess slot 23' in the mounting support or block 24 under a locking loop 23. The block 24 is rigidly secured to the automobile. The recess 23', locking loop 23 and hook 22 are so formed and arranged that when the strut 21 extends upwardly and outwardly from the automobile the strut will be locked to the block 24 and thus to the automobile, but when the upper end of the strut is swung downwardly and rearwardly (to the position illustrated in Fig. 16) the hook 22 will free itself from the recess 23' and the locking loop 23 on the block 24.

When the wings are to be demounted from the automobile portion of the assembly the locking pins are unlocked from the latch members 25 attached to the front spars of the wings. This permits the wings, while still resting on their struts 21, to be swung rearwardly on the flexible joint assemblies through which they are attached to their mount blocks 33. The joints at the top and bottom ends of the struts 21 enable the struts to swing rearwardly and downwardly while still carrying the wing weight. As a result, as each unlocked wing is pushed rearwardly it swings down and aft from the position of Fig. 1 through the position of Fig. 4 or Fig. 5, and through the subsequent position illustrated in Fig. 6, until the wing comes into substantial vertical position adjacent the tail portion.

When the wings 12 are brought into this latter position the outer, rear, or free ends of the wings are attached to each other and to the rear of the tail portion 11. Referring now to Fig. 18, a pair of eye-loops 45 are mounted on opposite sides of the tail portion 11 and are adapted for engagement by hooks 46 carried on the wings. The two wings also carry the two coupling members 47 and 48 respectively (Figs. 18 and 19), one of which, namely the member 48, terminates in a stub adapted to support the other member 47, the members 47 and 48 also terminating in eye-loops, thus enabling the two members 47 and 48 to be coupled by the insertion of a suitable pin 49. This pin 49 can in turn be held against inadvertent displacement by an ordinary safety pin type cotter pin (not shown). The extended ends of the members 47 and 48 are also arranged to have a yoke 50 attached to them by means of a horizontal pin 49'. The yoke 50 in turn is adapted to be connected with a trailer coupling 51 (Fig. 20), to which reference will be made later, by a pivotal and swivel connection.

Each wing 12 has a wheel chamber or cavity 27 (Fig. 12) located at the inner end of the leading edge of the wing, which cavity is enclosed by a hinged cover 28 when the wing is attached to the automobile in flying position. A wheel 26 is mounted in the forked end of a wheel arm 29 in each cavity 27. The wheel arm 29 is in the form of a bell crank and is pivotally mounted

on a support bracket 30. The opposite end of the wheel arm 29 is pivotally connected to an adjustment rod 31, the other end of which is threaded and which extends into a threaded sleeve 32. The sleeve 32 is slidably and rotatably carried in a support 35. A spring 36 is carried on the sleeve 32 between the support 35 and a fixed collar 36'. The channel wall in the outer end of the sleeve 32 is deformed in order to be rotatably engaged by the correspondingly surfaced end of a hand crank 37 or other suitable means. Thus when the wings 12 are to be demounted from the automobile by being swung rearwardly from the automobile, the wheels 26 in the wheel chambers 27 of the wings can be moved into outward position (illustrated by the broken lines in Fig. 12) by turning the sleeve 32 with the hand crank 37. These wing wheels are an important feature of my invention inasmuch as they constitute a pair of supporting and spring mounted wheels for the wings and tail portion when the wings and tail portion of the assembly are subsequently separated from the automobile. These wheels can also act as jacks for bringing the trailer (comprising the wings and tail portion) to the proper level or height when the tail portion is to be attached to the automobile in arranging the assembly for air travel as will later be apparent.

When the wings are demounted from the automobile and are swung back adjacent opposite sides of the tail portion, the bottom ends of the wing struts having been disconnected from their blocks 24 on the automobile, and when the wings are attached to each other and to the tail portion (as illustrated in Fig. 18), and when the wing wheels 26 are in engagement with the ground, the entire wing and tail portion of the assembly is then ready to be disconnected from the automobile portion. To facilitate the disconnecting of the wing and tail portion and in order to furnish a temporary support for the rear end of this wing and tail portion, I provide an adjustable wheel 52 and screw jack in the outer end of one of the wings, as shown in Fig. 14. This small supporting wheel 52 is mounted in a wheel fork 53 secured on the bottom end of the shaft 54. The shaft 54 is preferably square in cross section and is mounted for sliding in a guide bearing 56. A cavity 55 in the edge and end of the wing houses the wheel 52 and its fork 53 when this temporary supporting wheel is not being used. A threaded shaft 58 is rigidly secured to the top of the shaft 54 or formed integral with the shaft 54, and the threaded shaft 58 is supported in a drive nut 59 secured at the bottom of a drive tube 57, which in turn is mounted for rotation in a suitable bearing (not shown). The top end (not shown) of this drive tube 57, which is accessible when the wing is in demounted position, has suitable drive gear (not shown) with which crank means (not shown) is connected to facilitate the manual turning of the drive tube 57. By turning the tube 57 and therewith the nut 59 the wheel 52 can be lowered or raised. Thus when the wings are demounted and are secured to the rear end of the tail portion, as previously described, this wheel 52 is lowered and provides a temporary ground support for the tail and wings. The tail portion is now unlocked from the automobile, whereupon the automobile moves away from the tail and wings as illustrated in Fig. 8, leaving the tail and wings by themselves as a separate trailer vehicle. This separate trailer vehicle can either be left parked at the location where it is disconnected from the automobile or this may be towed by the automobile in the same manner as any trailer, its dimensions being such as to conform to existing highway codes and regulations.

If it is desired now to tow the wing and tail trailer, the automobile 10 moves around to the opposite end of the wing and tail trailer and thus from the position of Fig. 8 to the position of Fig. 9. A trailer coupling 51 (shown also in part in Fig. 20) is attached to the rear of the automobile on a suitable center support which is provided and at the same time points at which the tail portion had been attached, and is secured by similar locking means, and the outer end of this coupling 51 is connected to the yoke 50 (Fig. 20) as previously mentioned. The temporary supporting wheel 52, which will now no longer be required for supporting the coupled end of the wing and tail trailer, is raised into its cavity in the wing, and the wing and tail trailer can now be towed along by the automobile until the assembly is again to be used for air travel. The coupling 51 and its connection with the yoke 50 provides a tow attachment at a relatively high point from the ground, which facilitates the towing of the trailer in high winds since the center of gravity and the greater portion of the wing area which will be engaged by the winds are lower than the tow attachment, thus reducing to a minimum the possibility of the trailer being blown over while being towed.

The forming of the assembly into an aeroplane is accomplished easily in the exact reverse of the procedure described for demounting the wings and tail, and the manner in which the aeroplane is again set up does not require further explanation.

Thus, with my improved flying automotive vehicle assembly the change-over from air travel to land travel and vice versa is accomplished easily and expeditiously, and, when the assembly is used for land travel, the automobile portion, which comprises a vehicle actually suited for extensive highway travel, can be used either by itself, or can tow the remaining portion of the entire assembly, comprising the demounted parts and members needed for air travel only, as a separate trailer vehicle, until such time as air travel is to be resumed.

I claim:

1. In a convertible flying assembly, an automobile having a body, an aircraft tail section demountably secured on the rear of said body, stabilizers, elevators and rudder mounted on said tail section near the rear, a propeller mounted on the rear end of said tail section, a pair of wings, a flexible joint assembly connecting each wing to said tail section, cooperating wing-locking means on said automobile and on each wing for demountably securing each wing to said automobile near the leading edge of the wing, a strut for each wing extending upwardly and outwardly from said automobile to the underside of the wing when the wing is in flying position, a flexible joint connecting each strut to the corresponding wing, a detachable pivotal joint connecting the other end of the strut to said automobile, whereby, when said wing-locking means is unlocked, each of said wings may be swung rearwardly on said first mentioned flexible joint assembly while partly supported on said strut until brought into substantially vertical position adjacent the corresponding side of said tail section, and means for securing the outer ends of said wings to the rear end of said tail section when said wings are in rearwardly swung vertical position adjacent said tail section.

2. In a convertible flying assembly, an automobile having a body, a pair of front wheels and a pair of rear wheels on said automobile, an aircraft tail section demountably secured on the rear of said body and extending obliquely upwardly with respect to the plane of the axes of said wheels when said tail section is in secured position, stabilizers, elevators and rudder mounted on said tail section near the rear, a propeller mounted on the rear end of said tail section, a pair of wings, a joint assembly permanently connecting each wing to said tail section, cooperating wing-locking means on said automobile and on each wing for demountably securing each wing to said automobile near the leading edge of the wing, a strut for each wing extending upwardly and outwardly from said automobile to the underside of the wing when the wing is in flying position, a joint connecting each strut to the corresponding wing, a joint connecting the other end of the strut to said automobile, the length and weight of said tail section and the position and weight of said wings, with respect to the weight and

center of gravity of said automobile being such that the center of gravity of said flying assembly, when arranged for flying will be only slightly ahead of said rear wheels of said automobile, whereby said rear wheels of said automobile will serve as landing gear when said assembly is used for air travel.

3. In a convertible flying assembly, an automobile having a body, an aircraft tail section demountably secured on the rear of said body, stabilizers, elevators and rudder mounted on said tail section near the rear, a propeller mounted on the rear end of said tail section, a pair of wings, a flexible joint assembly permanently connecting each wing to said tail section, cooperating wing-locking means on said automobile and on each wing for demountably securing each wing to said automobile near the leading edge of the wing, a strut for each wing extending upwardly and outwardly from said automobile to the underside of the wing when the wing is in flying position, a flexible joint connecting each strut to the corresponding wing, a detachable pivotal joint connecting the other end of the strut to said automobile, whereby, when said wing-locking means is unlocked, each of said wings may be swung rearwardly on said first mentioned universal joint assembly while partly supported on said strut until brought into substantially vertical position adjacent the corresponding side of said tail section, means for securing the outer ends of said wings to the rear end of said tail section when said wings are in rearwardly swung vertical position adjacent said tail section, and adjustable ground-engaging means mounted in the outer end of one of said wings for temporarily supporting said outer end of said latter mentioned wing, and therewith the adjacent end of said tail section and the end of the other wing when said wings are in rearwardly swung vertical position with their outer ends secured to said tail section and said tail section and wings are disconnected from said automobile.

4. In a convertible flying assembly, an automobile having a body, an aircraft tail section demountably secured on the rear of said body, a pair of wings, a flexible joint assembly connecting each wing to said tail section, cooperating wing-locking means on said automobile and on each wing for demountably securing each wing to said automobile near the leading edge of the wing, a strut for each wing extending upwardly and outwardly from said automobile to the underside of the wing when the wing is in flying position, a flexible joint connecting each strut to the corresponding wing, a joint connecting the other end of the strut to said automobile, whereby, when said wing-locking means is unlocked, each of said wings may be swung rearwardly on said first mentioned universal joint assembly while partly supported on said strut until brought into substantially vertical position adjacent the corresponding side of said tail section, and a wheel mounted in the leading edge of each wing, whereby said wing wheels will act as partial supports for said wings and tail section when said wings and tail section are disconnected from said automobile.

5. In a convertible flying assembly, an automobile having a body, an aircraft tail section demountably secured on the rear of said body, a pair of wings, a flexible joint assembly connecting each wing to said tail section, cooperating wing-locking means on said automobile and on each wing for demountably securing each wing to said automobile near the leading edge of the wing, a strut for each wing extending upwardly and outwardly from said automobile to the underside of the wing when the wing is in flying position, a flexible joint connecting each strut to the corresponding wing, a detachable pivotal joint connecting the other end of the strut to said automobile, whereby, when said wing-locking means is unlocked, each of said wings may be swung rearwardly on said first mentioned universal joint assembly while partly supported on said strut until brought

into substantially vertical position adjacent the corresponding side of said tail section, and a wheel adjustably mounted in the inner end of the leading edge of each wing, means in each wing for lowering said wheel to ground-engaging position when said wing is in rearwardly swung vertical position, whereby said wing wheels will act as partial supports for said wings and tail section when said wings and tail section are disconnected from said automobile.

6. In a convertible flying assembly, an automobile having a body, an aircraft tail section demountably secured on the rear of said body, a pair of wings, a flexible joint assembly permanently connecting each wing to said tail section, cooperating wing-locking means on said automobile and on each wing for demountably securing each wing to said automobile near the leading edge of the wing, a strut for each wing extending upwardly and outwardly from said automobile to the underside of the wing when the wing is in flying position, a flexible joint assembly connecting each strut to the corresponding wing, a detachable pivotal joint connecting the other end of the strut to said automobile, whereby, when said wing-locking means is unlocked, each of said wings may be swung rearwardly on said first mentioned flexible joint assembly while partly supported on said strut until brought into substantially vertical position adjacent the corresponding side of said tail section, means for securing the outer ends of said wings to the rear end of said tail section when said wings are in rearwardly swung vertical position adjacent said tail section, a wheel adjustably mounted in the inner end of the leading edge of each wing, and means in each wing for lowering said wheel to ground-engaging position when said wing is in rearwardly swung vertical position, whereby said wing wheels will support the corresponding ends of said wings and therewith said tail section when said tail section and wings are disconnected from said automobile, the adjustable mounting for each of said wing wheels including a cushioning spring element.

7. The combination set forth in claim 1 with the addition of a wheel adjustably mounted in the inner end of the leading edge of each wing, means in each wing for lowering said wheel to ground-engaging position when said wing is in rearwardly swung vertical position, whereby said wing wheels will support the corresponding ends of said wings and therewith said tail section when said tail section and wings are disconnected from said automobile, and adjustable ground-engaging means mounted in the outer end of one of said wings for temporarily supporting said outer end of said latter mentioned wing and therewith the adjacent end of said tail section and the outer end of the other wing when said wings are in rearwardly swung vertical position with their outer ends secured to said tail section and said tail section and wings are disconnected from said automobile.

8. In a convertible flying assembly of the character described, an automobile having a body, an aircraft tail section demountably secured on the rear of said body, stabilizers, elevators and rudder mounted on said tail section near the rear, a propeller mounted on the rear end of said tail section beyond said rudder, a pair of wings, a joint assembly permanently connecting each wing to said tail section, cooperating wing-locking means on said automobile and on each wing for demountably securing each wing to said automobile near the leading edge of the wing, a strut for each wing extending upwardly and outwardly from said automobile to the underside of the wing when the wing is in flying position, a flexible joint connecting each strut to the corresponding wing, a detachable joint connecting the other end of the strut to said automobile, whereby, when said wing-locking means is unlocked, each of said wings may be swung rearwardly on said first mentioned joint assembly while partly supported on said strut until brought into substantially vertical position adjacent the corresponding

side of said tail section, means for securing the outer ends of said wings to the rear end of said tail section when said wings are in rearwardly swung vertical position adjacent said tail section, a wheel adjustably mounted in the inner end of the leading edge of each wing, means in each wing for lowering said wheel to ground-engaging position when said wing is in rearwardly swung vertical position, whereby said wing wheels will support the corresponding ends of said wings and therewith said tail section when said tail section and wings are disconnected from said automobile, adjustable ground-engaging means mounted in the outer end of one of said wings for temporarily supporting said outer end of said latter mentioned wing, and therewith the adjacent end of said tail section and the outer end of the other wing when said wings are in rearwardly swung vertical position with their outer ends secured to said tail section, a trailer support coupling attachable to the rear end of said automobile when said tail section is disconnected from said automobile, and cooperating coupling means on the outer ends of said wings enabling said latter ends of said wings and said tail section to be coupled as a trailer vehicle to said automobile and caused to travel on said wing wheels.

9. A convertible flying assembly of the character described including an automobile having a body, an aircraft tail section demountably secured on the rear of said body, a pair of front wheels and a pair of rear wheels on said automobile, the bottom line of said tail section extending rearwardly and obliquely upwardly with respect to said body when said tail section is in secured position, stabilizers, elevators and rudder mounted on said tail section near the rear, a propeller mounted on the rear end of said tail section beyond said rudder, a pair of wings, a pivotal-universal joint assembly permanently connecting each wing to said tail section, cooperating wing-locking means on said automobile and on each wing for demountably securing each wing to said automobile near the leading edge of the wing, a strut for each wing extending upwardly and outwardly from said automobile to the underside of the wing when the wing is in flying position, a substantially universal joint connecting each strut to the corresponding wing, a detachable pivotal and swivel joint connecting the other end of the strut to said automobile, a wheel adjustably mounted in the inner end of the leading edge of each wing, the length and weight of said tail section and the position and weight of said wings with respect to the weight and center of gravity of said automobile being such that the center of gravity of said assembly when arranged for flying will be only slightly ahead of said rear wheels of said automobile, whereby said rear wheels of said automobile will serve as landing gear when said assembly is used for air travel, the mounting of said wings being such that, when said wing-locking means is unlocked, each of said wings may be swung rearwardly on said first mentioned joint assembly while partly supported on said strut until brought into substantially vertical position adjacent the corresponding side of said tail section, and means in said wings for lowering said wing wheels to ground-engaging position when said wings are in rearwardly swung vertical position.

References Cited in the file of this patent

UNITED STATES PATENTS

1,603,697	Klemm _____ Oct. 19, 1926
1,855,574	Hubert _____ Apr. 26, 1932
2,011,254	Nightingale _____ Aug. 13, 1935
2,434,068	Geisse _____ Jan. 6, 1948
2,532,755	Bloomfield _____ Dec. 5, 1950
2,533,925	Fulton, Jr. _____ Dec. 12, 1950
2,624,530	Hanssen _____ Jan. 6, 1953

FOREIGN PATENTS

| 486,758 | Great Britain _____ June 9, 1938 |
| 559,319 | Great Britain _____ Mar. 7, 1944 |

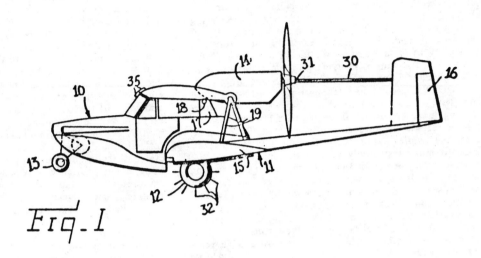

Fig_1

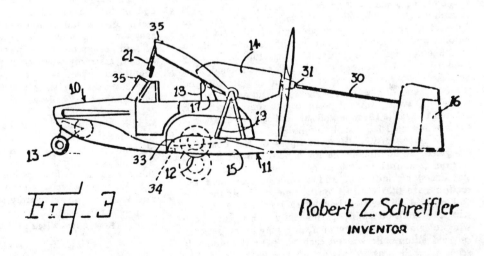

Fig_3

Robert Z. Schreffler

INVENTOR

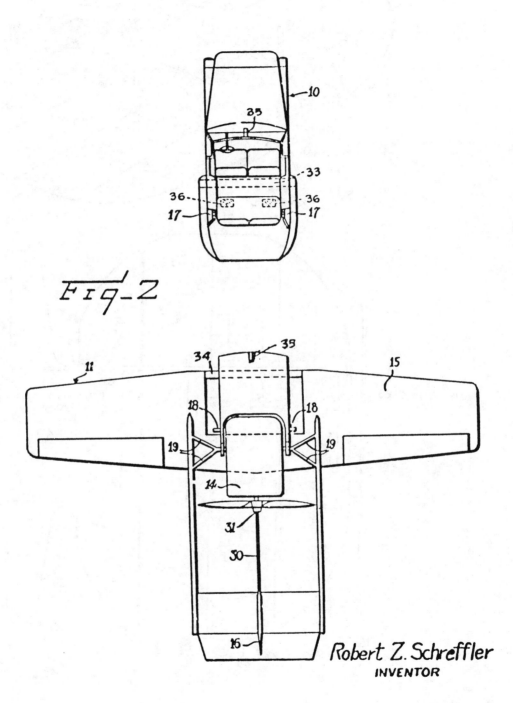

_Fig_2_

Robert Z. Schreffler
INVENTOR

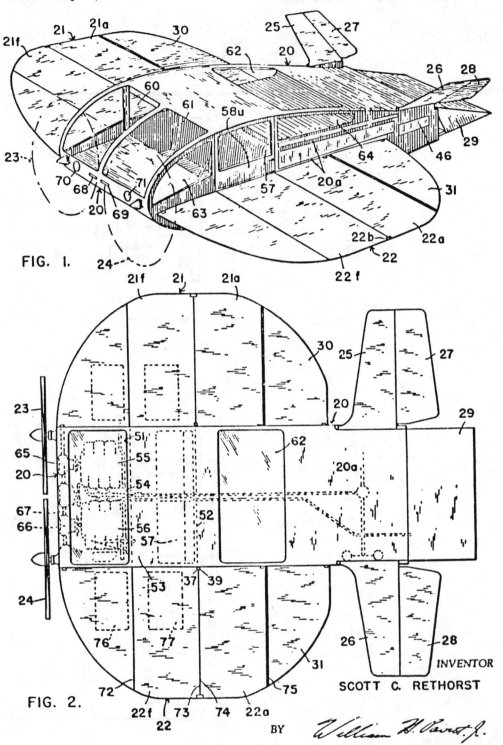

FIG. 1.

FIG. 2.

INVENTOR
SCOTT C. RETHORST

BY *William H. Parrott Jr.*

ATTORNEY

FIG. 3.

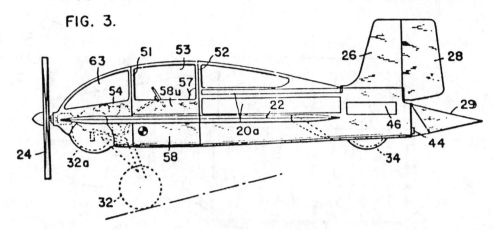

FIG. 5.

FIG. 4.

FIG. 15

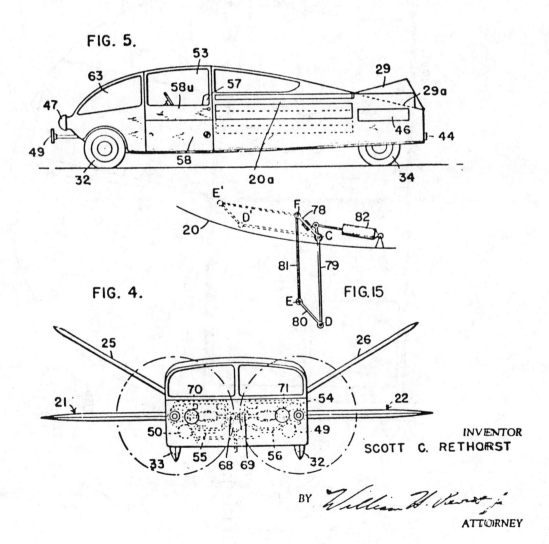

INVENTOR

SCOTT C. RETHORST

BY *William H. Kenway*

ATTORNEY

ROADABLE AIRCRAFT

Filed July 23, 1953 4 Sheets-Sheet 3

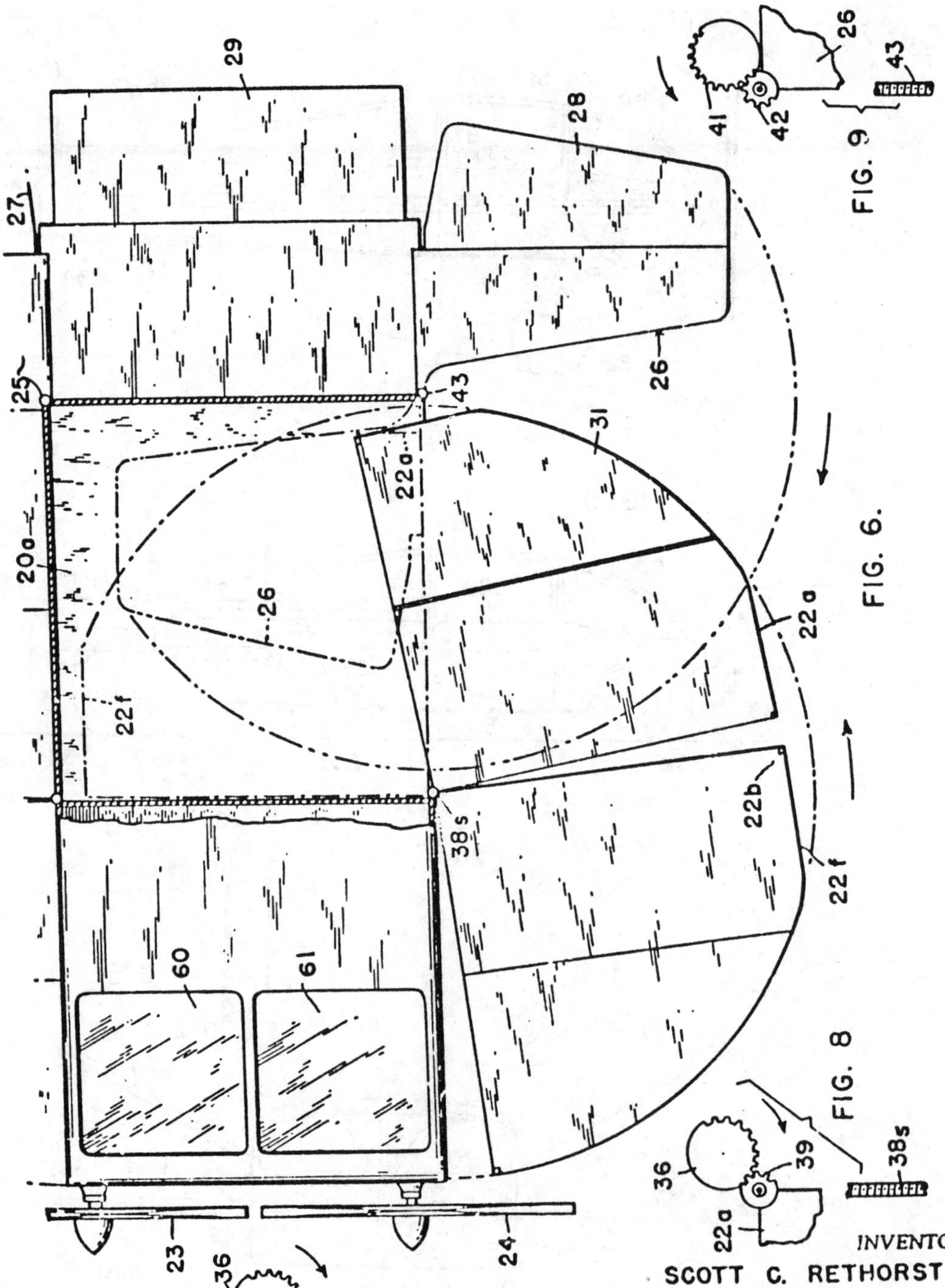

FIG. 6.

FIG. 9

FIG. 8

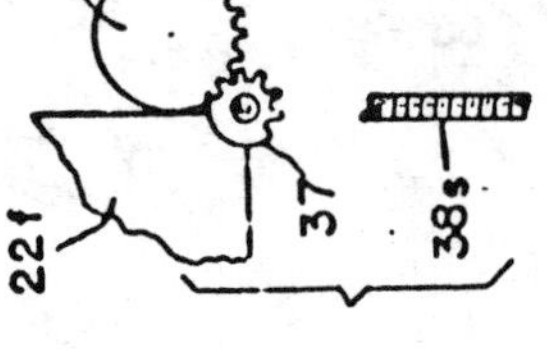

FIG. 7.

INVENTOR
SCOTT C. RETHORST

BY William H. Parrott, Jr.
ATTORNEY

Filed Doo. 27, 1954   2 Sheets-Sheet 1

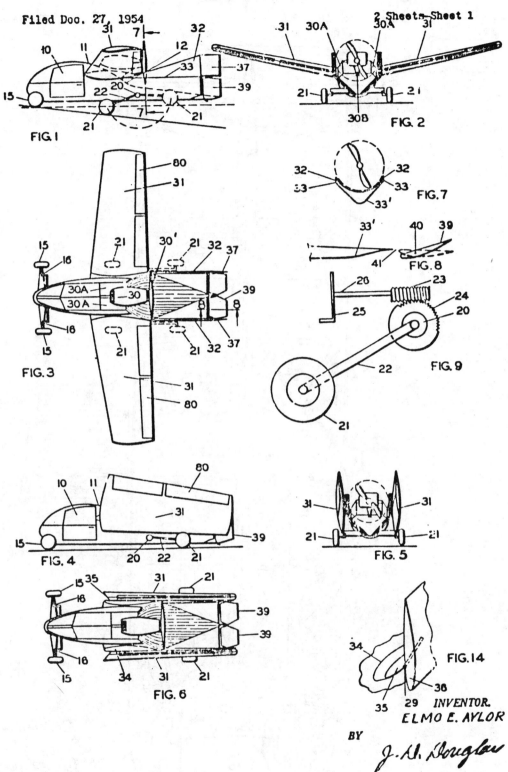

FIG.1

FIG. 2

FIG. 3

FIG. 4

FIG. 5

FIG. 6

FIG.7

FIG. 8

FIG. 9

FIG.14

INVENTOR.
ELMO E. AYLOR

BY
J. A. Douglas

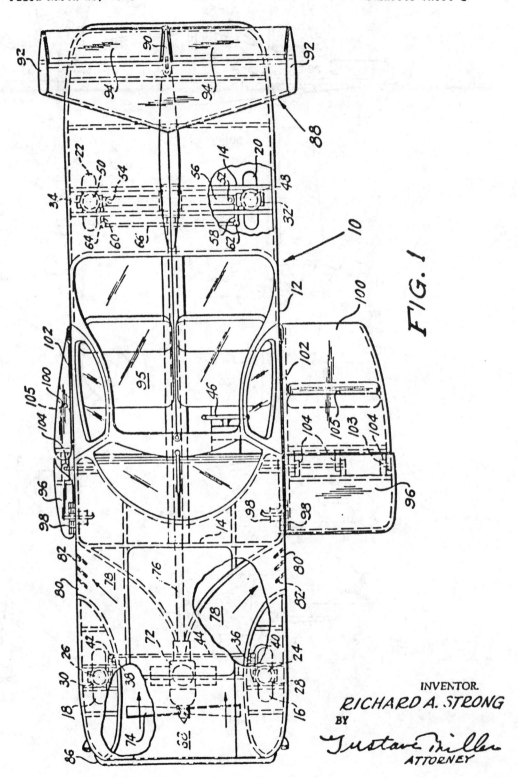

FIG. 1

INVENTOR.
RICHARD A. STRONG
BY

Gustave Miller
ATTORNEY

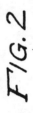

FIG.2

INVENTOR.
RICHARD A. STRONG
BY
ATTORNEY

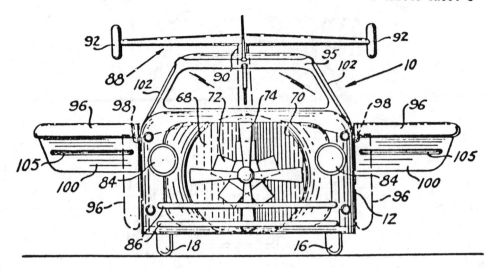

FIG.3

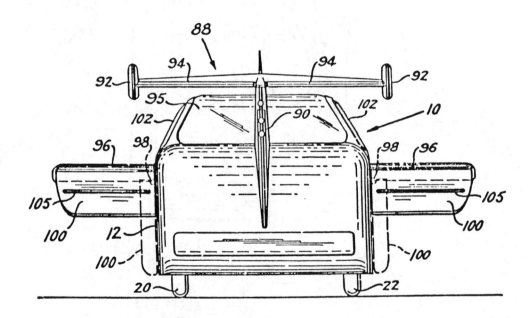

FIG.4

INVENTOR.

RICHARD A. STRONG

BY

Gustave Miller

ATTORNEY

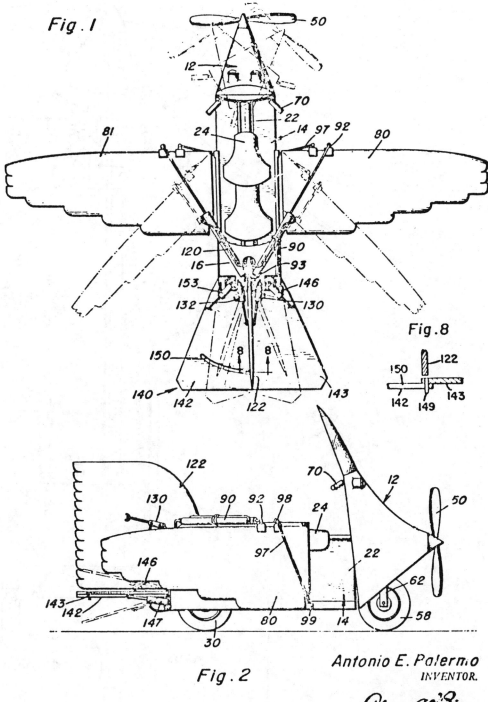

Fig. 1

Fig. 8

Fig. 2

Antonio E. Palermo
INVENTOR.

BY
Attorneys

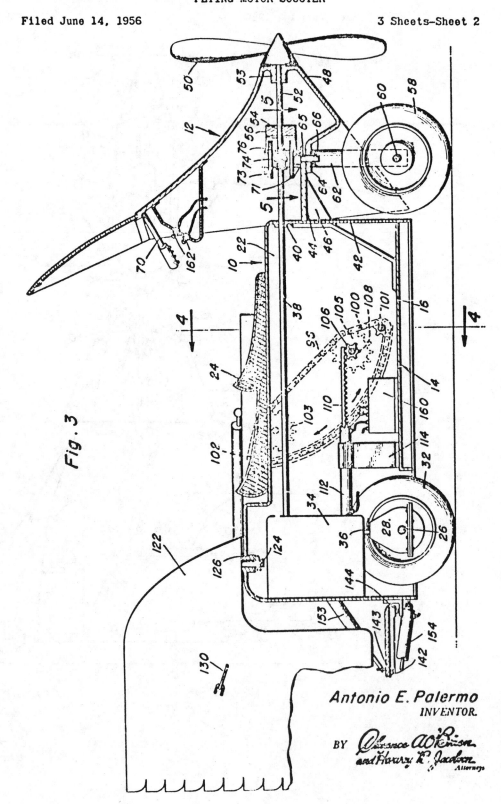

Fig. 3

Antonio E. Palermo
INVENTOR.

BY
Attorneys

June 14, 1960
E. F. BLAND
2,940,688
ROADABLE AIRCRAFT AND SAILBOAT

Filed Aug. 27, 1956
6 Sheets—Sheet 1

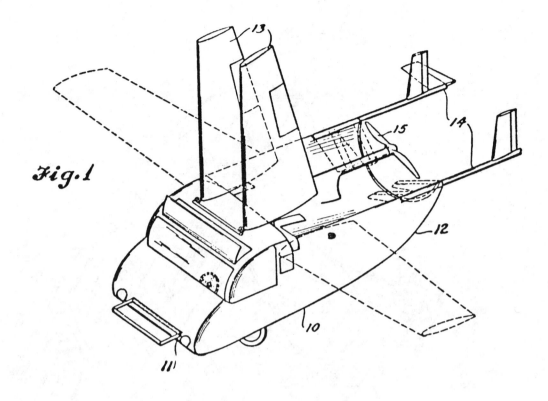

Fig.1

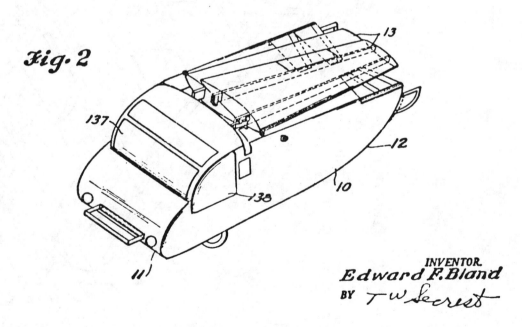

Fig.2

INVENTOR.
Edward F. Bland
BY T W Secrest

ATTORNEY

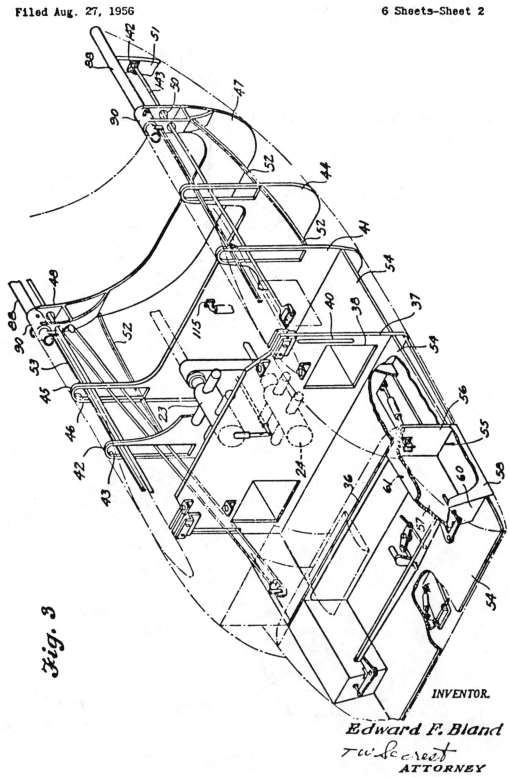

Fig. 3

INVENTOR.

Edward F. Bland

T. W. Secrest

ATTORNEY

Fig. 5

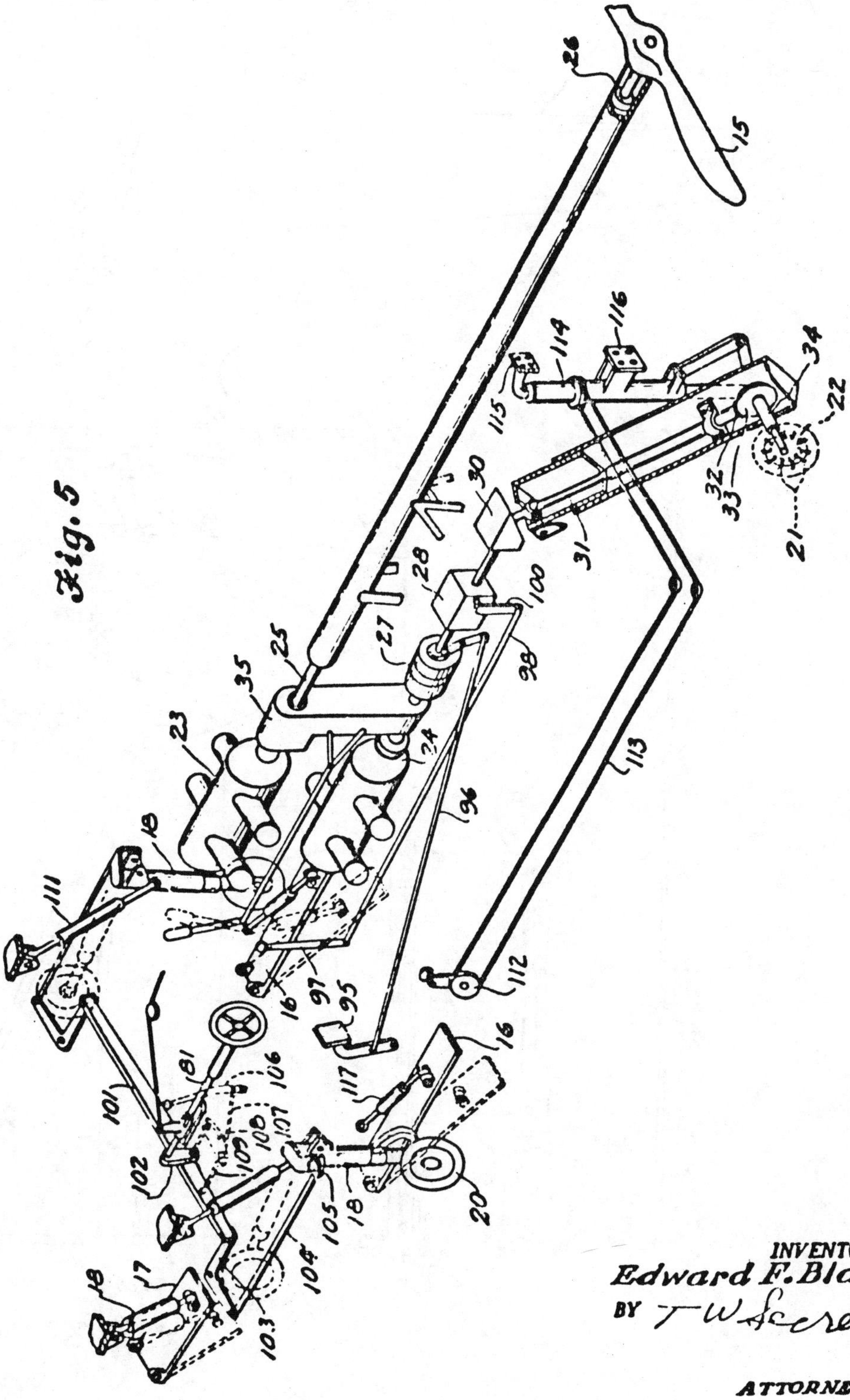

INVENTOR.
Edward F. Bland
BY *T. W. Secrest*

ATTORNEY

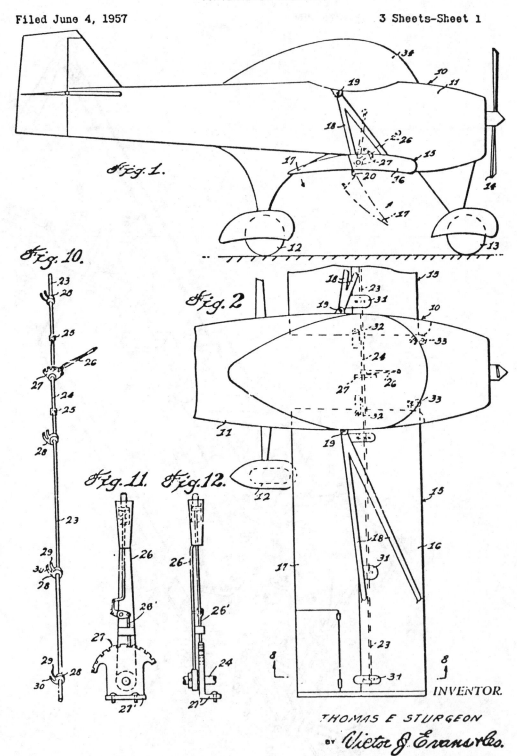

Fig. 1.

Fig. 10.

Fig. 2.

Fig. 11.   *Fig. 12.*

INVENTOR.

THOMAS E STURGEON

BY *Victor J. Evans & Co.*

ATTORNEYS

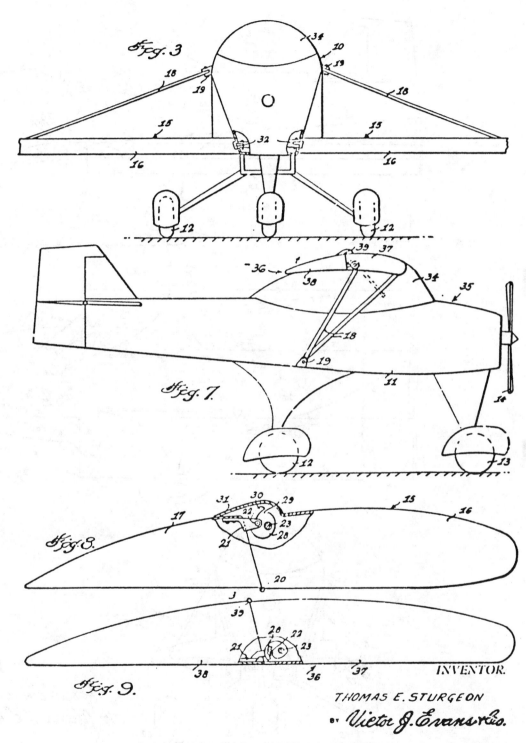

Fig. 3

Fig. 7

Fig. 8.

Fig. 9.

INVENTOR.

THOMAS E. STURGEON

BY Victor J. Evans & Co.

ATTORNEYS

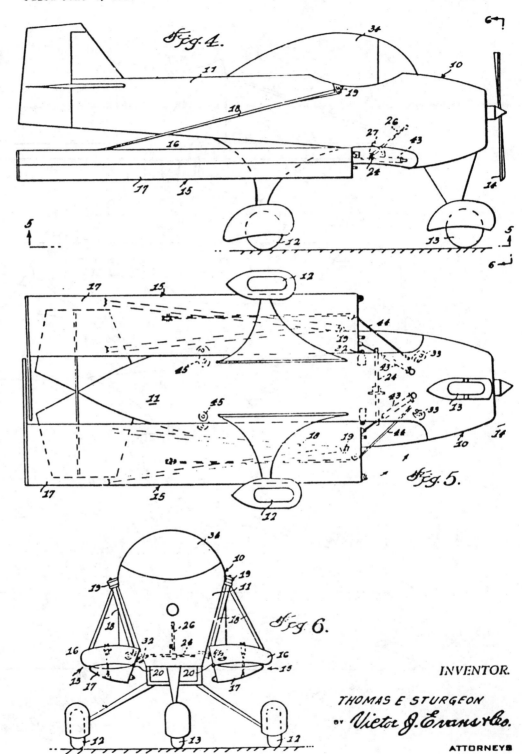

INVENTOR.

THOMAS E STURGEON

by Victor J. Evans & Co.

ATTORNEYS

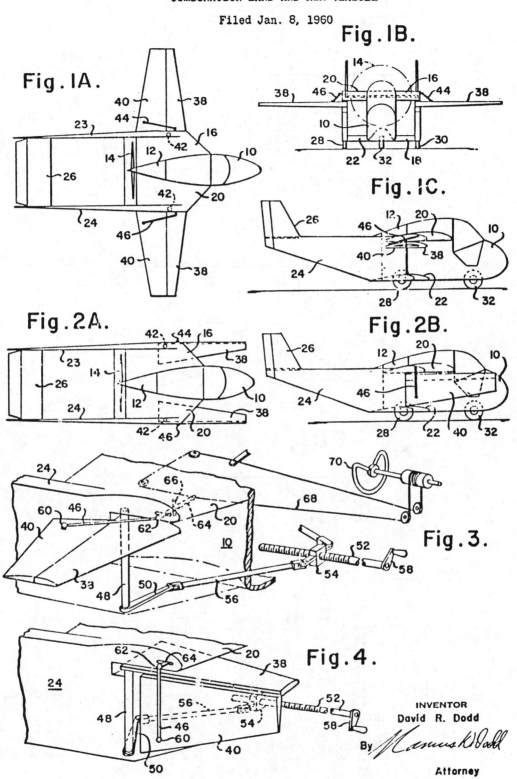

Fig.1A.

Fig.1B.

Fig.1C.

Fig.2A.

Fig.2B.

Fig.3.

Fig.4.

INVENTOR
David R. Dodd

By

Attorney

Fig.1

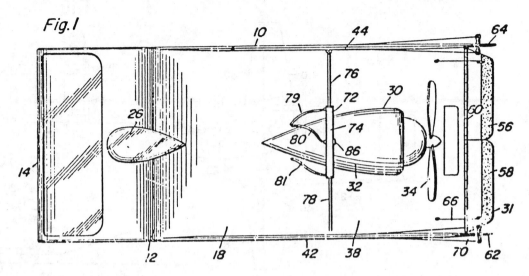

Fig. 2

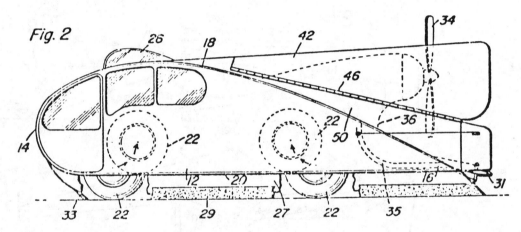

Fig. 3

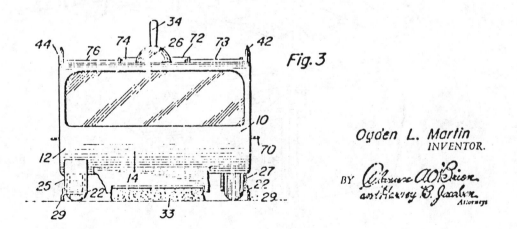

Ogden L. Martin
INVENTOR.

BY
Attorneys

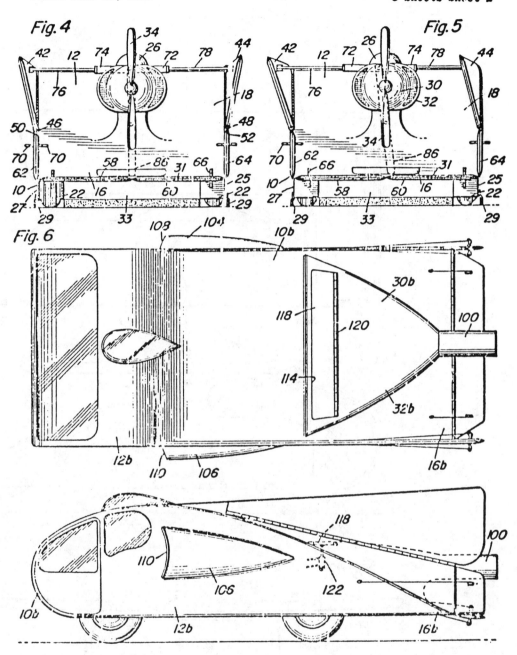

Fig.4

Fig.5

Fig.6

Fig.7

Ogden L. Martin
INVENTOR.

BY

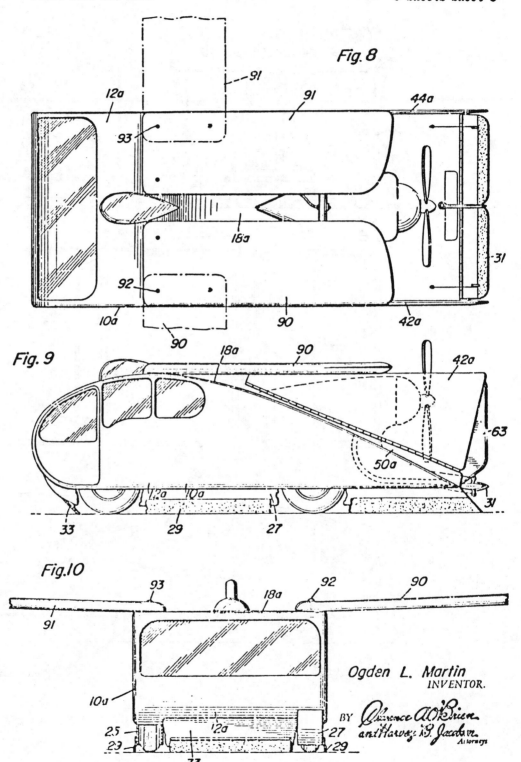

Fig. 8

Fig. 9

Fig. 10

Ogden L. Martin
INVENTOR.

BY
and Harvey B. Jacobson
Attorneys

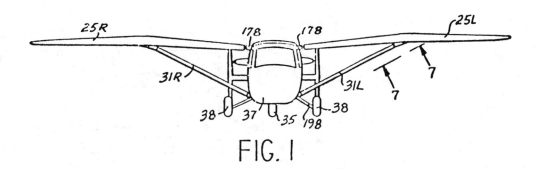

FIG. 1

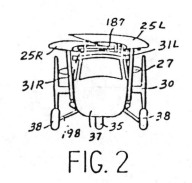

FIG. 2

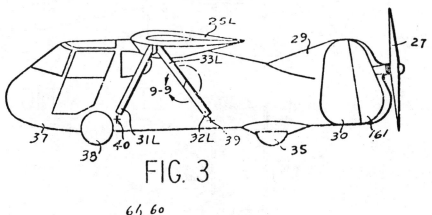

FIG. 3

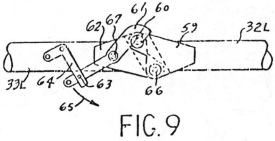

FIG. 9

INVENTOR.

Daniel R. Zuck

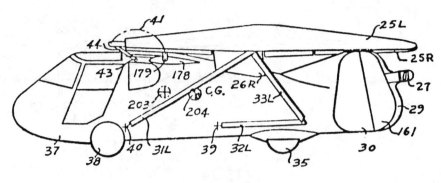

FIG. 4

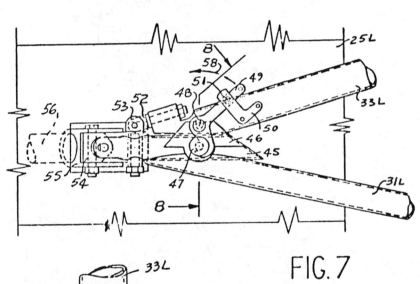

FIG. 7

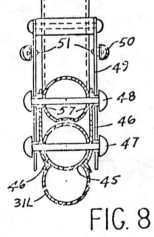

FIG. 8

INVENTOR.

Daniel R. Zuck

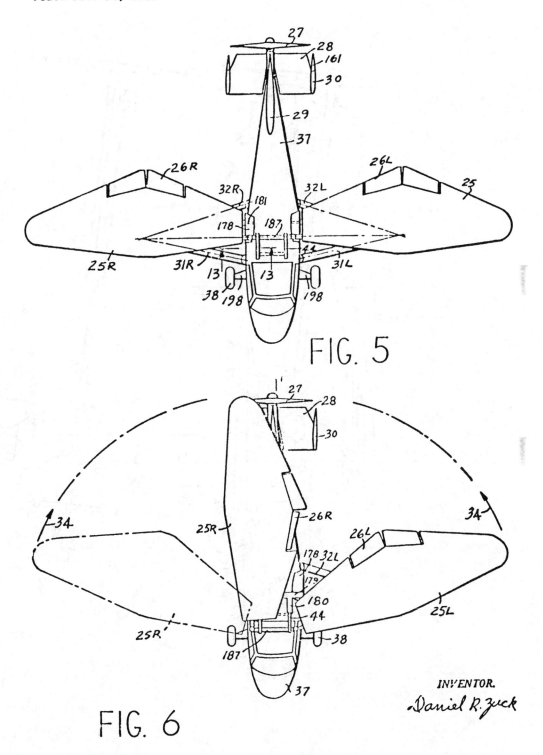

FIG. 5

FIG. 6

INVENTOR.
Daniel R. Zuck

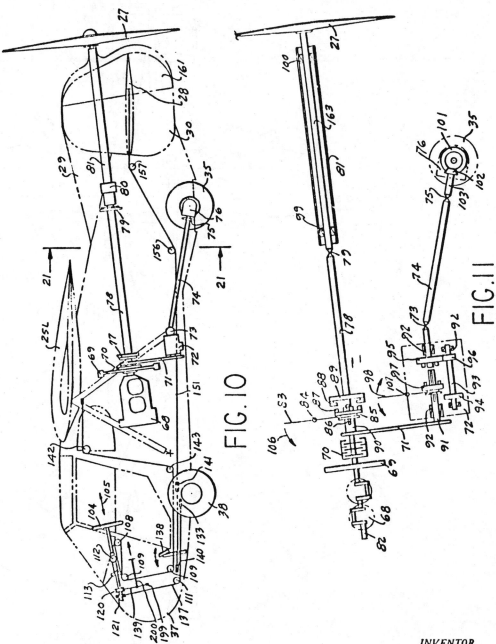

FIG.10

FIG.11

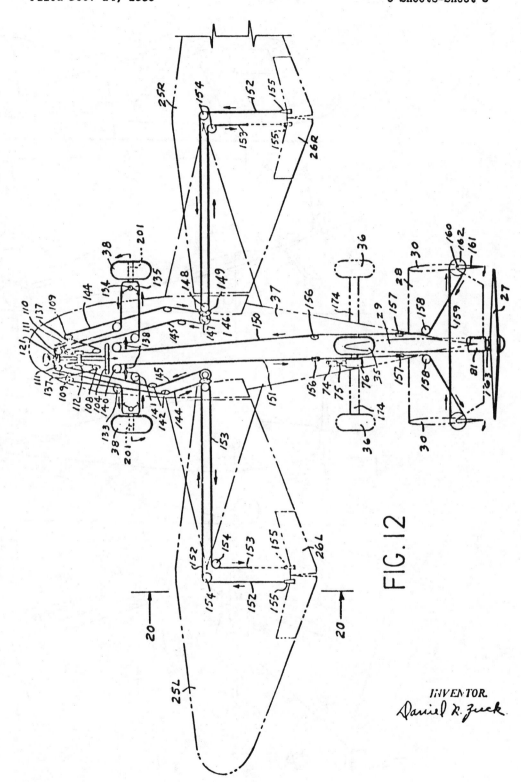

FIG. 12

INVENTOR.

Daniel R. Zuck

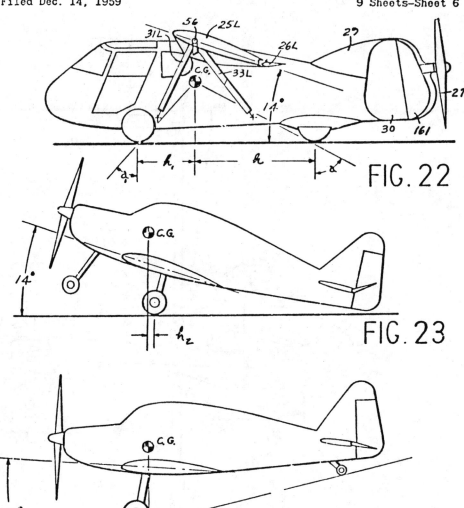

FIG. 22

FIG. 23

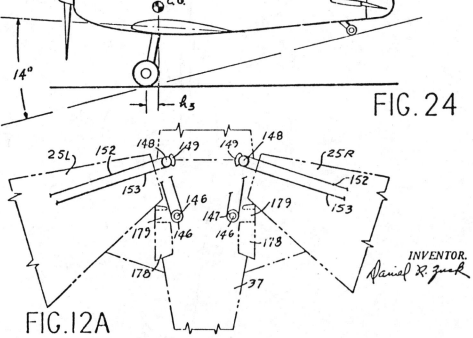

FIG. 24

FIG.12A

INVENTOR.

Daniel R. Zuck

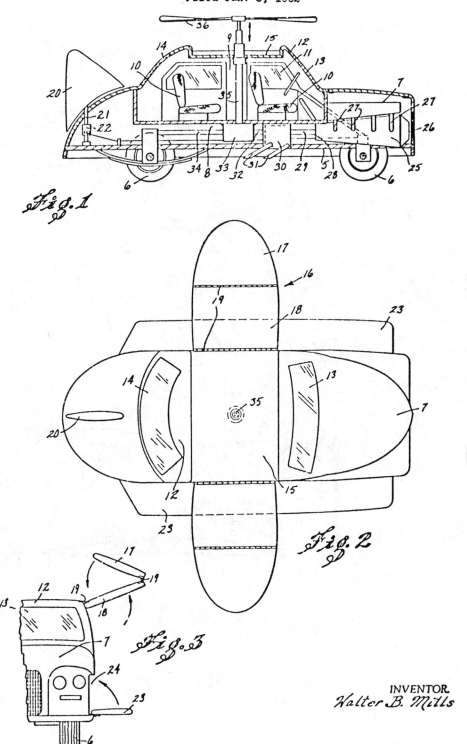

Fig. 1

Fig. 2

Fig. 3

INVENTOR.
Walter B. Mills

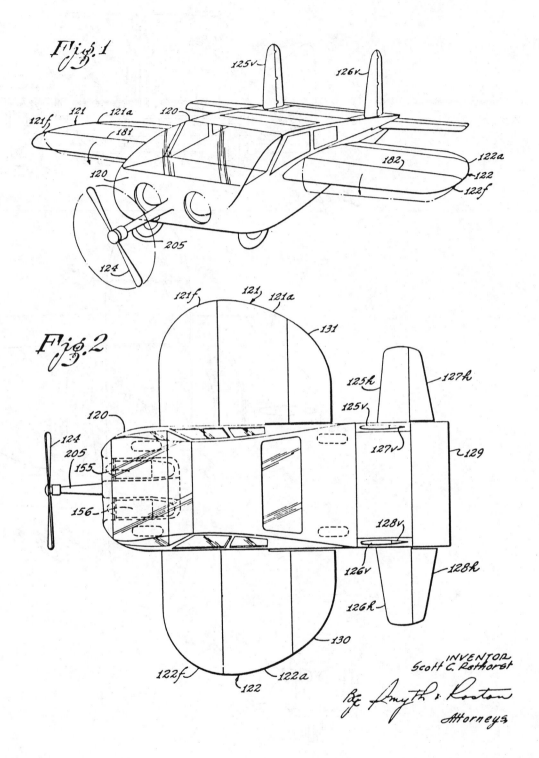

Fig. 1

Fig. 2

INVENTOR
Scott C. Rethorst

By Smyth & Roston

Attorneys

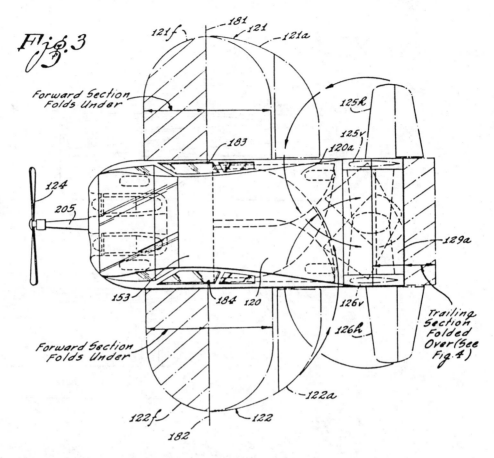

Fig.3

Forward Section Folds Under

Forward Section Folds Under

Trailing Section Folded Over (See Fig. 4)

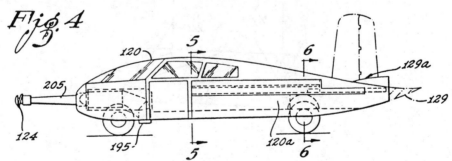

Fig.4

INVENTOR:
Scott C. Rethorst

By Smyth, Roston
Attorneys

Fig. 5

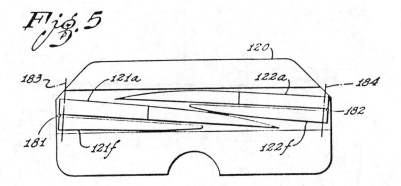

Fig. 6

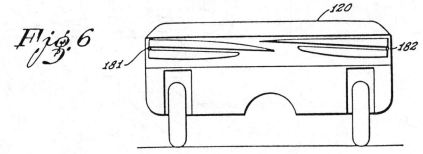

Fig. 7

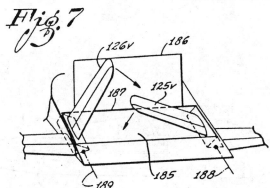

INVENTOR:
Scott C. Rethorst

By Smyth & Roston
Attorneys,

Fig. 8

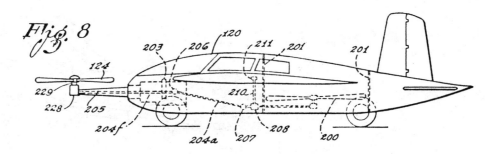

Fig. 9

Fig. 10

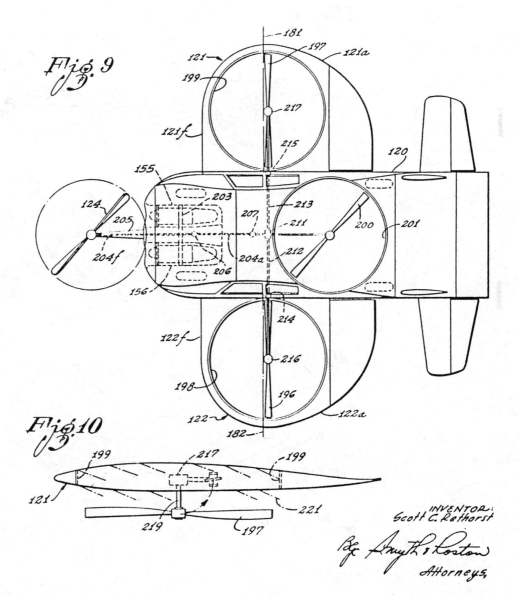

INVENTOR:
Scott C. Rethorst

By Smyth & Roston
Attorneys

May 21, 1963 E. EINARSSON 3,090,581

FLYING CAR

Filed Aug. 12, 1959 3 Sheets-Sheet 1

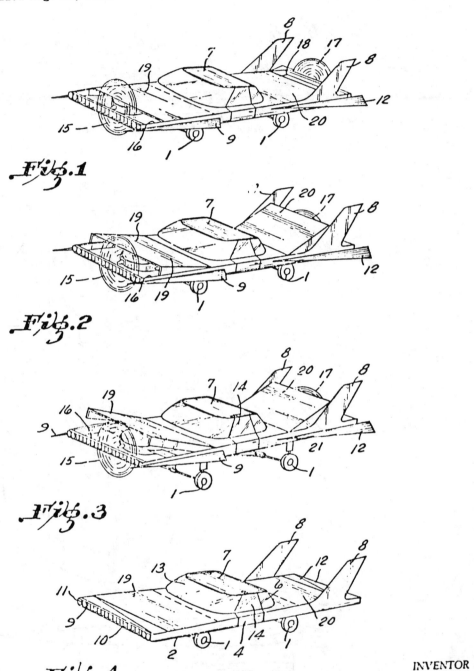

Fig. 1

Fig. 2

Fig. 3

Fig. 4

INVENTOR
EINAR EINARSSON

BY
Watson Cole Grindle & Watson
ATTORNEYS

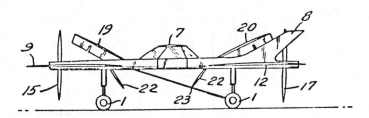

Fig.5

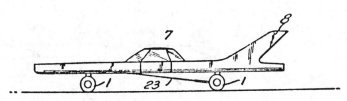

Fig.6

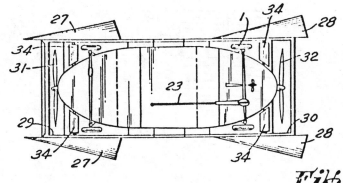

Fig.7

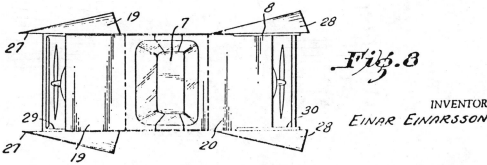

Fig.8

INVENTOR
EINAR EINARSSON

BY
V. Watson Cole Grindle & Watson
ATTORNEYS

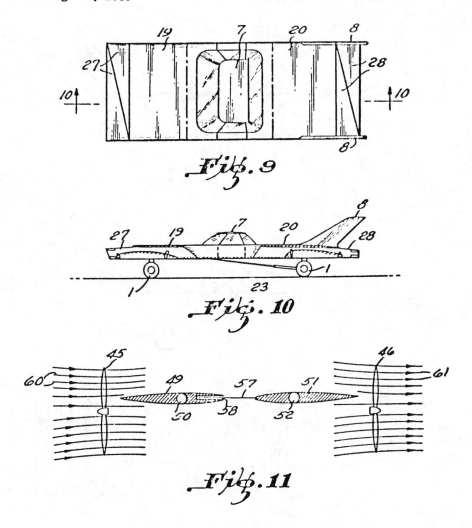

Fig. 9

Fig. 10

Fig. 11

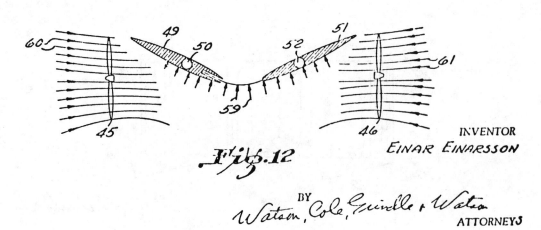

Fig. 12

INVENTOR

EINAR EINARSSON

BY *Watson, Cole, Grindle & Watson*

ATTORNEYS

1

3,090,581
FLYING CAR
Einar Einarsson, 7 Eastern Parkway, Farmingdale, N.Y.
Filed Aug. 12, 1959, Ser. No. 833,334
10 Claims. (Cl. 244—2)

This invention relates to a flying car, that is one capable of conversion from flying to one able to travel on the ground as well as from a ground automobile to a flying vehicle.

It is an object of this invention to provide a ground vehicle with propellers and wings as well as wing flaps so that the vehicle may take off and fly in the air. Another object of the invention resides in the use of a common power plant to supply the motive power for rotating the propellers as well as to rotate the wheels of the vehicle.

A further object of the invention resides in the provision of spaces in the vehicle both front and back to mount removable propellers and to provide space for the rotation of the propellers. The spaces for the rotating propellers is utilized to receive the side flaps or wings so that when the vehicle is used for ground transportation the propeller spaces will be completely filled. Another object of the invention resides in the provision of a pair of adjustable main wings which are in front and back of the driver's compartment which when raised at an angle to the horizontal, serve to support the vehicle in the air.

Another object of the invention resides in a flying car in which a pair of stabilizers are pivotally mounted on the front and back of the car. The stabilizers when folded against the car will cover the spaces for the front and rear propellers.

A further object of the invention resides in a flying car with front and rear propellers of which the front propeller is of the pulling type and the rear propeller is of the pusher type. The propellers may be feathered so that each propeller may be converted from a pulling propeller to a pushing propeller. A still further object of the invention resides in a pair of interconnected wing sections between which the operator of the car or airplane is seated. The wings are interconnected by a light metal or plastic sheet which is bendable to accommodate the bent wings.

Further objects will be apparent from the following description when considered in connection with the accompanying drawings in which:

FIGURES 1 to 4 are perspective views of the flying car in flying position as in FIGURES 1 to 3 and in ground locomotion position as in FIGURE 4,

FIGURE 5 is a side view of the car of FIGURES 1 to 4 showing take-off and landing adjustment,

FIGURE 6 is a side view showing the car as a land vehicle.

FIGURE 7 is a bottom plan view of the flying car,

FIGURE 8 is a top plan view of the car of FIGURE 7,

FIGURE 9 is a top plan view of the car in non-flying condition,

FIGURE 10 is a longitudinal section of the car taken on line 10—10 of FIGURE 9 in the direction of the arrows,

FIGURE 11 is a diagrammatic view showing one position of the propellers and the wings with interconnecting surface member, and

FIGURE 12 is a diagrammatic view showing another position of the propellers and wings with the interconnecting surface member of FIGURE 11.

In the structure of FIGURES 1 to 4 the car shown is capable of cruising on the ground as well as in the air and FIGURE 4 shows the car assembled and adjusted

2

ready for ground travel on the wheels 1. For ground travel power is derived from an engine which drives the propellers and by transmission means, as shown in U.S. Patent No. 2,446,528 of August 10, 1948, also drives the wheels. The body or frame 2 of the car has a raised portion 3 composed of doors 4, windshield 13 and glass windows 6. A roof 7 covers the space to be occupied by the operator and passengers. Two upwardly extending stabilizing fins or rudders 8 are provided on the rear end of the car and as shown the front end has two interfitting surface fins 9 adjacent a front grill 10 with the usual head lights 11 therein. The rear end is also provided with two interfitting surface fins 12 and as shown in FIGURE 3 which illustrates the car in flight, the front fins 9 are secured along the front sides of the car and the rear fins 12 are mounted along the rear sides of the car. The fins 9 and 12 may be secured to the side of the car by any suitable means such as bolts or lock pins.

The car of FIGURES 1 to 4 may be provided with a full vision windshield 13 and each door 4 may have a side window 14 with the windows and windshield made of glass or clear plastic. A front propeller 15 is rotatably mounted to rotate in the space 16 in the car to be driven by any suitable transmission members connected to a motor in the car. There is also a rear propeller 17 mounted to rotate in the rear space 18. In FIGURE 4 the space 18 is covered by the fins 12 but FIGURE 1 best shows this rear space. The car is also provided with a pivoted front wing 19 and a pivoted rear wing 20 with FIGURES 1 and 4 showing the wings down in horizontal position in non-flying condition, whereas FIGURES 2 and 3 show the wings 19 and 20 raised for flying position of the parts.

FIGURE 7 shows the lower wing or flap sections 22 used to create air lift or brake surfaces depending upon the demands made on the car. A transmission rod 23 is utilized to provide motive power to the rear wheels 1 when the car is traversing the ground as shown in FIGURE 8.

The car shown in FIGURES 6 to 10 is quite similar to the car of FIGURES 1 to 4 and as shown in FIGURES 6 and 7 the side fins or stabilizers 27 and 28 are in flying position whereas in FIGURES 9 and 10 they are in position to close over the propeller spaces. The propeller spaces 29 and 30 accommodate propellers 31 and 32 respectively and as best shown in FIGURE 6 a small propeller 33 is for use when the vehicle is used as a boat. Stabilizing vanes 34 are mounted front and back in pairs, for pivotal adjustment and as shown in FIGURES 1 to 4, wings 19 and 20 are also provided on the car of FIGURES 6 to 10.

FIGURES 11 and 12 illustrate a modified form of flying car in which the front propeller 45 as well as the rear propeller 46 are entirely in the open.

As shown in FIGURES 11 and 12 the wings 49 and 51 are shown as interconnected by a resilient sheet member 57 which may be connected to one wing such as 51 and is slidable in a slot 58 in the wing 49. When the wings 49 and 51 are adjusted on their axes 50 and 52 as shown in FIGURES 11 and 12, the member 57 flexes into a bow or curved shape as shown in FIGURE 12 with the arrows 59 indicating the thrust of the air on the wings 49 and 51 and member 59 when the vehicle is in flight. The arrows 60 in the stream for the propeller 45 and the arrows 61 for the air stream for the propeller 46 shows direction of the air flow even when the propeller 46 is feathered to the position of FIGURE 12 where the stream 61 is reversed.

The operation of the flying car has been referred to in the foregoing in that the car after travelling on land may be easily converted for air travel by removing the stabilizers and wings and placing them in position on the outside of the vehicle. The road wheels may be raised and the propellers are now in position for operation. By suitable adjustment of the wings the car can take-off and when in the air the wings are further adjusted for cruising speed.

FIGURES 11 and 12 also illustrate the take-off position of the parts as in FIGURE 12 with the blades of the propeller 46 suitably adjusted to force the air back of the wings so that the air as indicated by the arrows 59 will force the vehicle upward until high enough when the parts are adjusted so that the air streams will follow the one direction indicated. Also when cruising in the air the wings 49 and 51, FIGURE 11, are adjusted practically horizontal.

As already referred to each car may have a common motor plant to drive both the ground wheels as well as the propellers with suitable clutch devices to control one or the other cruising power. Separate power plants may be used and for air travel jet engines may also be used with and without the use of propellers.

I claim as my invention:

1. A vehicle capable of cruising on land and in the air comprising a body, a plurality of wheels mounted under the body to support the vehicle while on the ground, means for supplying power to the wheels for cruising on the ground, front and rear propellers mounted on the body to provide for take-off and cruising power when in the air, and a pair of pivotally mounted wings secured on the body and being adjustable as to the angles to the horizontal for take-off and cruising positions for the wings, said propellers being connected to receive power from the power supplying means and the wings forming a wing extending from the front propeller to the rear propeller with a bridging element to receive the pressure between the propellers.

2. A vehicle capable of cruising on land and in the air comprising a body, a plurality of wheels mounted under the body to support the vehicle while on the ground, means for supplying power to the wheels for cruising on the ground, front and rear propellers mounted on the body to provide for take-off and cruising power when in the air, and a pair of pivotally mounted wings secured on the body and being adjustable as to the angles to the horizontal for take-off and cruising positions for the wings, said propellers being connected to receive power from the power supplying means and one of the propellers having reversible blades to adjust for take-off and cruising of the vehicle and the wings forming a wing extending from the front propeller to the rear propeller with a bridging element to receive the pressure between the propellers.

3. A vehicle capable of cruising on land and in the air comprising a body, a plurality of wheels mounted under the body to support the vehicle while on the ground, means for supplying power to the wheels for cruising on the ground, front and rear propellers mounted on the body to provide for take-off and cruising power when in the air, a pair of pivotally mounted wings secured on the body and being adjustable as to the angles to the horizontal for take-off and cruising positions for the wings, said propellers being connected to receive power from the power supplying means, and two pairs of stabilizers removably attachable on the sides of the body at the front and rear ends of the vehicle, said stabilizers interfitting for placement on the front and rear ends of the body to cover the propellers when the vehicle is travelling on the ground.

4. A vehicle capable of cruising on land and in the air

comprising a body, a plurality of wheels mounted under the body to support the vehicle while on the ground, means for supplying power to the wheels for cruising on the ground, front and rear propellers mounted on the body to provide for take-off and cruising power when in the air, a pair of pivotally mounted wings secured on the body and being adjustable as to the angles to the horizontal for take-off and cruising positions for the wings, said propellers being connected to receive power from the power supplying means, and two pairs of stabilizers pivotally mounted on the front and rear ends of the body so that each stabilizer may be adjusted to flying position or against and over the body for land cruising said wings forming a wing structure with a bridging element between the propellers.

5. A flying vehicle comprising a body having landing wheels secured thereto, a front propeller and a rear propeller mounted on the body, a pair of wings one behind the front propeller and the other in front of the rear propeller to form a wing structure with a bridging element, each wing having means to adjust it relative to the horizontal to increase or decrease the lift on the wings, said propellers having power means to rotate the propellers so that the pressure between the propellers will be utilized on the wings, and the rear propeller having reversing blades so that the vehicle may take-off from the ground in a vertical direction.

6. A land vehicle capable of conversion to an aircraft comprising a body provided with a compartment for the operator, a plurality of wheels for locomotion on the ground, at least one propeller mounted on the body for use of the vehicle as an aircraft, means for supporting the wheels and connected to the body to adjust the wheels vertically and when close to the body the vehicle is operated as an aircraft and a pair of wings pivotally mounted on the body adjustable upwardly at an angle to the horizontal to provide lift for the vehicle as an aircraft and when horizontal the vehicle is adjusted for operation on the ground, said wings forming a wing structure with a bridging element to utilize the pressure of the propeller.

7. A land vehicle according to claim 6, in which a pair of propellers are provided one in front and the other at the back of the vehicle with the rear propeller having blades adjustable to reverse the direction of airflow toward the center of the vehicle body for take-off of the vehicle for air travel.

8. A land vehicle according to claim 6, in which a plurality of stabilizer fins are provided mounted on the body to control the vehicle while travelling in the air.

9. A land vehicle according to claim 6, in which a plurality of stabilizer fins are provided mounted on the body to control the vehicle while travelling in the air, and in which a pair of vertical rudder members are secured on the body at the rear end thereof with one on each side of the vehicle.

10. A vehicle according to claim 1, in which said bridging element is secured to one of the wings and slidable in the other wing.

References Cited in the file of this patent

UNITED STATES PATENTS

1,130,125	Wilkins	Mar. 2, 1915
1,579,654	Harpstrite	Apr. 6, 1926
1,814,115	Blain	July 14, 1931
1,938,171	Braley	Dec. 5, 1933
2,446,528	Clark	Aug. 10, 1948
2,681,773	Rethorst	June 22, 1954
2,811,323	Rethorst	Oct. 29, 1957

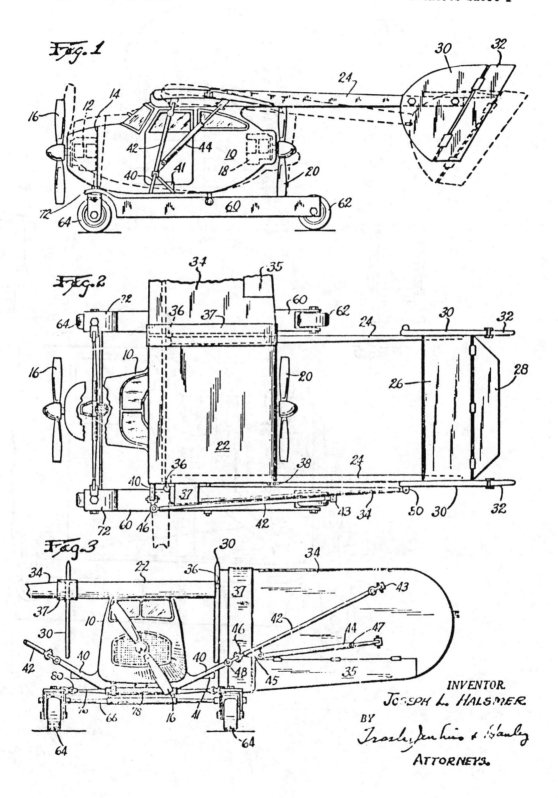

Fig.1

Fig.2

Fig.3

INVENTOR.
Joseph L. Halsmer
BY
Trasher, Jenkins & Stanley
ATTORNEYS.

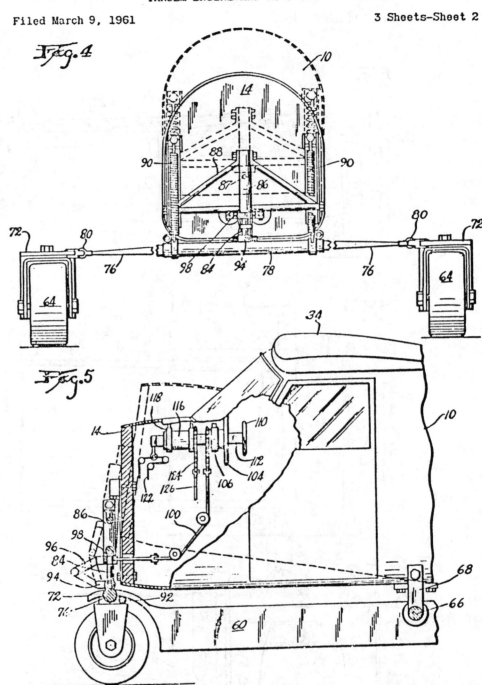

Fig.4

Fig.5

INVENTOR.

JOSEPH L. HALSMER

BY

Trask, Jenkins & Hawley

ATTORNEYS.

Fig. 6

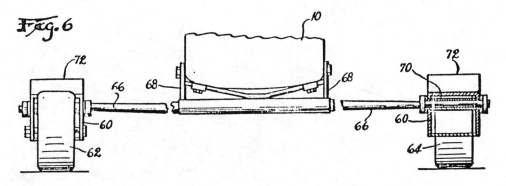

Fig. 7

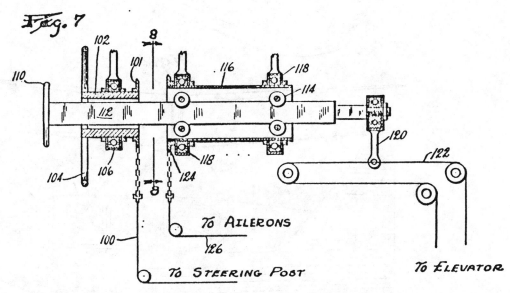

To AILERONS

To STEERING POST

To ELEVATOR

Fig. 8

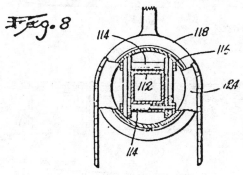

INVENTOR.

JOSEPH L. HALSMER

BY

Trash, Jenkins & Hanley

ATTORNEYS.

Fig.1

Fig.2

Fig.3

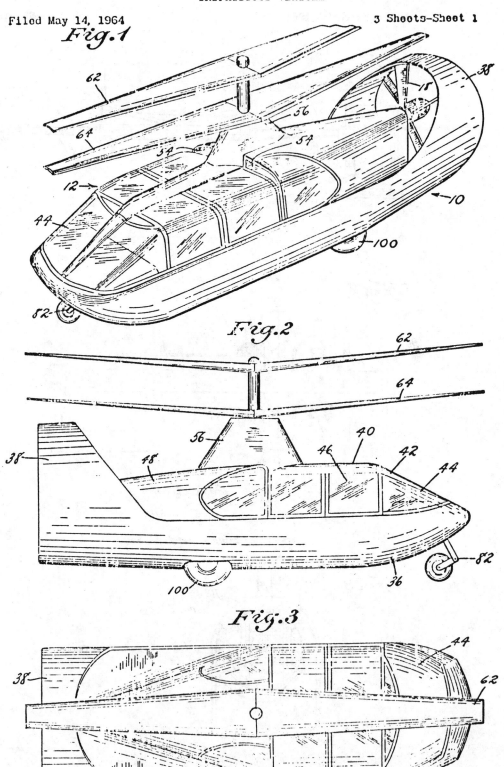

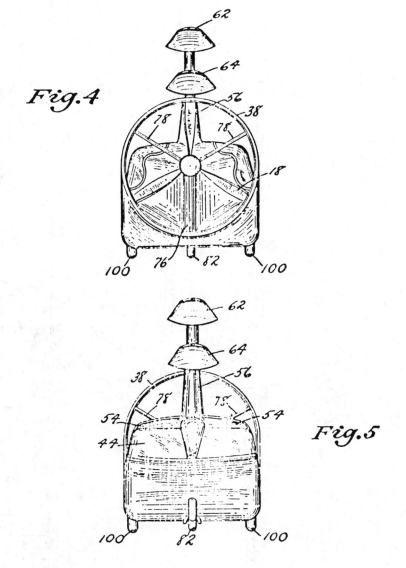

Fig.4

Fig.5

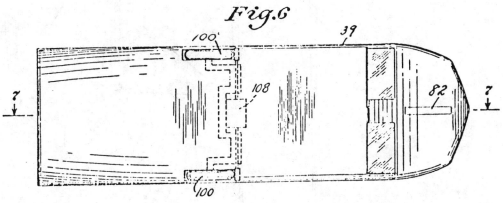

Fig.6

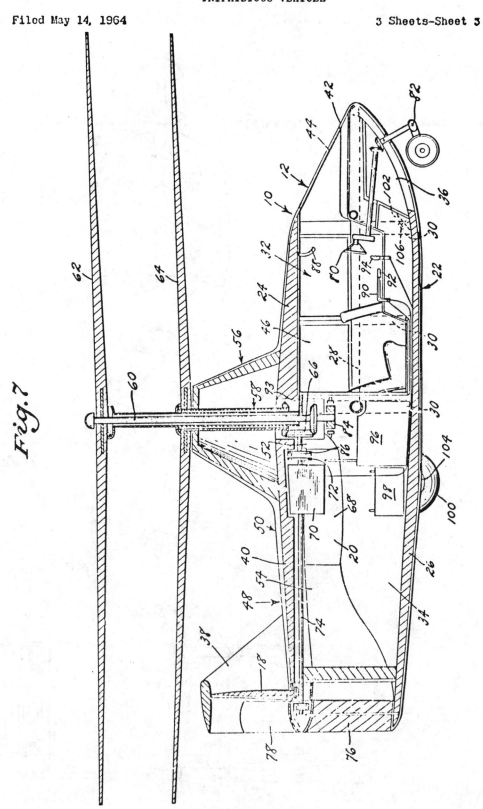

Fig. 7

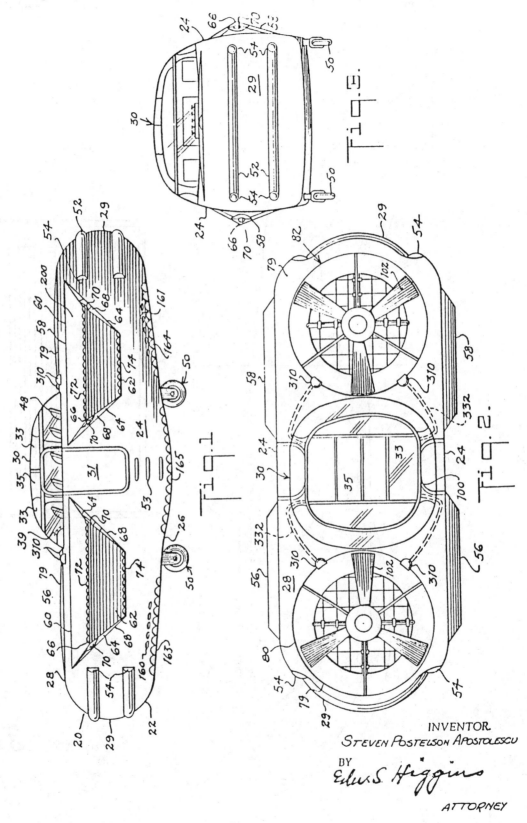

Fig. [1]

Fig. 1

Fig. 2

INVENTOR.
STEVEN POSTELSON APOSTOLESCU

BY

Edw S. Higgins

ATTORNEY

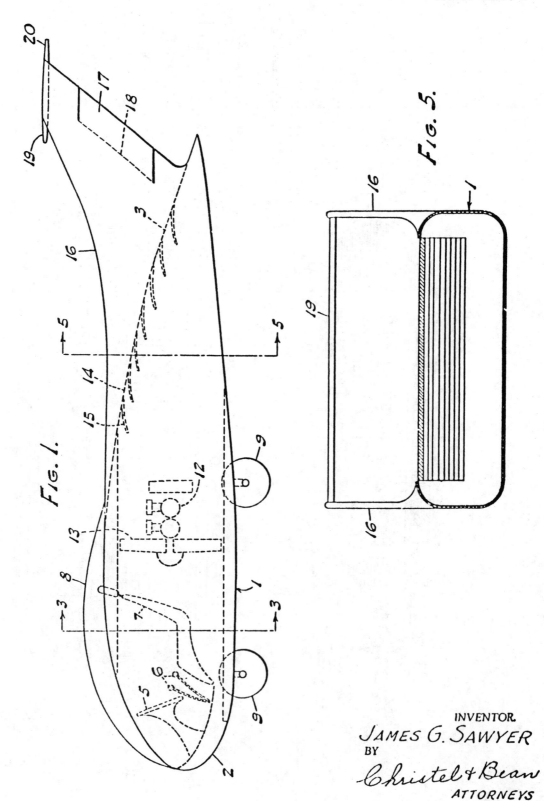

INVENTOR.
JAMES G. SAWYER
BY
Christel & Bean
ATTORNEYS

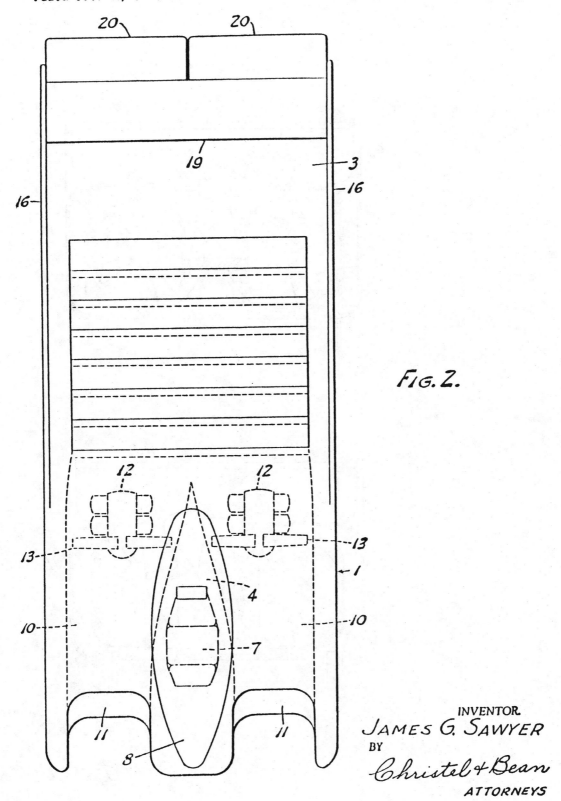

FIG. 2.

INVENTOR.

JAMES G. SAWYER

BY

Christel & Bean

ATTORNEYS

FIG. 3.

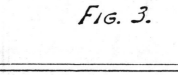
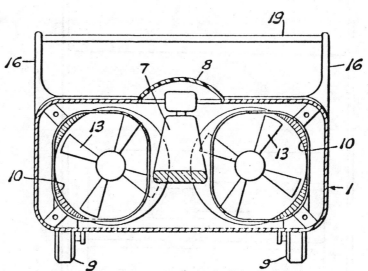

FIG. 4.

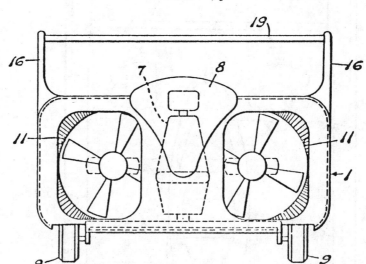

INVENTOR.

JAMES G. SAWYER

BY

Christel & Bean

ATTORNEYS

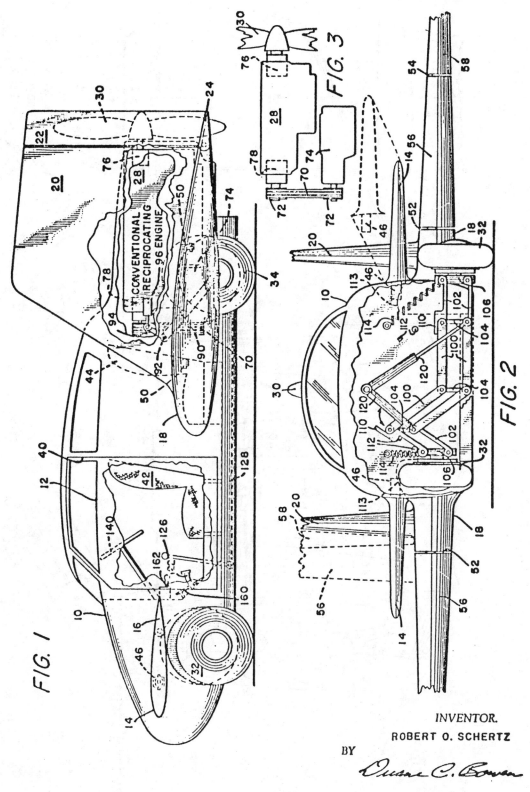

INVENTOR.
ROBERT O. SCHERTZ

BY

ATTORNEY

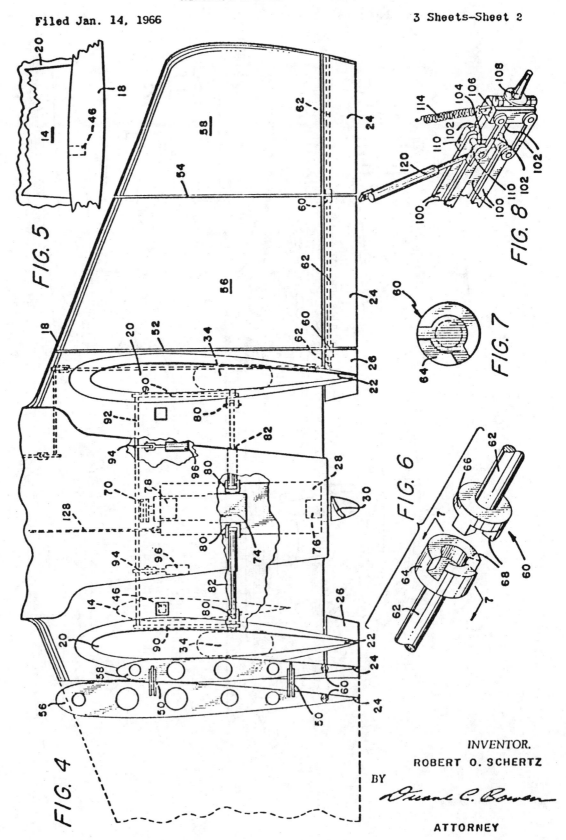

INVENTOR.

ROBERT O. SCHERTZ

BY

ATTORNEY

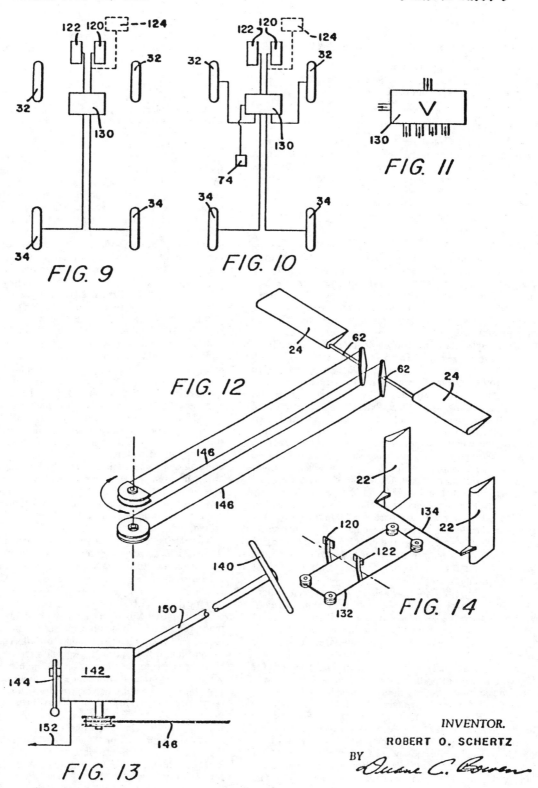

FIG. 9

FIG. 10

FIG. 11

FIG. 12

FIG. 13

FIG. 14

INVENTOR.

ROBERT O. SCHERTZ

BY Duane C. Bowen

ATTORNEY

1

3,371,886
AIRCRAFT ADAPTED FOR HIGHWAY USAGE
Robert O. Schertz, 12 E. 2nd St.,
El Paso, Ill.   61738
Filed Jan. 14, 1966, Ser. No. 520,732
12 Claims. (Cl. 244—2)

ABSTRACT OF THE DISCLOSURE

An aircraft adapted for highway travel has a canard configuration; a removable forward horizontal stabilizer; rear foldable main load-carrying wings; a side opening cabin door between horizontal stabilizer and main wings; wheel means used for highway travel, takeoff and landing, and retractible during flight; a power plant used for highway travel and flight, and controls having dual highway and flight usage.

My invention relates to an aircraft usable for highway travel when needed and to achieve this adaptability includes a canard configuration, a removable horizontal stabilizer, foldable main load-carrying wings, wheel means adapted for highway usage and for retraction during flight, related flight controls and automotive type controls, and other features.

In the light plane field it would often be desirable to have an air auto vehicle usable for highway travel as well as flight. At present an operator of a light plane has to provide other surface transportation to and from his home airfield and at other airfields to get between airport and other destinations. Most often at airfields away from home he must bear the expense of renting a car or using taxis and public transportation to get from airport to other destinations whether a half-mile away or many miles from the nearest landing facility. Business usage of a light plane by an owner can involve trips to large cities, smaller communities, rural areas (as in farm related enterprises), or relatively unsettled areas (as in oil and gas drilling, mining prospecting, and ranching related businesses). Conventional light aircraft are particularly limited in many types of vacationing wherein it would be desirable to fly to the general area but then the vacationers want to travel on highways through areas or want to get to one or more locations remote from airports. Such an aircraft also has potential military uses.

Reduced visibility and low ceiling weather have a definite adverse effect upon the use and practicability of conventional aircraft. A roadable type aircraft would make it possible to safely complete trips in this vehicle even though a part of the trip was to be made through unflyable weather.

In fact, the applications for an aircraft adapted for highway travel are pertinent on occasion or frequently to most business or private light airplane owners to save money and time or for convenience. For example, a private light plane owner to reach his home airfield usually has to drive himself to the airport and leave the car there (and sometimes pay parking charges) and his family is unable to use it in his absence; or another member of his family must accompany him on his departure and meet him on his arrival (however inconvenient the hour or circumstances) in order that the family is able to use the car in his absence, or he must pay for transportation other than his own automobile.

Owning a light plane may be difficult to finance in the family budget and may be foregone partly because of inconvenience, extra expenses for surface transportation away or at home, or even the purchase of an additional car to avoid the situation outlined. The economic impor-

2

tance of dual air and highway usage will be understood as to a family that can substitute such aircraft and a single automobile for a conventional aircraft, a first car and a second car. Many business light plane owners, large or small, will have similar considerations of expense and convenience.

It is an object of my invention to devise an aircraft usable for highway travel to meet the above needs of present and potential, private and business light plane owners.

An observation should be made at this point that a practical aircraft usable for highway travel should substantially increase light plane sales because the additional usefulness and the reduction in expenses of such aircraft over conventional aircraft could be the decisive factor in sales to parties now indecisive on purchase. It can be safely forecast that air and surface travel will undergo substantial changes in the relatively near future because this prediction is in keeping with the rate and type of present technological development, and an aircraft usable in highway travel is consistent with those technological developments and is one of the forms those changes may take.

Of course to meet the needs it is not enough merely to provide an aircraft that qualifies under the minimum requirements to travel down a highway. The vehicle, instead, must have due convenience, economy, etc. The conventional automobile is at a high state of development and, in general, the more details the aircraft has that are comparable to those of such automobile the better for highway transportation. Conversely, the conventional light aircraft is highly developed and, in general, the more similar the vehicle is to such aircraft the better for flight purposes. However, direct combination of conventional automobile and aircraft features is inapplicable as there is not sufficient compatibility and dual usefulness for much direct copying of features, although the development of systems having some similarity is possible and leads to suitable compromises. It is an object of my invention to provide an aircraft usable for highway travel having as much similarity to conventional aircraft and automobiles as is suitable and is compatible with arriving at the best overall design.

The design of automotive vehicles is difficult and the design of aircraft may be even more difficult because of the requirements of air flight, the great importance of minimizing weight, safety problems, etc. Aircraft design is particularly complex in arriving at final compromises among desirable features, needed characteristics, and absolute requirements. It is an object of my invention to make the best possible compromises among desirable features, needed characteristics and absolute requirements for air and highway travel including such factors as providing suitable speed in the air and on the highway; minimizing weight, sales price, maintenance and other costs, fuel consumption, and complexity; providing due safety, riding comfort, visibility in air and highway use, rapid change between flight and highway configurations, good flight and highway control characteristics, etc.

To list only a part of the considerations in more detail, the wheels should be retractable, should adapt for landing, and should have supports including resilient means for highway travel which lead to a safe and comfortable ride. The controls in flight should be like those in aircraft and the controls in highway travel should be like those in automobiles and the operator should be able to readily shift from one to the other, and dual use of some system components is desirable to minimize cost, weight, etc. The maximum width of the vehicle during highway travel (which will be understood to primarily involve main load carrying wings and horizontal stabilizer) must not exceed legal limits which are usually eight feet, and I have provided wing folding and horizontal stabilizer removal to achieve this end. I have arrived at a canard configuration partly because of the need for highway visibility like that of the ordinary automobile, as the canard configuration puts the horizontal stabilizer (which is small compared with the main load-carrying wing) up front where it can be removed to achieve such visibility. Having the main wing aft permits having front doors not obstructed by wing structure, which is a feature convenient for passengers in getting in and out of the vehicle. Further objects of my invention include devising the best solution to the above and other design subjects.

My invention will be best understood, together with other objectives and advantages of my vehicle, from a reading of the following description, read with reference to the drawings, in which:

FIGURE 1 is side view of an aircraft forming a specific embodiment of my invention, portions being broken away to show hidden structure.

FIGURE 2 is a front view of the aircraft of FIGURE 1 in which certain features involved in changing the structure between configurations for flight and for highway travel are indicated in dotted lines.

FIGURE 3 is a partial side view of power plant and combined transmission and differential.

FIGURE 4 is a partial top view showing the wing in full lines on the right hand side in flight condition and on the left hand side in condition for highway travel.

FIGURE 6 is an enlarged perspective view of means at wing hinge joints for transmitting control movement to ailerons and adapted for disengagement upon wing folding.

FIGURE 7 is a view taken on line 7—7 of FIGURE 6 showing one of the elements in end view.

FIGURE 8 is a partial perspective view of front wheel support means adapted for wheel retraction during flight.

FIGURES 9 and 10 are schematical views of rudder pedal systems including, in FIGURE 9, the system adaptation for braking during takeoff and landing and, in FIGURE 10, the system adaptation for braking and clutching during highway travel.

FIGURE 11 is a schematical view of the control valve of the FIGURES 9 and 10 systems.

FIGURE 12 is a view in perspective of elevator control system details.

FIGURE 13 is a side view of control means for steering during highway travel and for elevator and aileron control in flight configuration.

FIGURE 14 is a view in perspective of rudder control by rudder pedals.

The drawings show an aircraft configuration adaptable for flight or for highway travel and includes fuselage 10, passenger compartment 12, horizontal stabilizers 14, elevator 16, main load-supporting wings 18, vertical stabilizers 20, rudders 22, ailerons 24, flaps 26, power plant 28, propeller 30, front wheels 32, and rear wheels 34.

The aircraft has canard configuration with horizontal stabilizer 14 mounted forwardly on fuselage 10 in extended position, main load-carrying wings 18 to the rear, and propeller 30 rearwardly directed in a pusher manner. The canard configuration is considered to be of considerable importance in designing an aircraft practical for both flight and highway travel. One feature is that horizontal stabilizer 14 is removable from its extended portion so that forward vision in highway travel is not impeded. In fact, the forward structure of the fuselage 10, passenger compartment 12 and front wheels 32 has strong similarity to the configuration of a conventional automobile once the horizontal stabilizer is removed. This is consistent with the objective of the invention to design as closely as is practical to an automobile for highway travel and as closely as practical to a conventional light aircraft for flight purposes. It will be noted, however, that this objective can be met only partly and involves various

compromises, but the general philosophy is that the conventional automobile and light plane are at a high state of development, are well adapted for their purposes, and the present design will benefit by considerable similarity.

Another advantage of a canard configuration is that the side-opening front doors 40 are behind horizontal stabilizer 14, and the main wing 18 is positioned aft of front doors 40 so that passengers have access to the front seat 42 in the normal manner of a two-door car without having to climb over wing structure, etc., in the manner of many airplanes. Although the vehicle may be adapted for carrying various numbers of people, it is shown as basically four-place with two people on front seat 42 and two people on seat 44 behind the front seat. It will be understood that for highway travel, more people could be carried in the manner of an automobile but for aircraft use because of maximum passenger weight consideration an aircraft is designed as two-place, four-place, etc.

Horizontal stabilizer 14 is shown in dotted lines on the right in FIGURE 2 as being removed. Stabilizer 14 may be stored on the aircraft during highway travel in various places, such as behind rear seat 44, but it is shown in FIGURES 4 and 5 as being stored with one section on the inner side of each vertical stabilizer 20. The securing means 46 for horizontal stabilizer 14 in flight condition can be accommodated in stored position in a recess in wing 18 (as shown in FIGURE 5) and conveniently can be made part of the securing system in stored condition.

There are other advantages of the canard configuration including the propeller is to the rear (and in fact is partly boxed in by rudders 22) which minimizes danger to passengers getting in and out of the vehicle etc.; the propeller has high efficiency in this rear pusher position; propeller and engine are remote from passenger compartment 12 to minimize noise; and power plant 28 is in a position involving minimum length (and weight) of transmitting means to get power to rear wheels 34 and the engine weight is above rear wheels 34 which is advantageous for traction purposes.

Twin vertical stabilizers 20 are mounted on main wing 18. As before observed, this canard configuration avoids problems of forward visibility in highway travel which would be present if main wing 18 were forward. Of course a basic problem in highway use of aircraft is to reduce width in the configuration for highway travel to the maximum legal limit for a highway transportation vehicle. This limit is eight feet in most localities in the United States. This maximum width for highway travel is achieved in my vehicle as to the main load-carrying wing (which is the widest part of an aircraft) by wing folding.

Wing folding is accomplished by providing hinges 50 at two locations 52 and 54 at each side of the wing medial portion, thereby forming inner wing end portions 56 and outer wing end portions 58. The hinges can include suitable locking means for the wing in flight and in folded portions or separate lock means can be provided. Systems connecting to the wing must be adapted for such folding and these may be adapted to be hinged or disconnected during wing folding (and adapted for automatic re-engagement). FIGURES 6 and 7 show such means 60 associated with the torque tubes 62 involved in aileron control and include interengaging parts 64, 66 with tongue and groove means 68 adapted for automatic disengagement and re-engagement.

The wing folding is about horizontal axes provided by hinges 50 and involves pivoting outer wing end portions 58 into superposition to inner wing end portions 56 and pivoting inner wing portions 56 into upright positions wherein there is juxtaposition to vertical stabilizers 20, as shown in FIGURES 2 and 4. It will be seen that by these means, control of width to eight feet or less is provided, rear vision has minimum obstruction, the vehicle has good air flow characteristics for highway travel, and this is a good choice aesthetically for appearance in highway travel.

HELICOPTER-AUTOMOBILE-BOAT AND AIR SUSPENSION CAR COMBINATION

Original Filed July 26. 1966 5 Sheets-Sheet 1

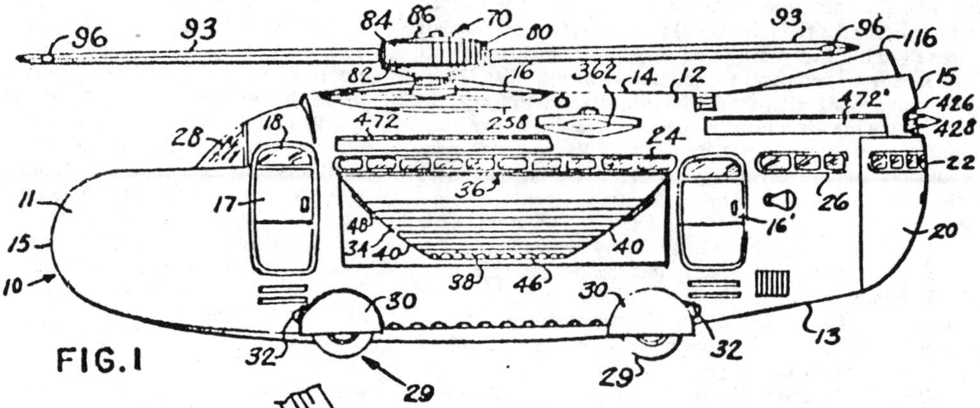

FIG. 1

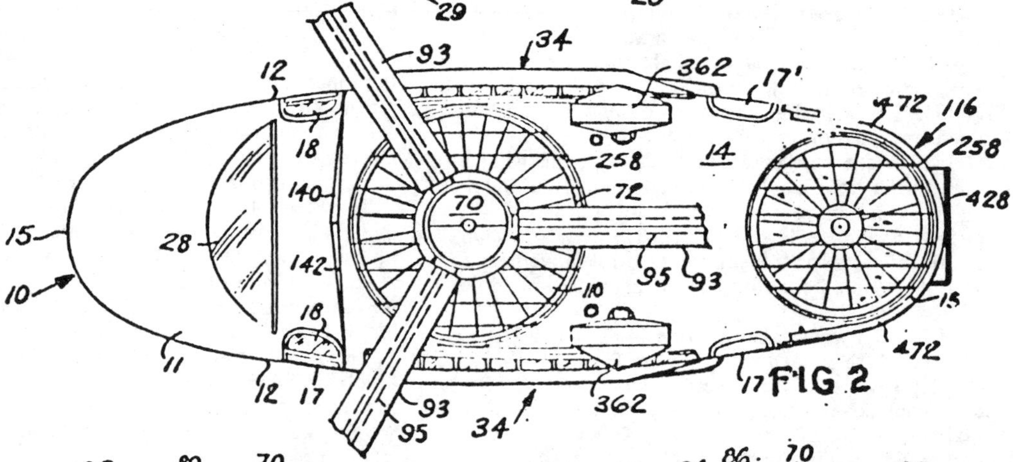

FIG 2

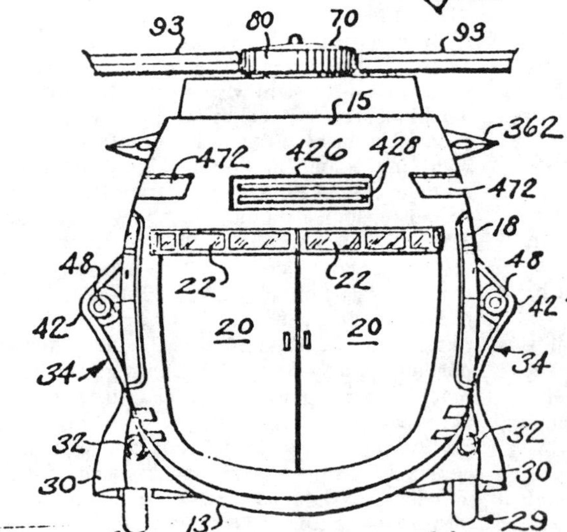

FIG. 3

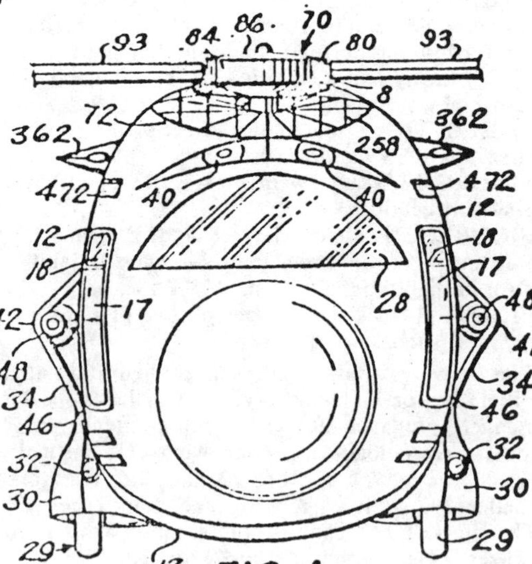

FIG. 4

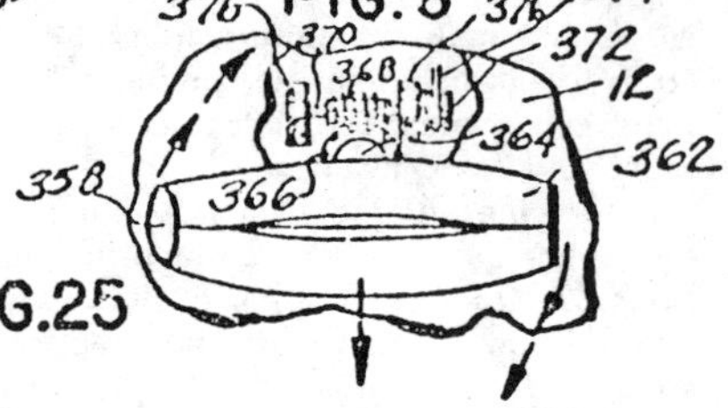

FIG. 25

INVENTOR.
STEVEN POSTELSON APOSTOLESCU

United States Patent

[11] 3,612,440

[72] Inventor Richard A. Strong
6106 Hope Drive, Washington, D.C. 20031
[21] Appl. No. 855,084
[22] Filed Sept. 4, 1969
[45] Patented Oct. 12, 1971

[54] WARP ACTION SPOILER PLATE AILERON AND COMBINED AIRPLANE AND AUTOMOBILE
9 Claims, 6 Drawing Figs.

[52] U.S. Cl. 244/2
[51] Int. Cl. B64c 37/00
[50] Field of Search 244/2, 7,
49, 40, 41, 45, 90

[56] References Cited
UNITED STATES PATENTS

2,174,542	10/1939	Weick	244/90 A
2,402,118	6/1946	Ashkenas	244/90 A
2,573,271	10/1951	Perl	244/2
2,609,167	9/1952	Gero, Jr.	244/2 X
2,811,323	10/1957	Rethorst	244/2
2,812,911	11/1957	De Jean	244/49
2,940,688	6/1960	Bland	244/2
3,012,737	12/1961	Dodd	244/2
3,439,890	4/1969	Stits	244/49
1,749,769	3/1930	Johnson	244/49
2,539,489	1/1951	Smith	244/2
2,673,047	3/1954	Scarato	244/49
3,056,564	10/1962	Zuck	244/2

Primary Examiner—Milton Buchler
Assistant Examiner—Carl A. Rutledge
Attorney—Gustave Miller

ABSTRACT: The invention relates to an aircraft having roadability features and includes wing structures which fold from operative positions to inoperative positions nested within the body of the aircraft.

The wing has a warp action spoiler plate aileron in it and has a full span flap which, with the wing, may be swung into overlapping position in the fuselage with the other wing similarly positioned. It is an improvement on my prior U.S. Pat. No. 2,923,494 of Feb. 2, 1960.

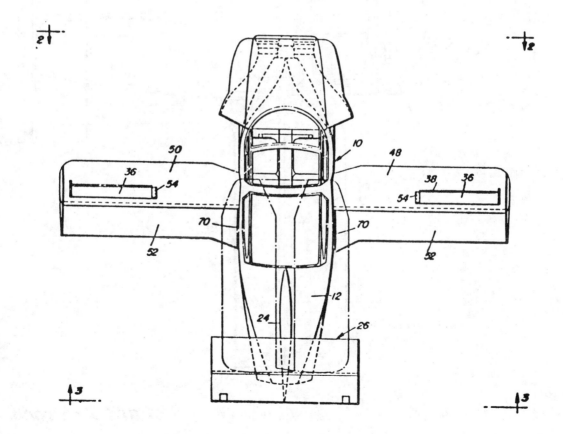

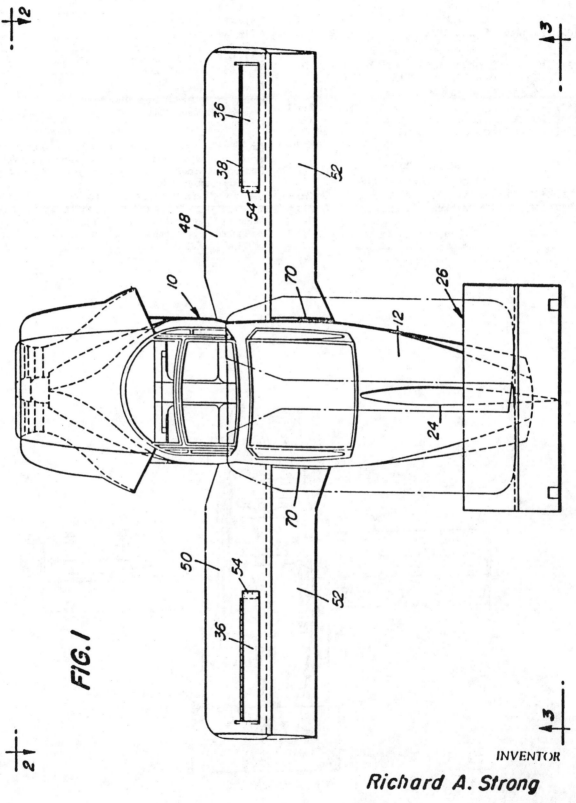

FIG. I

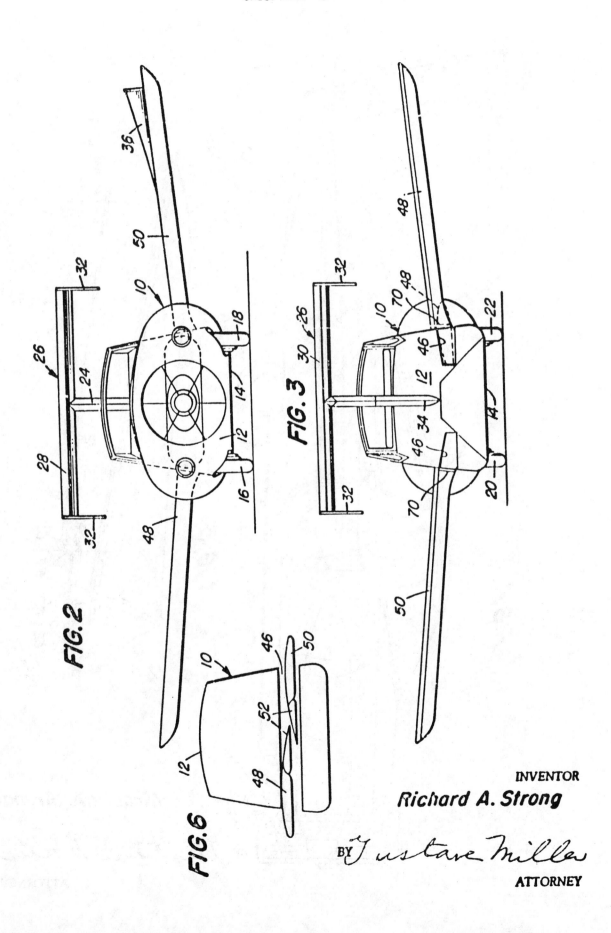

FIG.2

FIG.3

FIG.6

INVENTOR
Richard A. Strong

BY *Gustave Miller*

ATTORNEY

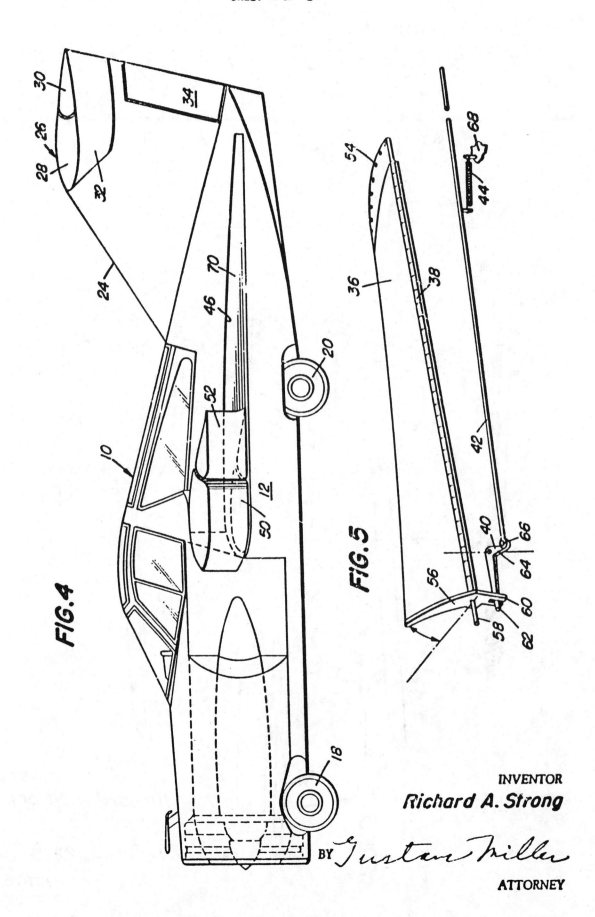

FIG.4

FIG.5

INVENTOR

Richard A. Strong

BY *Gustave Miller*

ATTORNEY

United States Patent

Arbuse

[15] 3,645,474

[45] Feb. 29, 1972

[54] **COMBINED LAND AND AIR VEHICLE**

[72] Inventor: Samuel H. Arbuse, P.O. Box 244, Palm Beach, Fla. 33480

[22] Filed: May 8, 1970

[21] Appl. No.: 35,683

[52] U.S. Cl..244/2
[51] Int. Cl..B64c 37/00
[58] Field of Search....................................244/2

[56] **References Cited**

UNITED STATES PATENTS

2,562,491	7/1951	Hall	244/2
2,593,785	4/1952	Nye et al	244/2
2,624,530	1/1953	Hanssen	244/2
2,373,467	4/1945	Frakes	244/2
2,410,234	10/1946	Read et al	244/2

Primary Examiner—Milton Buchler
Assistant Examiner—Carl A. Rutledge
Attorney—Eliot S. Gerber

[57] **ABSTRACT**

A combined land and air vehicle includes an automobile having an engine for travel on land and a detachable air structure. The automobile is adapted to be connected with the air structure which includes wings, tail assemblies and an airplane engine, for air travel. To become ready to fly, the steering wheel of the automobile is disconnected from the front automobile wheels and is connected with the elevator and aileron controls. A rudder-steering pedal trolley system is engaged, which has pedals that are removed when driving on land and which are connected for flying. A power transmission system permits the automobile engine to rotate the propeller in case of failure of the airplane engine.

10 Claims, 16 Drawing Figures

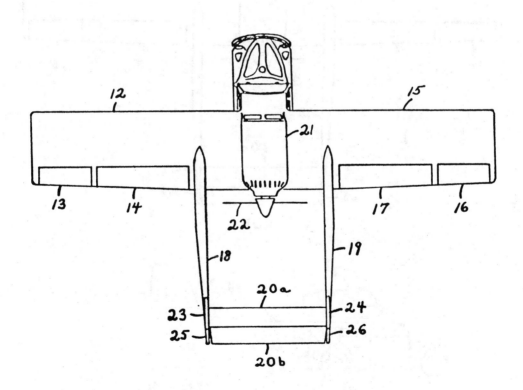

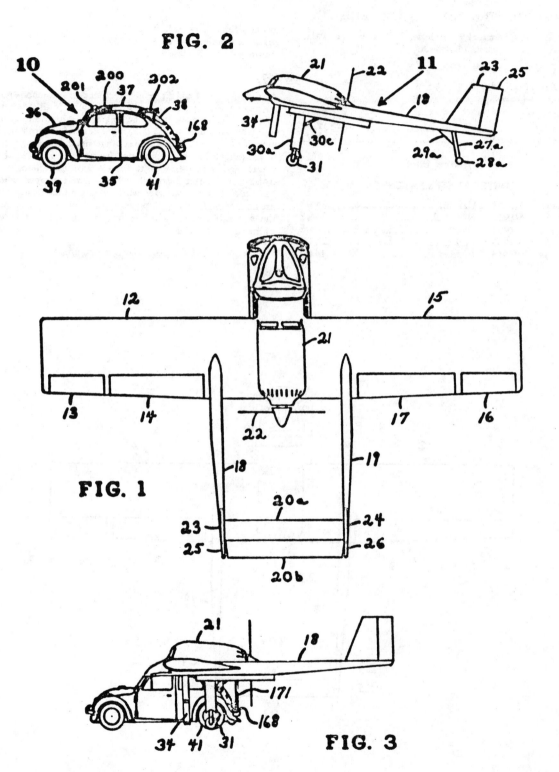

FIG. 2

FIG. 1

FIG. 3

INVENTOR.
SAMUEL H. ARBUSE
BY
Eliot S. Gerber
ATTORNEY.

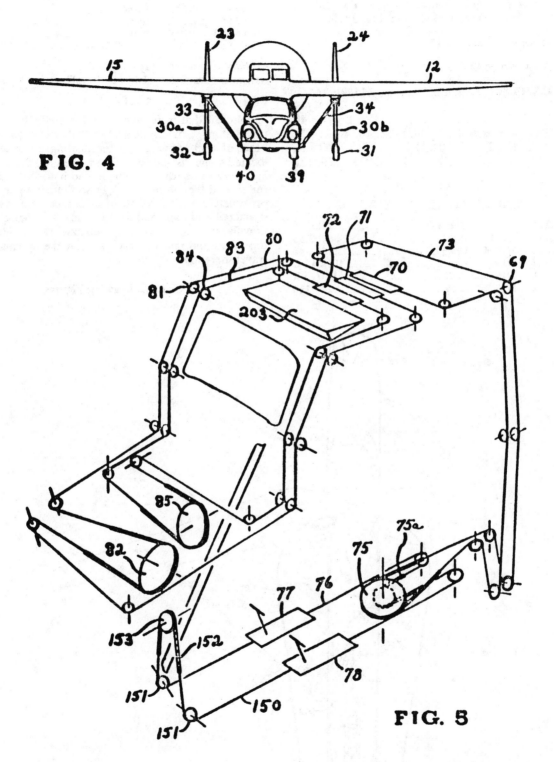

FIG. 4

FIG. 5

INVENTOR.

SAMUEL H. ARBUSE

BY

Eliot S. Gerber

ATTORNEY.

[54] **CONVERTIBLE AIRCRAFT**

[76] Inventor: **Louis Francois Chiquet, P.O. Box 3134, Jacksonville, Fla. 32206**

[22] Filed: **Jan. 28, 1976**

[21] Appl. No.: **643,475**

[52] U.S. Cl. 244/46; 244/2; 244/49

[51] Int. Cl.² B64C 3/40

[58] Field of Search .... 244/38, 2, 46, 49, 114 R, 244/115, 116; 104/23 R, 23 FS; 105/215 R, 215 C; 238/127, 128

[56]   **References Cited**

UNITED STATES PATENTS

141,217	7/1873	Ghirardini	238/128
2,319,446	5/1943	Dowty	244/102.55
3,140,842	7/1964	Craigo et al.	244/46
3,701,323	10/1972	Cox	105/215 C
3,715,991	2/1973	Boyd	104/23 R
3,830,452	8/1974	Seay	244/116

FOREIGN PATENTS OR APPLICATIONS

54,814	8/1950	France	244/49
372,863	7/1939	Italy	244/114 R
566,334	8/1957	Italy	244/46
672,959	5/1952	United Kingdom	244/49

Primary Examiner—Trygve M. Blix
Assistant Examiner—Galen L. Barefoot

[57]   **ABSTRACT**

An aircraft that is designed to additionally be able to travel along a railroad track so that it can get into a heart of a city, instead of terminating at an airport located some distance away from the city; the aircraft including wings which can be folded inwardly adjacent the side of the aircraft fuselage so that it requires approximately a same width of clearance as a conventional railroad train, and the railroad tracks being additionally fitted with a system of channel rails welded on top of the old railroad track so that the airplane can travel thereupon.

1 Claim, 2 Drawing Figures

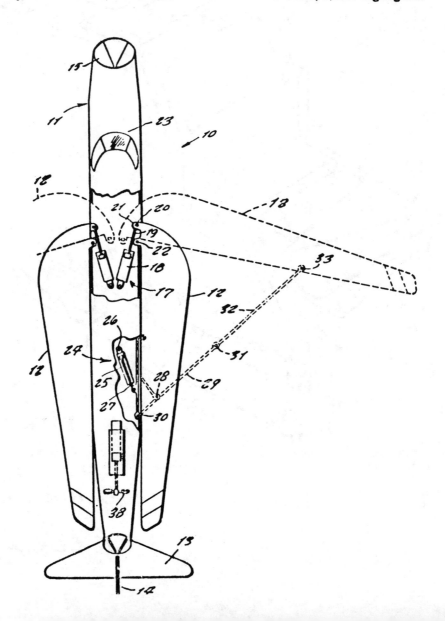

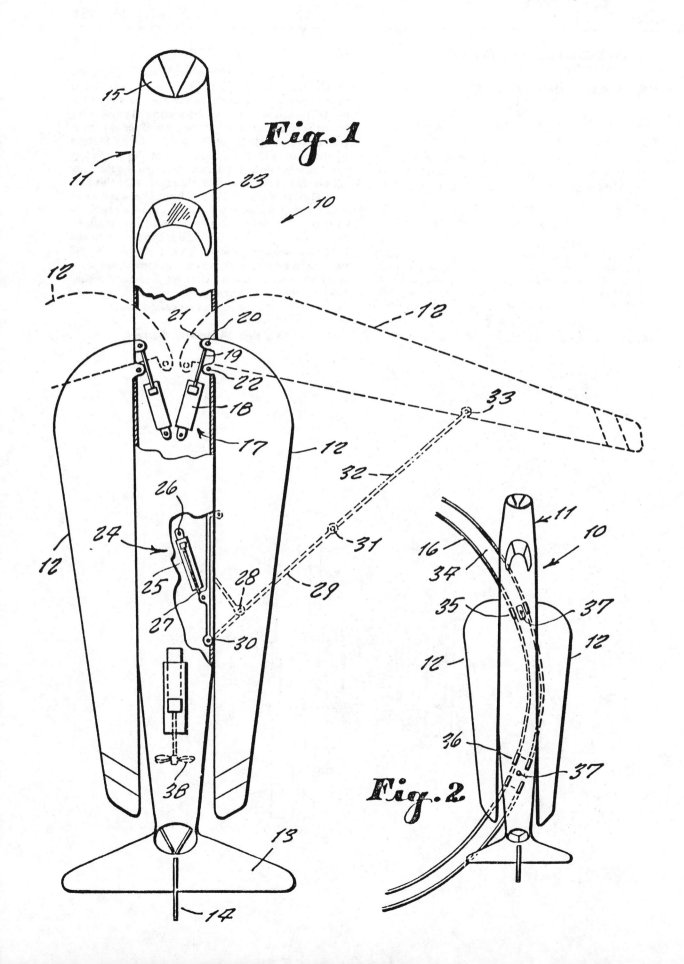

Fig.1

Fig.2

United States Patent [19]

Miller

[11] **4,269,374**

[45] **May 26, 1981**

[54] **COMBINED ROAD VEHICLE AND AIRCRAFT**

[76] Inventor: Harvey R. Miller, 3655 E. Amazon, Eugene, Oreg. 97405

[21] Appl. No.: **1,876**

[22] Filed: **Jan. 8, 1979**

[51] Int. Cl.³ B64C 37/00; B64C 3/56
[52] U.S. Cl. 244/2; 244/49
[58] Field of Search 244/2, 49, 36, 50, 87

[56] **References Cited**

U.S. PATENT DOCUMENTS

2,573,271	10/1951	Perl	244/49
2,811,323	10/1957	Rethorst	244/2
2,940,688	6/1960	Bland	244/2
2,989,269	6/1961	Le Bel	244/36
3,083,936	4/1963	Rethorst	244/49
3,371,886	3/1968	Schertz	244/2

Primary Examiner—Charles E. Frankfort
Attorney, Agent, or Firm—Eugene M. Eckelman

[57] **ABSTRACT**

The apparatus is convertible between road vehicle and aircraft forms having wing and tail assemblies as well as propelling structure that are movable outwardly for the flying form and movable inwardly in stored position for the road vehicle form. All of the parts of the apparatus remain intact in both the road and flying forms. Storage for the wing and tail assemblies and the propelling structure is in side and end compartments, and the wing and tail assemblies have foldable sections for this purpose. The apparatus has a pair of front wheels and a pair of rear wheels, the latter wheels being movable between a narrowed rearward position for road use which allows storage of the wings in the side compartments and a forward widened position for aircraft use. The tail assembly is supported on a slide mechanism which extends downward in a forward longitudinal direction whereby the tail assembly is lowered as it is moved forwardly for storage in the rear compartment.

5 Claims, 18 Drawing Figures

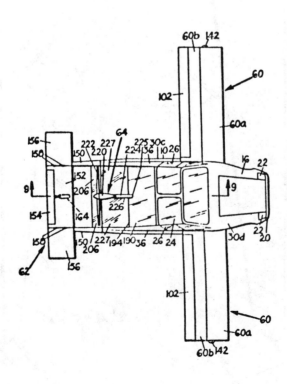

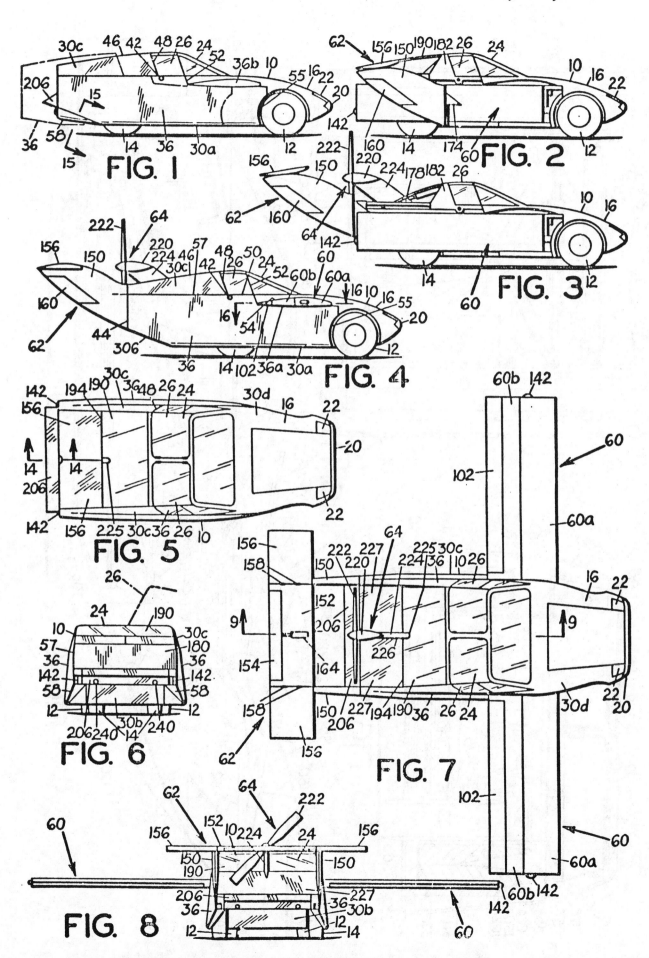

FIG. 1

FIG. 2

FIG. 3

FIG. 4

FIG. 5

FIG. 6

FIG. 7

FIG. 8

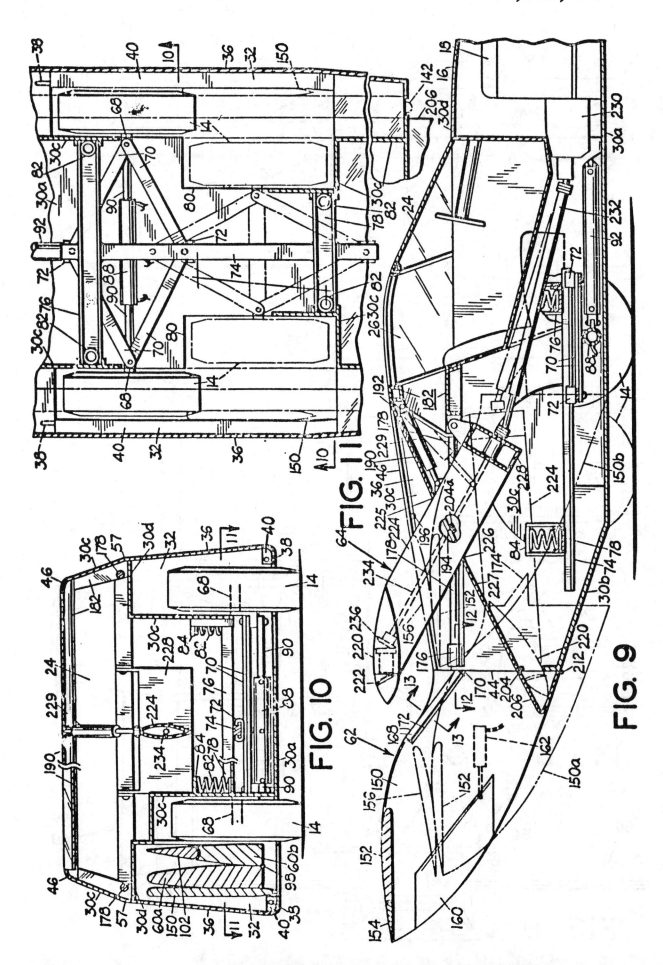

FIG. 11

FIG. 10

FIG. 9

United States Patent [19]

Williamson

[11] **4,358,072**

[45] **Nov. 9, 1982**

[54] **LAND VEHICLE AND AIRCRAFT COMBINATION**

[76] Inventor: Roger Williamson, 2862 S. 2nd East, Apt. 62, Salt Lake City, Utah 84115

[21] Appl. No.: 138,320

[22] Filed: Apr. 8, 1980

[51] Int. Cl.³ B64C 39/00
[52] U.S. Cl. 244/2; 244/120; 244/234
[58] Field of Search 244/2, 120, 140, 224, 244/234; 180/198

[56] **References Cited**

U.S. PATENT DOCUMENTS

2,014,769	9/1935	Kossakowski	180/198
2,410,234	10/1946	Read et al.	244/2
2,462,462	2/1949	Boggs et al.	244/2
2,535,164	12/1950	Seibel	244/120
2,650,049	8/1953	Fowler	244/2
3,833,190	9/1974	Gaio	244/224
4,143,841	3/1979	Roeder	244/140

FOREIGN PATENT DOCUMENTS

994341 11/1951 France 244/2

Primary Examiner—Galen L. Barefoot
Attorney, Agent, or Firm—Trask & Britt

[57] **ABSTRACT**

A combination road and air vehicle having separate engines for each craft is disclosed. The aircraft has an air frame with wings and tail elements attached to a fuselage with a tricycle landing gear attached to the air frame. A nose platform extends forward from the bottom of the fuselage. The platform is adapted to receive and support a small land vehicle. The aircraft controls are mounted on a folding stalk attached to the top side of the platform. The land vehicle has a central opening in its body through which the control stalk may be elevated to a vertical position. The aircraft and land vehicle each have its own power plant and control system.

13 Claims, 9 Drawing Figures

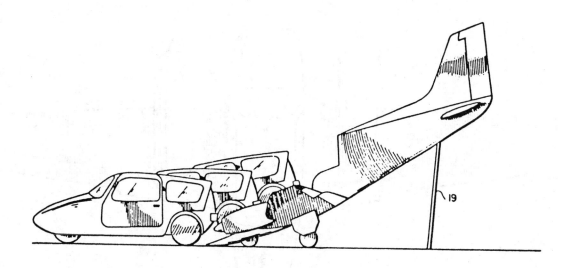

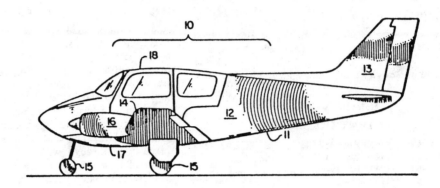

Fig. 1

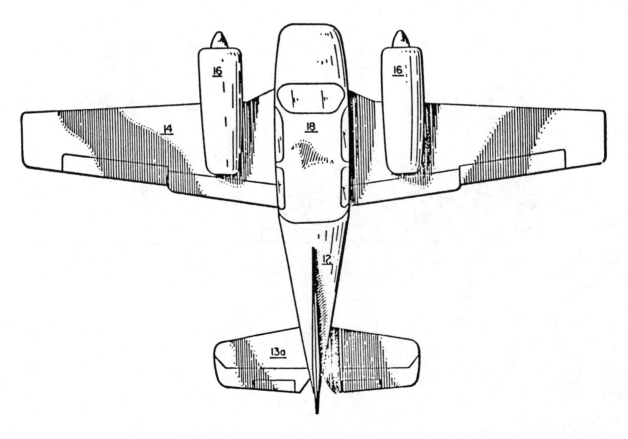

Fig. 2

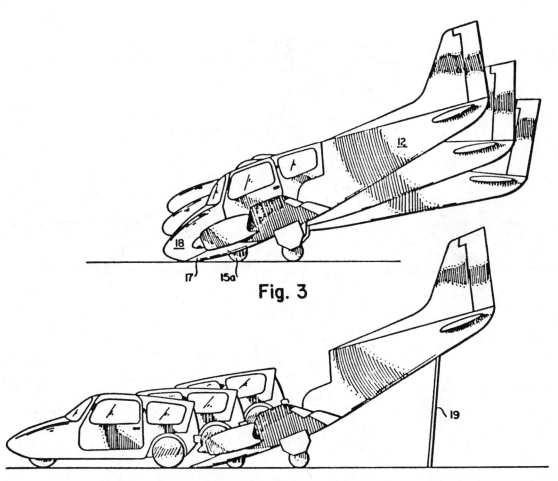

Fig. 3

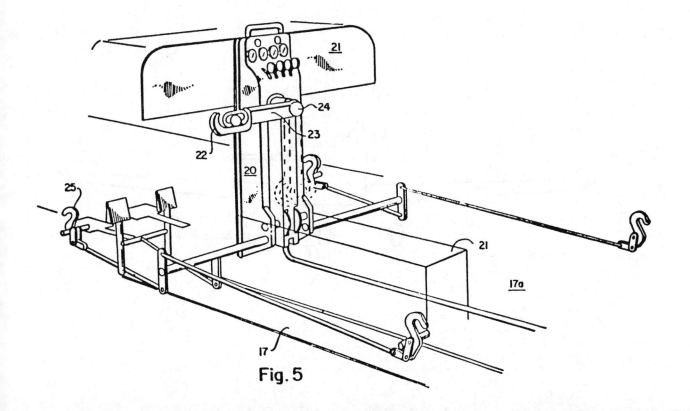

Fig. 4

Fig. 5

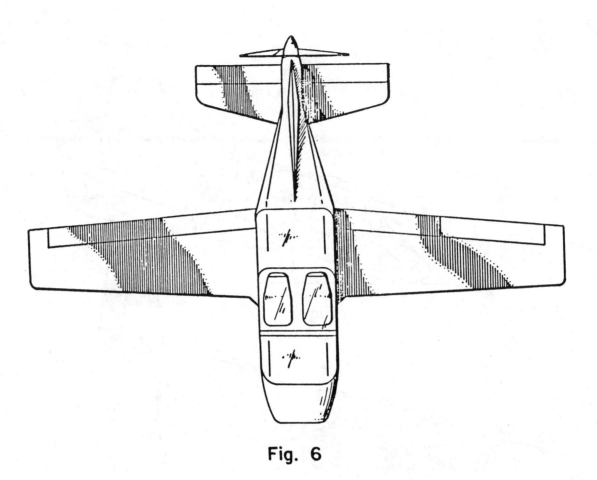

Fig. 6

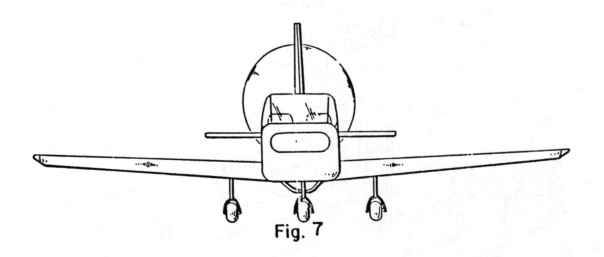

Fig. 7

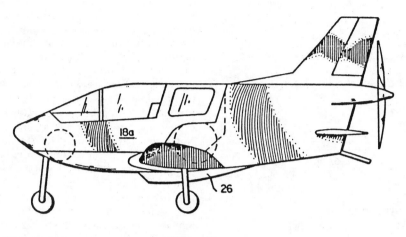

Fig. 8

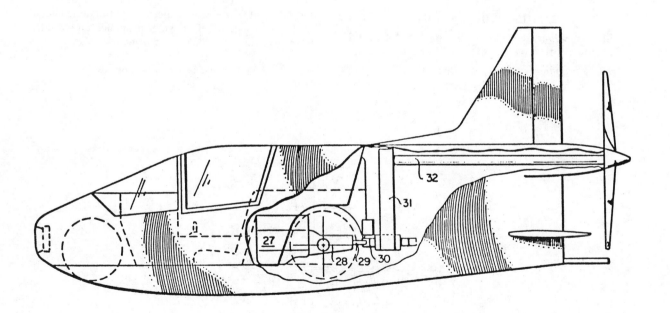

Fig. 9

[54] **AIR, LAND AND SEA VEHICLE**

[75] Inventor: Joseph N. Ayoola, P.O. Box 17532, Los Angeles, Calif. 90017

[73] Assignee: Joseph N. Ayoola, Los Angeles, Calif.

[21] Appl. No.: 645,800

[22] Filed: Aug. 30, 1984

Related U.S. Application Data

[63] Continuation-in-part of Ser. No. 493,431, May 11, 1983, abandoned.

[51] Int. Cl.⁴ B64D 37/00
[52] U.S. Cl. 244/2; 244/50; 244/49; 244/106; 114/270
[58] Field of Search 244/2, 49, 50, 58, 218, 244/106; 114/270

[56] **References Cited**

U.S. PATENT DOCUMENTS

2,563,731	8/1951	Masterson	244/2
2,940,688	6/1960	Bland	244/2
3,082,975	3/1963	Cardwell et al.	244/2
3,134,561	5/1964	Clejan	244/58
3,306,249	2/1967	Chase	114/270
3,666,210	5/1972	Look et al.	244/218

OTHER PUBLICATIONS

"Filtron", advertisement, the Filtron Co. Inc., 38-25 Bell Boulevard, Bayside, NY, NY, 3-13-50.

Primary Examiner—Trygve M. Blix

Assistant Examiner—Rodney Corl

[57] **ABSTRACT**

Air, Land and Sea vehicle is convertible between aircraft form, road vehicle form and boat form. The conversion between aircraft form and road vehicle forms having (4) four tires as an automobile as well as a roadable vehicle structure that are movable outwardly for highway usage, and inwardly into stored position for the aircraft form or boat form, and having storage for the wing and tail assemblies which has a foldable section for this purpose. For conversion between aircraft form and boat forms, the apparatus has a retractable or extendable water propeller as propelling means in the water, and parts arranged for steering. The wings and tail assemblies are moved inwardly into stored position including auto and aero tires moved inwardly into their water-leak-proof compartments. The conversion between boat form and aircraft forms having wings and tail assemblies as well as propelling structures that are movable outwardly for the flying form including wing-lifter to lift the wings upwardly for the sufficient clearance between the wing-level and the water-level in order to accommodate sufficient relative wind to propel the invention as a lift means, during water takeoff. The water-rudder will maintain a straight forward movement. The auto and aero engines operate until the invention takes off on the water, then, the automobile engine must be turned off. The water-propeller and rudder move inwardly into their compartments respectively.

6 Claims, 14 Drawing Figures

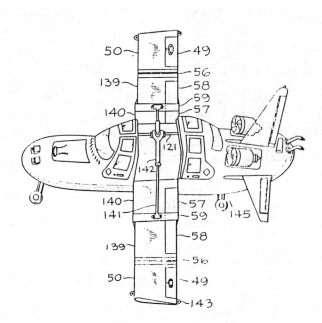

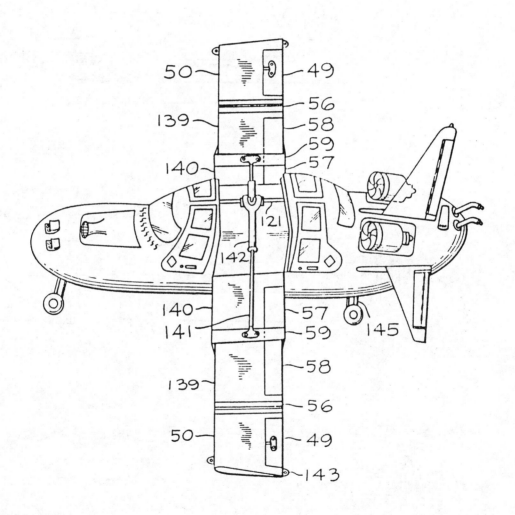

FIG. 1

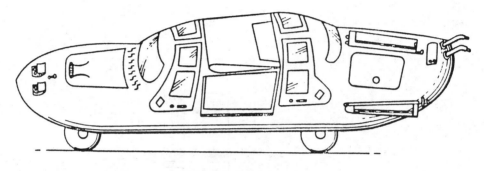

FIG. 2

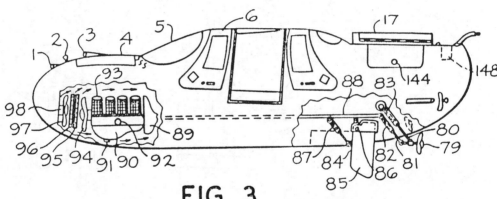

FIG. 3

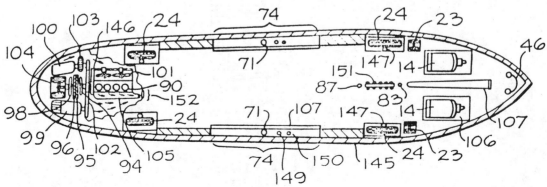

FIG. 4

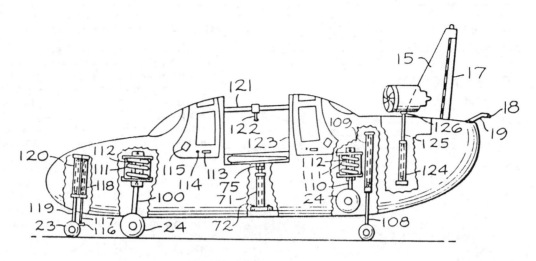

FIG. 5

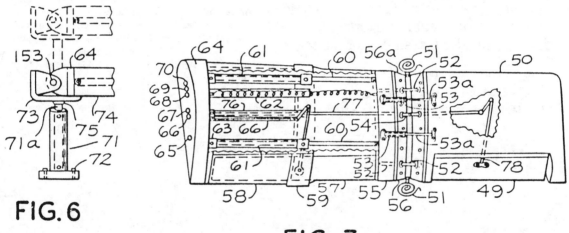

FIG. 6

FIG. 7

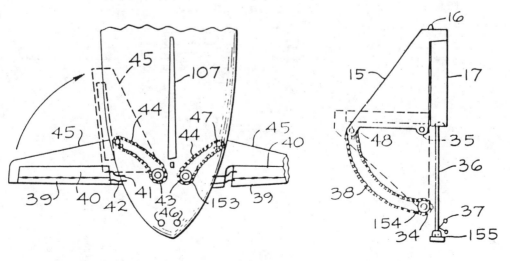

FIG. 8

FIG. 9

[11] Patent Number: 4,627,585

[45] Date of Patent: Dec. 9, 1986

[54] PUSHER TYPE AUTO-PLANE

[76] Inventor: Harry Einstein, 25 Midvale Dr., Springfield, N.J. 07081

[21] Appl. No.: 624,521

[22] Filed: Jun. 25, 1984

[51] Int. Cl.⁴ B64C 3/56; B64C 37/00
[52] U.S. Cl. 244/2; 244/49
[58] Field of Search 244/2, 49, 50

[56] References Cited

U.S. PATENT DOCUMENTS

1,393,820	10/1921	Osborne	244/49
1,731,757	10/1929	Tubbe	244/49
2,713,465	7/1955	Novinger	244/2
2,940,688	6/1960	Bland	244/2
3,065,927	11/1962	Mills	244/2
4,240,601	12/1980	Reed	244/49
4,269,374	5/1981	Miller	244/49

FOREIGN PATENT DOCUMENTS

635259 4/1950 United Kingdom 244/49

OTHER PUBLICATIONS

Dewoitine, Published U.S. Ser. No. 323,201, May 25, 1943.
Scientific American, Mar. 1935, p. 151.

Primary Examiner—Galen L. Barefoot
Attorney, Agent, or Firm—Kenneth P. Glynn

[57] ABSTRACT

An improved auto-plane has been invented which has been adapted for air travel and road travel using a Pusher type design. The present invention auto-plane has two main wings which are cut approximately parallel to an imaginary fuselage centerline at about two-thirds the distance in from the wing's outer tip to the imaginary centerline, one of the two main wings being hinged along its cut and above its top surface at a height sufficient to allow both of the two wings to be folded inward 180° with one resting atop the other. The auto-plane includes a rear stabilizer system which can be retracted forward to reduce the overall length for road use, a Pusher type propeller, and a Pusher type aviation engine which is located within the fuselage to drive the propeller. Landing wheels are located on the underside of the fuselage in an aviation landing relationship, e.g. tricycle, and aviation controls are located within the fuselage to control the aviation engine, propeller and elevons and rudders. An independent land vehicle engine is located within the fuselage and connected to drive one or more of the wheels for land use. In an alternative embodiment, each wing is cut twice, once about one-quarter the distance in and once about three-quarters in, with hinges to allow unique double (spiral) folding to permit compact stocking of the twice folded wings.

8 Claims, 6 Drawing Figures

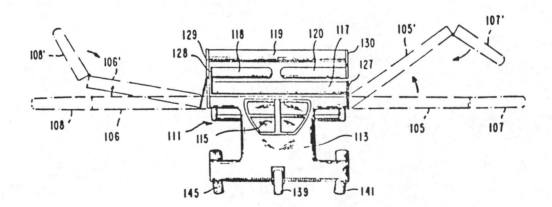

FIG. 1

FIG. 2

FIG. 3

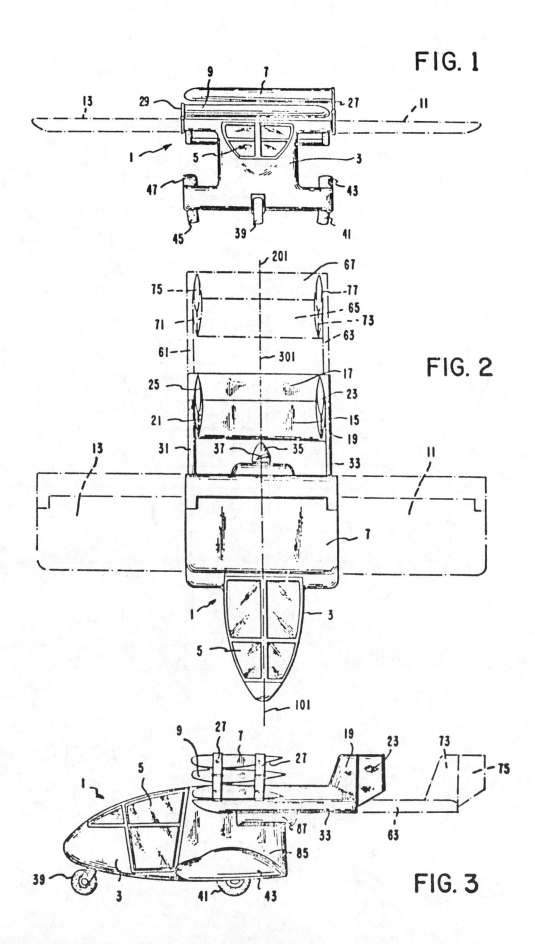

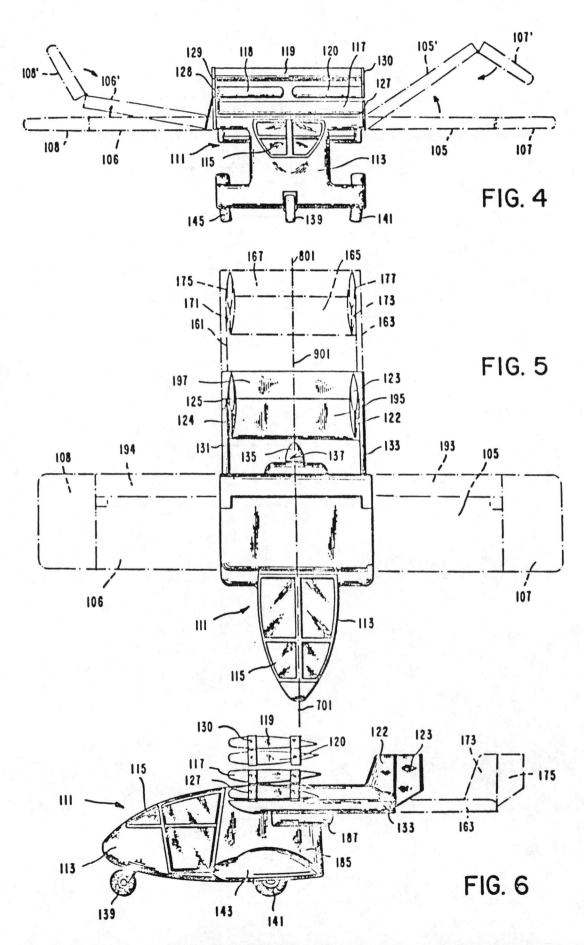

FIG. 4

FIG. 5

FIG. 6

United States Patent [19]

Rutan

[11] **Patent Number:** **4,641,800**

[45] **Date of Patent:** **Feb. 10, 1987**

[54] **TANDEM OR MULTI-WINGED HIGH PERFORMANCE AIRCRAFT**

[76] Inventor: **Elbert L. Rutan,** Hangar 73, Mojave Airport, Mojave, Calif. 93501

[21] Appl. No.: **524,332**

[22] Filed: **Aug. 18, 1983**

[51] Int. Cl.⁴ B64C 3/54; B64C 3/40
[52] U.S. Cl. .... 244/218; 244/45 A; 244/45 R; 244/46
[58] Field of Search .... 244/45 A, 46, 45 R, 244/201, 218, 203, 49

[56] **References Cited**

U.S. PATENT DOCUMENTS

2,744,698	5/1956	Baynes	244/218
3,330,501	7/1967	Barber	244/46
3,738,595	6/1973	Bouchnik	244/218
3,776,491	12/1973	Oulton	244/218
4,093,156	6/1978	Coe, Jr.	244/45 A

FOREIGN PATENT DOCUMENTS

413781	8/1910	France	244/218
493655	10/1938	United Kingdom	244/218
814450	6/1959	United Kingdom	244/45 A

OTHER PUBLICATIONS

Flight International, "Canards: Design With Care", pp. 19–21, Feb. 23, 1985.
"Notes on the Tail–First Aeroplane", RAE Report BA 1542, S. B. Gates, Nov. 18, 1941.
"Aircraft Design Part I, Parametric Studies", A. A. Lebedinski, Dept. of Aeronautical Eng., Indian Institute of Science, Bangalore, India, 1963.
NACA RM–L8614, "Study of the Canard Config. with Particular Ref. to Transonic Flight Characteristics and Low Speed Characteristics at High Lift", C. W. Mathews, Nov. 16, 1949.
NACA TN–1499, "Flight Tests of the Miles Libellula Tandem Biplane", P. Brotherhood, et al., Aug. 1944.

Primary Examiner—Galen L. Barefoot
Assistant Examiner—Rodney Corl
Attorney, Agent, or Firm—Edwin L. Spangler, Jr.

[57] **ABSTRACT**

This invention relates to a tandem or multi-winged aircraft wherein a primary wing system is so designed and equipped that it is capable of being actuated in a manner to bring about a shift in the neutral point of the craft relative to its center of gravity and wherein a secondary wing system located ahead of the primary one and movable fore and aft relative to the latter is deployed and angled during its excursion so as to effectively counteract the neutral point shift that would be brought about by deploying the primary wing system alone thereby maintaining the neutral point at approximately its former location in at least both the cruise mode as well as the high-lift mode preferred for landing and take-off.

23 Claims, 7 Drawing Figures

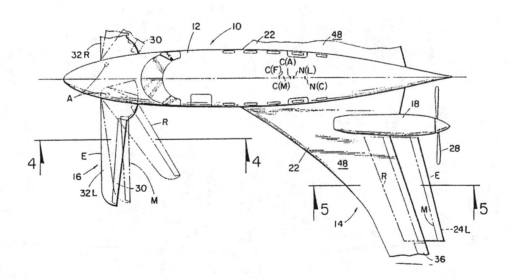

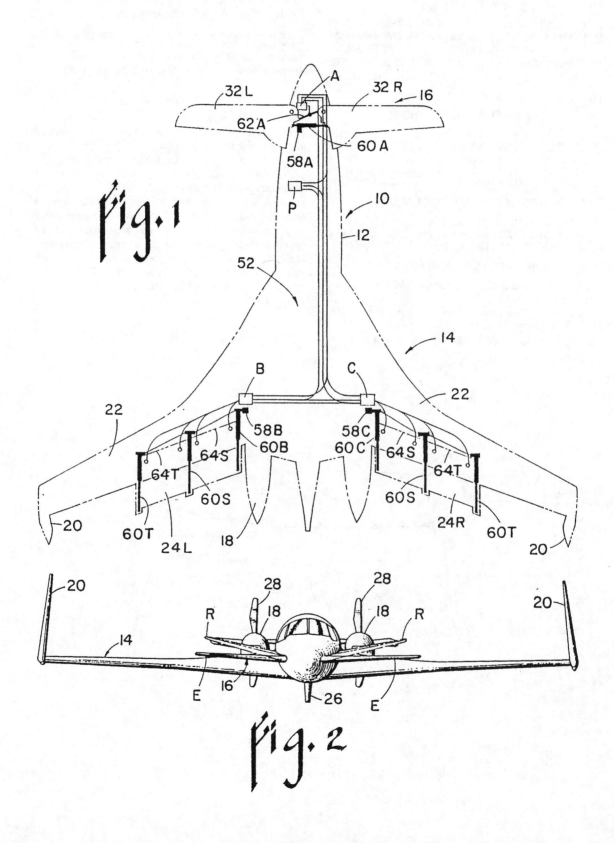

Fig. 1

Fig. 2

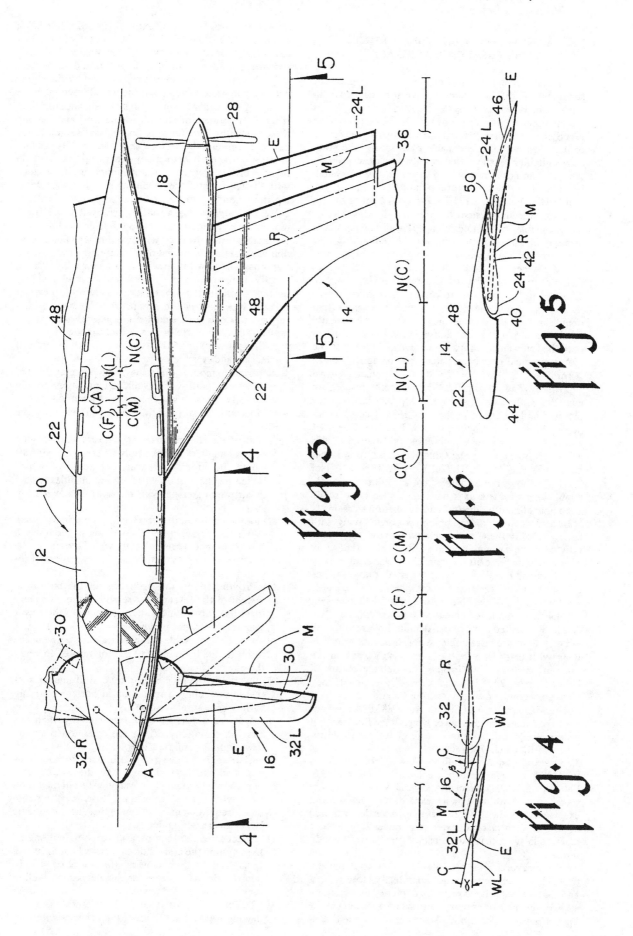

Fig. 3

Fig. 6

Fig. 5

Fig. 4

TANDEM OR MULTI-WINGED HIGH PERFORMANCE AIRCRAFT

High-speed aircraft, most of which are designed for supersonic flight, have been known for years that include some type of extendable so-called "canard" wings which upon deployment create a lift force about an aerodynamic center located forwardly of the craft's center of gravity that is capable of offsetting the nose-down pitching moment that results when the primary wing system positioned behind the canard wing system is actuated to shift the neutral point aft. Lockheed Aircraft's U.S. Pat. No. 2,271,226 employs a more or less fixed canard wing system having high-lift elevators or flaps capable of counteracting the diving moment brought about through actuation of similar high-lift elements associated with the main wing that become effective when actuated to shift the aft or main wings center of pressure rearward. Creasey et al U.S. Pat. No. 2,982,496 uses a fixed canard wing in association with a main wing having jettisonable wing extensions that double in function as fuel tanks. Still other essentially fixed tandem-winged aircraft using coordinated flaps on both the fore and aft wings are known in addition to the aforementioned Lockheed patent, one being Blackburn Aircraft's U.S. Pat. No. 2,470,602. Applicant's own "VariEze" and "Long-EZ" home built planes are equipped with canards, several such planes having been pictured and described in the May 1983 issue of Technology Illustrated. Lockheed U.S. Pat. No. 2,511,504 employs a canard wing tiltable about its "spanwise" axis and it is probably this patent that is referred to in Lockheed U.S. Pat. No. 2,271,226. Howard U.S. Pat. No. 2,747,816 shows canard wings that are not only tiltable about their spanwise axes but independently so while encompassing both dihedral and catahedral versions.

Instead of tilting or equipping the canard wing with flaps, probably the most common alternative approach is to move the canard between a fully-deployed position effective to increase lift forward of the center of gravity and a stowed condition having essentially no influence on the flight characteristics. Examples of such canards are found in U.S. Pat. Nos. 2,601,962; 3,642,234; and, 2,924,400. In the latter patent as well as U.S. Pat. No. 3,955,780 directed to a heavier-than-air hovercraft, both wing systems are retractable. Aircraft having only one wing with extendable portions are also known in the prior art such as those forming the subject matter of U.S. Pat. Nos. 2,858,091 and 4,181,277; however, they have no secondary wing system or canard.

The Messerschmitt U.S. Pat. No. 3,883,094 does not stow the canard wing inside or beneath the fuselage, but instead, folds it down into a more or less vertical attitude. McDonnell Douglas in their U.S. Pat. No. 3,680,816 also shows the forward wing folding down while the aft wing sweeps backward. Calderon U.S. Pat. No. 3,218,005 describes several variable lift designs, some with sweepable canards and main wing extensions, another that rotates about a vertical axis and even one with stacked extensions depending from a main delta wing that sweep back into a stowed condition.

Of the several prior art patents known to applicant, probably the majority do not completely stow the canard but instead leave it partially deployed as a continuation of the main or primary wing when operating in the high speed or cruise mode. Among such patented con-

figurations are U.S. Pat. Nos. 3,104,082; 3,489,375; 3,738,595; 3,926,389; and 4,093,156. In each of the latter patents, the canard wing sweeps rearward and remains partially extended as an integral part of a delta wing.

While the prior art aircraft exemplified by the above patents, published articles and the like all recognize the ability of the canard wing system to enhance the low speed performance of aircraft for take-off and landing they, evidently, have failed to appreciate its significance insofar as refining the performance and stability characteristics of the craft in its many other flight regimes. In other words, applicant has now found in accordance with the teaching of the instant invention that by leaving the secondary or canard wing system at least partially, and always significantly, deployed in all flight modes such that it has a marked influence on the flight characteristics of the craft while, at the same time, coordinating its effect with that of lift-increasing flaps operatively associated with the main or primary wing system, greatly improved overall performance and stability become possible. It is not enough, therefore, to extend or otherwise deploy the secondary wing system and rely upon it solely to enhance the performance of the craft in the high angle of attack flight mode. To do so robs the system of potential as yet unrealized in terms of stable, safe and reliable performance.

Applicant, among others, has long recognized that the tandem or multi-winged aircraft possesses certain inherent advantages over the more conventional main wing forward, tail-aft design, such as, for example, the ability to:

(1) Introduce stall progression patterns that provide defined angle of attack limits whereby the aircraft cannot be forced to exceed an angle of attack which results in such unsafe flying qualities as stall departure or spin entry throughout the normal c.g. range.

(2) Reduce induced drag by having the primary wing system take advantage of operating in the upwash flow field that is created outboard of the tips of the secondary wing system located forwardly and inboard thereof.

(3) Provide an overall reduction in the structural weight of the fuselage by reason of the more uniform load distribution attainable and to the lower shear and moment intensities.

(4) Increase the usable cabin volume for a given size fuselage due to smaller aft section needed to carry the empennage group.

(5) Distribute the load among several lifting surfaces thereby effecting a reduction in horizontal flying surface structural weight.

(6) Achieve a greater stick-free stability than the stick-fixed stability of the aforementioned single-wing tail-aft configurations.

(7) Separate the primary and secondary wing systems and load the latter higher than the former thus improving the ride qualities under turbulent conditions while, at the same time, lessening the structural requirements necessary to accommodate larger than average loads.

(8) Effect a reduction in parasitic drag by not having to rely upon the conventional vertical tail for directional stability while using the so-called "Whitcomb" winglet systems for this purpose as well as that of reducing induced drag.

(9) Reduce wing to fuselage interference drag by making it possible to mount the primary wing sys-

[54] **AIRBORNE VEHICLE WITH HYDRAULIC DRIVE AND CONTROL**

[76] Inventor: Karl Eickmann, 2420 Isshiki, Hayama-machi, Kanagawa-ken, Japan

[21] Appl. No.: 45,638

[22] Filed: May 1, 1987

[51] Int. Cl.⁴ B64C 37/00
[52] U.S. Cl. 244/2; 244/12.4; 244/56; 244/66
[58] Field of Search .... 244/12.4, 2, 12.6, 23 R, 244/23 A, 26, 29, 56, 66, 60

[56] **References Cited**

U.S. PATENT DOCUMENTS

1,957,896	5/1934	Marguglio	244/23 R
3,012,738	12/1961	Bertin et al.	244/12.4
3,276,528	10/1966	Tucknott et al.	244/23 R
3,417,943	12/1968	Page et al.	244/23 R
3,497,162	2/1970	Zickmann .	

FOREIGN PATENT DOCUMENTS

1506048 7/1969 Fed. Rep. of Germany 244/12.4

Primary Examiner—Galen L. Barefoot

[57] **ABSTRACT**

An airborne craft with at least four propellers arranged in a front propeller pair and a rear propeller pair having substantial vertical or forwardly inclined axes has hydraulic motors which drive the propellers. A pumping device supplies two pairs of separated flows to the motors. One pair of the flows has fixed delivery and equal flow quantities per revolution of the pump while the other pair has variable flow-rates but the flow quantities of both flows of the variable flow pair are also equal relatively to each other. One of the flow pairs drives the front propellers at equal speeds and the other pair of flows drives the rear propellers with equal speeds. But the variability of the rates of flow of one of the pairs of flows is utilized to let one of the pairs run with a different rotary velocity of the propellers than the other pair. The so obtained difference of rotary speeds of the propeller pairs relatively to each other is utilized to incline the vehicle in a desired and controlable extent in the desired direction of flight to obtain and control the forward speed of the vehicle. The variable flow pair has a common control means which assures an equality of the rates of flows in the variable flow pair, whereby a straight forward flight path of the vehicle is assured and departures to the right or left of the desired flight path are prevented. The invention also makes it possible to set the arrangement to the most effective and fuel saving speed as well as to employ control means, which prevent too stiff descents or ascents. In the specific embodiment whereto the claims are directed, the invention is utilized to provide a vehicle with the lateral size of a passenger car to be able to run on the road and lift away from it to fly through the air, borne by eight propellers which are located and revolve in eight ducts.

1 Claim, 28 Drawing Sheets

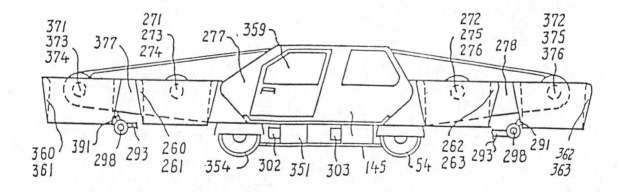

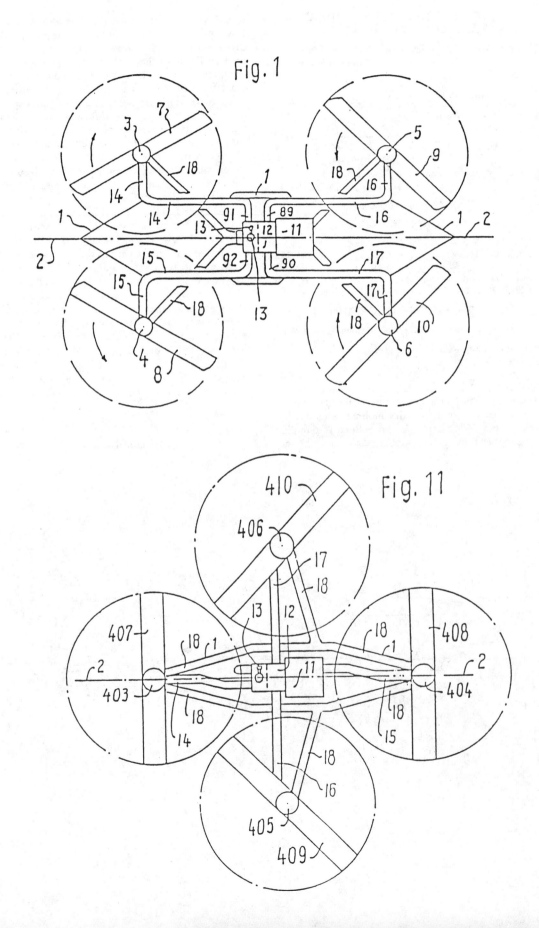

Fig. 1

Fig. 11

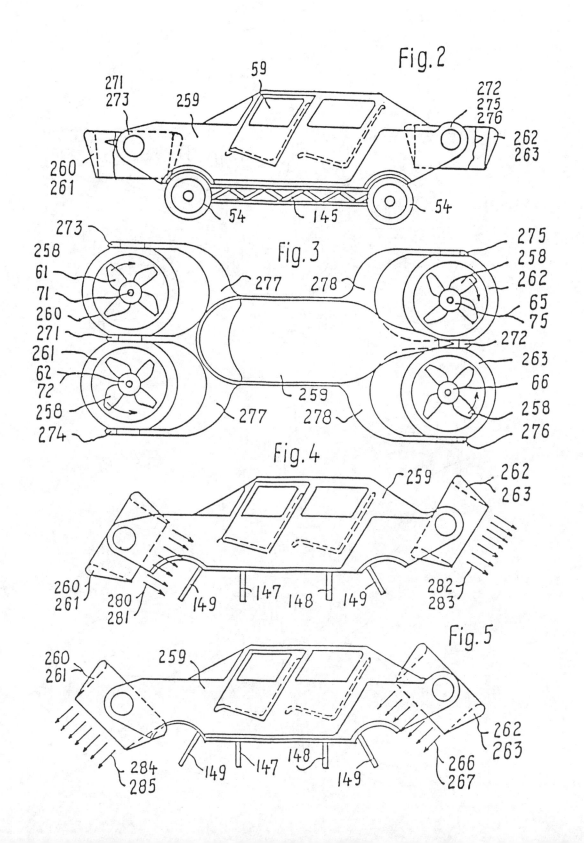

Fig.2

Fig.3

Fig.4

Fig.5

Fig.6

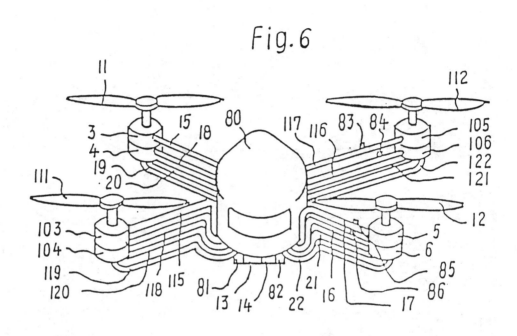

Fig.7

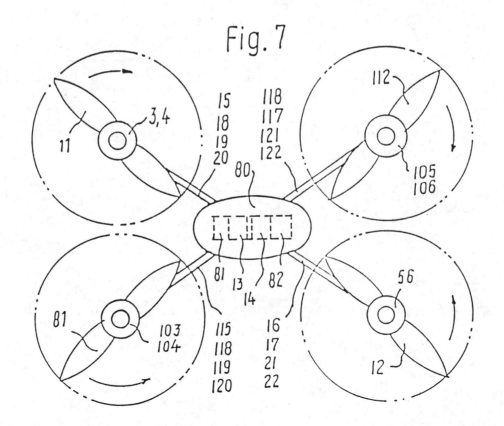

Fig. 14

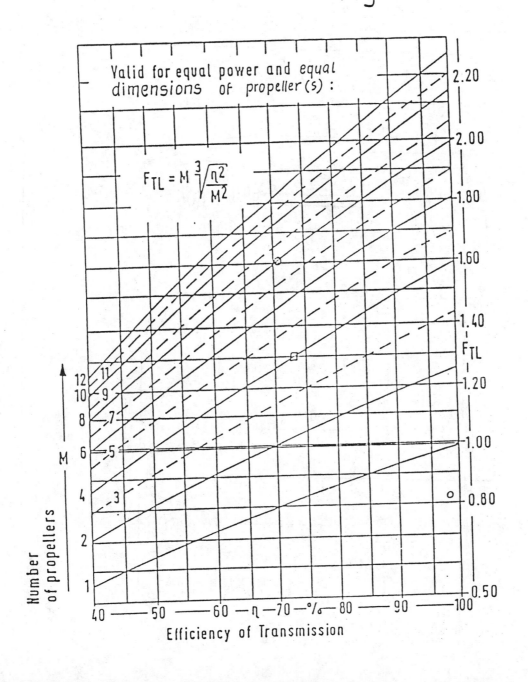

$$F_{TL} = M \sqrt[3]{\frac{\eta^2}{M^2}}$$

Valid for equal power and equal dimensions of propeller(s) :

Fig. 15

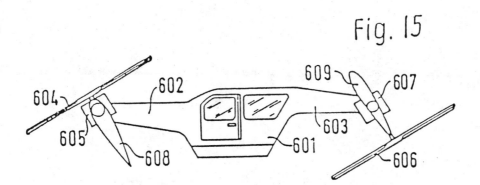

Fig. 16

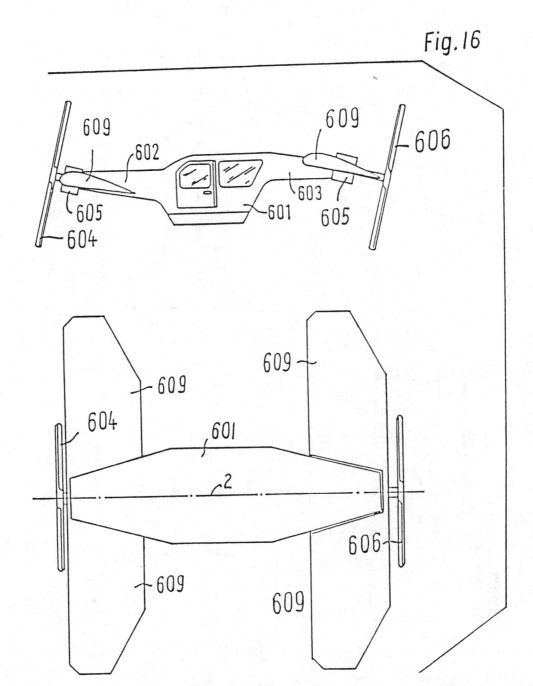

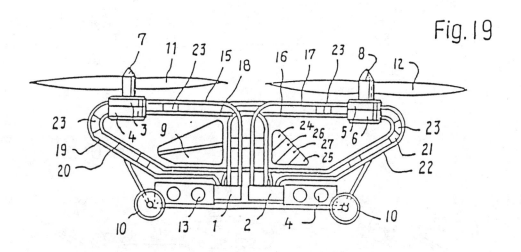

Fig.19

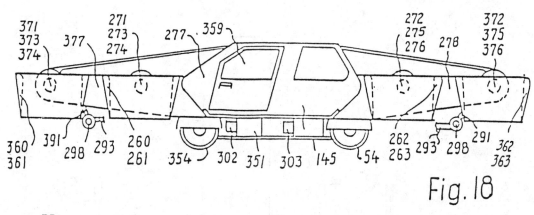

Fig.17

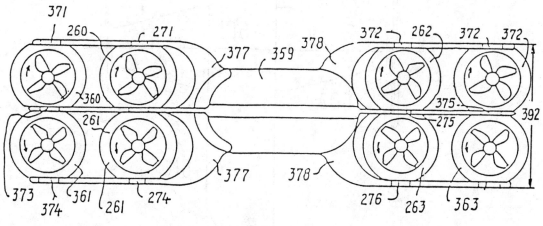

Fig.18

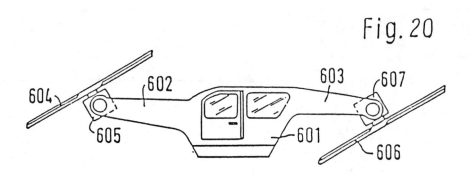

Fig. 20

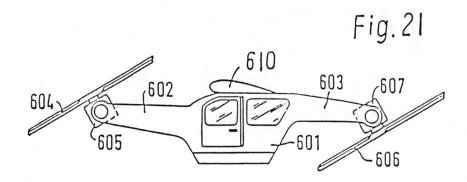

Fig. 21

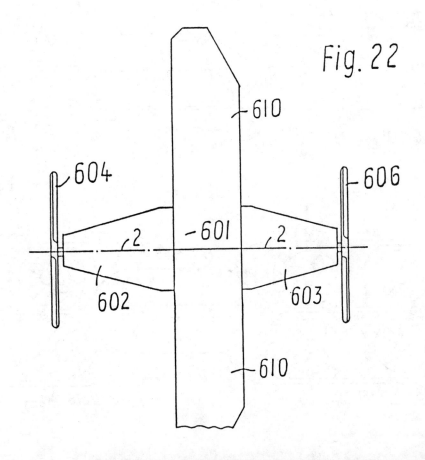

Fig. 22

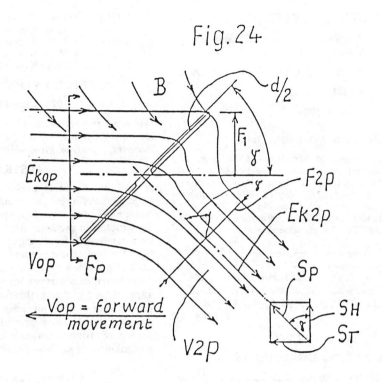

Fig. 24

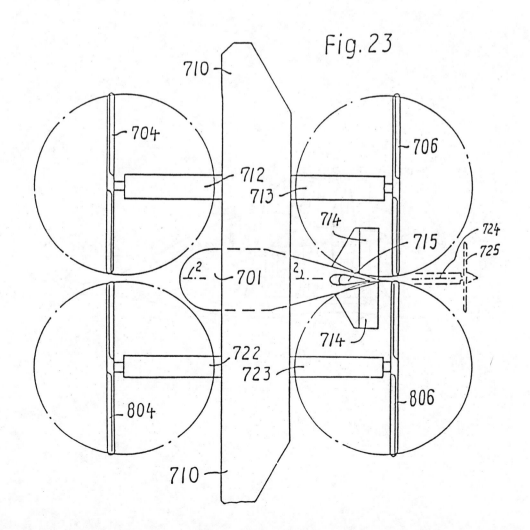

Fig. 23

United States Patent [19]

Thompson

[11] Patent Number: 4,865,275

[45] Date of Patent: Sep. 12, 1989

[54] **LAND, WATER AND AIR CRAFT**

[75] Inventor: Harold L. Thompson, Okmulgee, Okla.

[73] Assignee: Alpha Images, Ltd., Henryetta, Okla.

[21] Appl. No.: 63,721

[22] Filed: Jun. 16, 1987

Related U.S. Application Data

[63] Continuation-in-part of Ser. No. 894,754, Aug. 11, 1986, abandoned, which is a continuation of Ser. No. 800,083, Nov. 19, 1985, abandoned, which is a continuation of Ser. No. 611,371, May 16, 1984, abandoned, which is a continuation of Ser. No. 502,694, Jun. 9, 1983, abandoned, which is a continuation of Ser. No. 276,031, Jun. 22, 1981, abandoned.

[51] Int. Cl.^{4} B64C 3/52
[52] U.S. Cl. 244/219; 244/36;
244/214; 244/215; 244/2
[58] Field of Search 244/2, 12.1, 12.2, 12.6,
244/23 R, 23 C, 36, 38, 34 A, 50, 213, 214, 219;
441/65, 66

[56] **References Cited**

U.S. PATENT DOCUMENTS

1,836,319	12/1931	Gehrung	244/54
3,055,613	9/1962	Taylor	244/12.2
3,261,572	7/1966	Gorton	244/2
3,341,125	9/1967	Sweeney et al.	244/23 C
3,734,432	5/1973	Low	244/76 C
3,785,592	1/1974	Kerruish	244/12.2

FOREIGN PATENT DOCUMENTS

1331655	9/1973	United Kingdom	244/12.2

Primary Examiner—Joseph F. Peters, Jr.
Assistant Examiner—Rodney Corl
Attorney, Agent, or Firm—Robert B. Stevenson

[57] **ABSTRACT**

A multi-media craft particularly designed and constructed for efficient and economical utilization on land, water and in the air and comprising a light weight body constructed in modular form for economy and power by a removable lightweight engine of the motorcycle type for fuel efficiency and ease of maintenance. The craft is provided with forward and rearward sections constructed in a manner for variable in-flight or in-use alteration or molding thereof for achieving the optimum planar or contour design for the craft as required during variable fluid conditions when airborne, thus providing efficient and safe flying operation for either an unskilled or skilled operator.

8 Claims, 12 Drawing Sheets

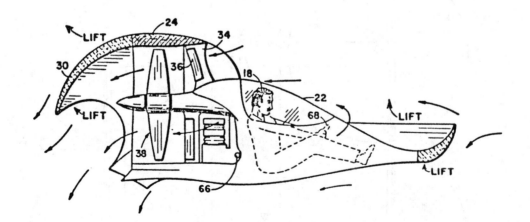

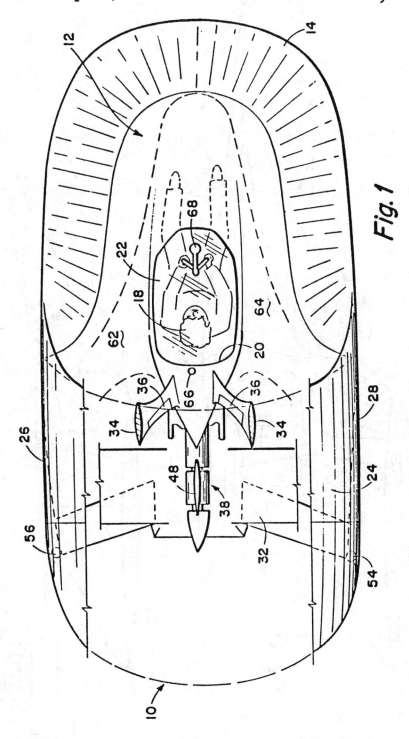

Fig. 1

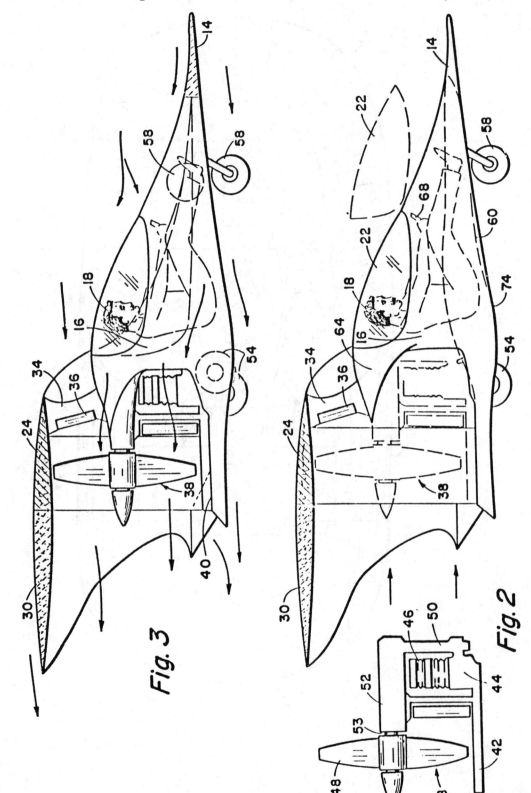

Fig. 3

Fig. 2

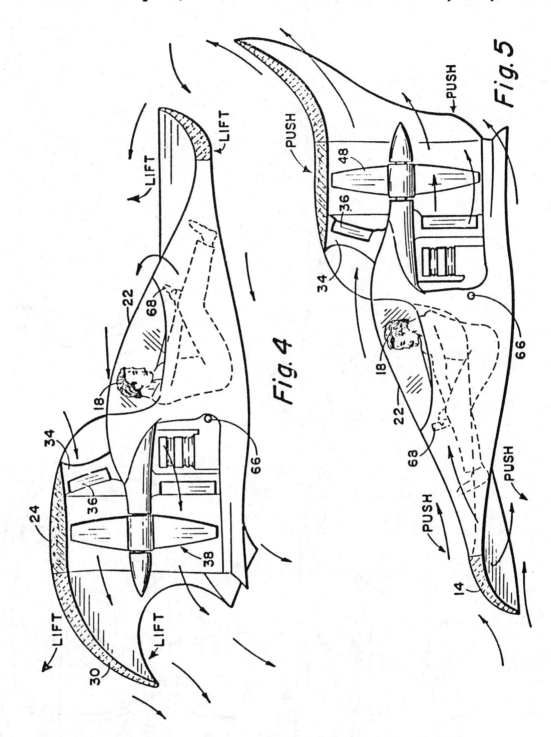

Fig.4

Fig.5

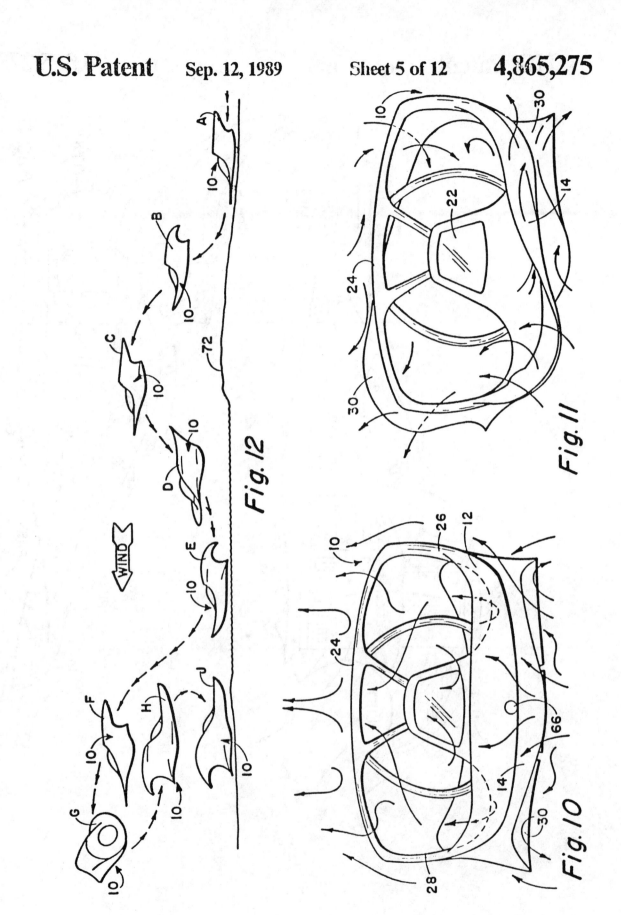

Fig. 12

Fig. 11

Fig. 10

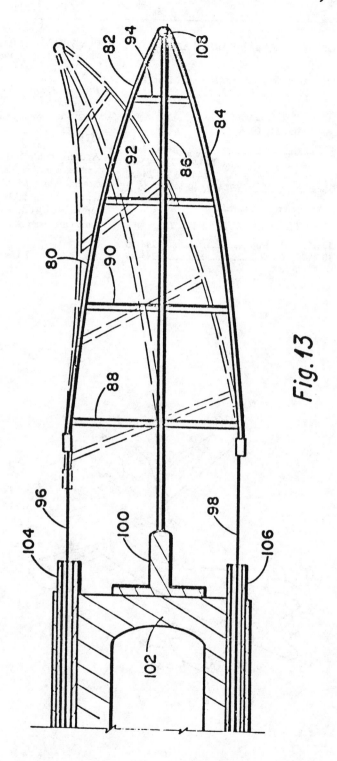

Fig. 13

United States Patent [19]

Bullard

[11] Patent Number: 4,881,701

[45] Date of Patent: Nov. 21, 1989

[54] **COMBINATION AUTOMOBILE AND AIRPLANE**

[76] Inventor: Gary M. Bullard, Rte. #1, Box 177, Accomac, Va. 23301

[21] Appl. No.: 168,015

[22] Filed: Mar. 14, 1988

[51] Int. Cl.⁴ B64C 3/56
[52] U.S. Cl. .... 244/49; 244/45 R; 244/45 A; 244/2
[58] Field of Search .... 244/2, 49, 45 A, 45 R

[56] References Cited

U.S. PATENT DOCUMENTS

1,393,820	10/1921	Osborne	244/49
1,731,757	10/1929	Tubbe	244/49
3,012,737	12/1961	Dodd	244/2
3,371,886	3/1968	Schertz	244/2
4,627,585	12/1986	Einstein	244/2

Primary Examiner—Joseph F. Peters, Jr.
Assistant Examiner—Rodney Corl
Attorney, Agent, or Firm—John B. Dickman, III

[57] **ABSTRACT**

A convertible airplane to automobile and visa versa, having a fuselage and three wings, including a forward canard wing, a foldable main wing and a secondary lift wing. The foldable wing is capable of folding to a size for safely driving the automobile on a roadway. All wings are used as ground effect airfoils for roadway use.

7 Claims, 4 Drawing Sheets

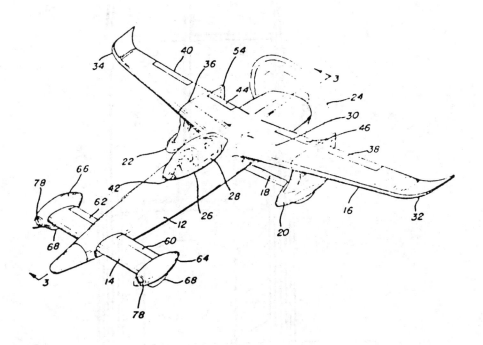

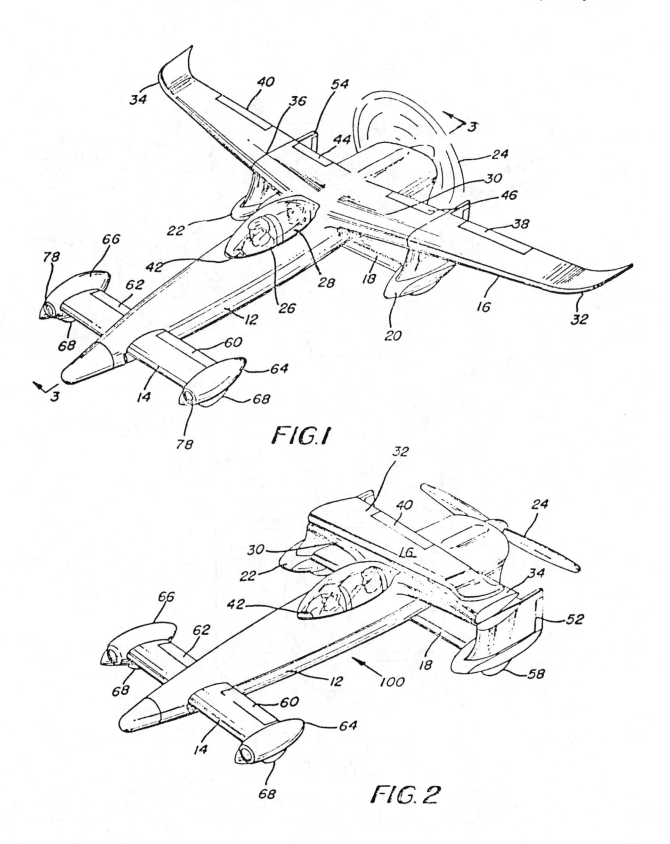

FIG.1

FIG.2

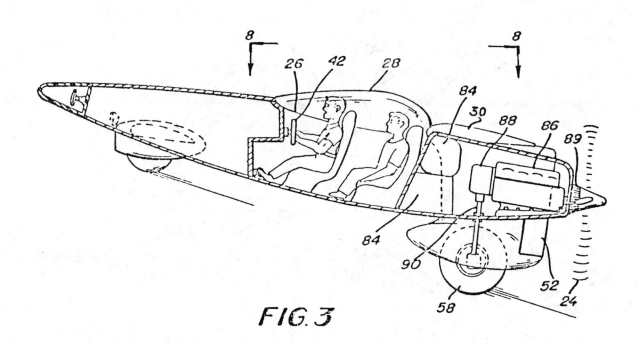

FIG. 3

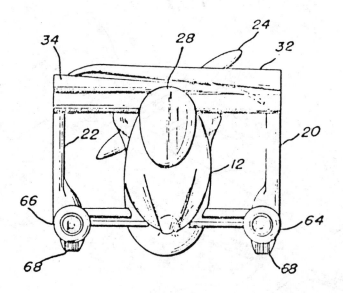

FIG. 4

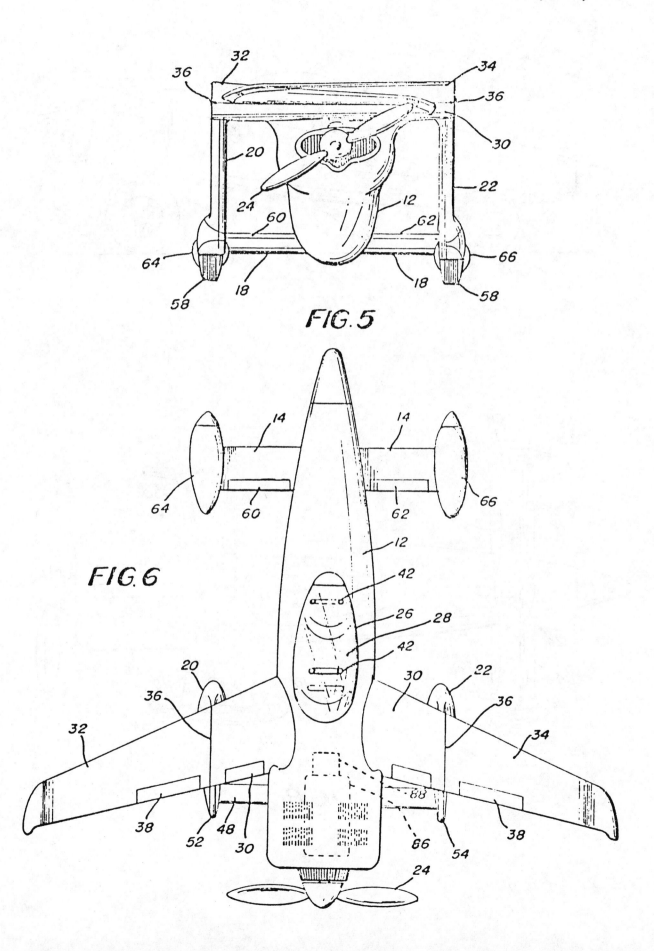

FIG.5

FIG.6

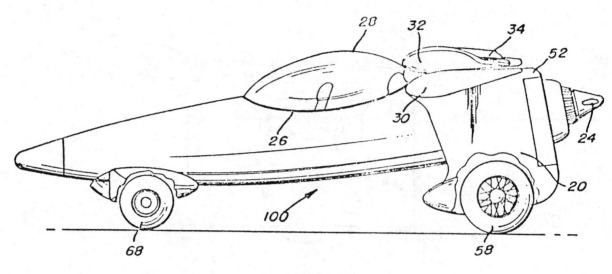

FIG 7

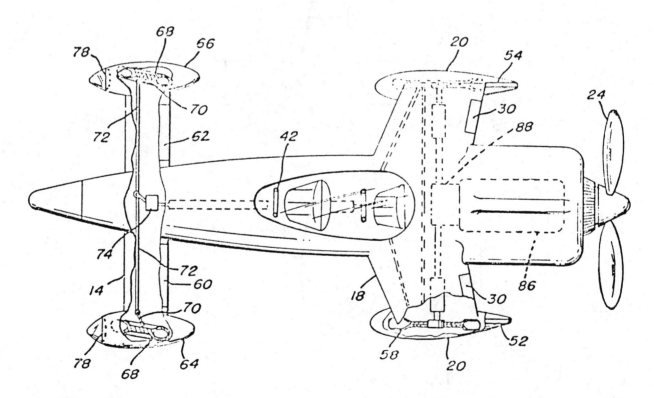

FIG. 8

United States Patent [19]

Pruszenski, Jr.

[11] **Patent Number:** 4,899,954

[45] **Date of Patent:** Feb. 13, 1990

[54] **GROUND-AIR-WATER CRAFT**

[76] Inventor: **Anthony Pruszenski, Jr.**, No. 3, 44th St., Plum Island, Mass. 01951

[21] Appl. No.: **192,544**

[22] Filed: **May 11, 1988**

[51] Int. Cl.⁴ B64C 37/00; B64C 39/08; B64C 39/12

[52] U.S. Cl. .... 244/2; 244/45 R; 244/45 A; 244/50; 244/91

[58] Field of Search .... 244/2, 36, 45 R, 45 A, 244/50, 91

[56] **References Cited**

U.S. PATENT DOCUMENTS

1,714,170	5/1929	Jette	244/50
2,713,465	7/1955	Novinger	244/2
2,814,482	11/1957	Anderson et al.	244/50
3,034,748	5/1962	Koup	244/50
3,371,886	3/1968	Schertz	244/2
3,834,654	9/1974	Miranda	244/91
4,579,297	4/1986	Ayoola	244/2

FOREIGN PATENT DOCUMENTS

0084686	8/1983	European Pat. Off.	244/45 A
1039983	10/1953	France .	

OTHER PUBLICATIONS

NASA Technical Memorandum 75872, "The High Lift Characteristics in the Case of the V–Wing Concept"–Z. Zimmer (Nov. 1980).

Primary Examiner—Sherman D. Basinger
Assistant Examiner—Rodney Corl
Attorney, Agent, or Firm—Felfe & Lynch

[57] **ABSTRACT**

A ground-air-water craft comprises a fuselage body with a passenger compartment mounted thereon, a box-type main wing connected to the fuselage and extending outwardly on both sides thereof, the main wing comprising an upper wing and a lower wing which are substantially horizontal and which have a total wing span in the range of 5 to 10 feet, as well as a right side member and a left side member, each side member extending substantially vertically and connected between the lateral ends of the upper and lower wings on the respective right and left sides of the craft. The craft also comprises a control or canard wing connected to the fuselage and extending outwardly on both sides of the fuselage with a wing span no greater than 10 feet. The craft also comprises front and rear wheels with balance wheels mounted therebetween, air propelling means which may constitute a propeller or a jet engine mounted on the craft, water propelling means driven by a hydraulic or electric drive motor, and fuel tanks mounted in the upper wing. The control wing is pivotable about its longitudinal axis, and all of the wings have moveable control surfaces comprising flap means for controlling the lift as well as air spoiler means disposed on the upper surfaces thereof. The front and rear wheels may be retractable and the body portion of the fuselage is water tight and includes a hydroplane bottom surface for a reduced resistance to water.

44 Claims, 3 Drawing Sheets

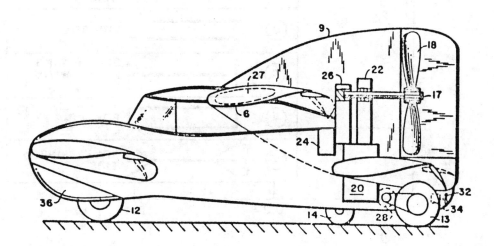

FIG.I
PRIOR ART

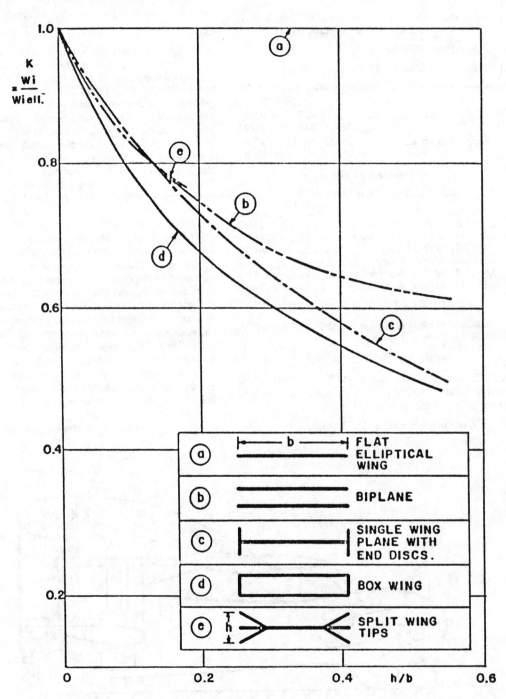

FIG.2

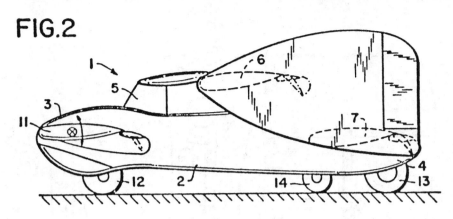

FIG.3

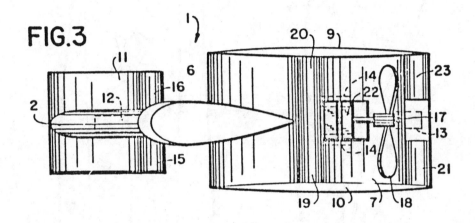

FIG.4

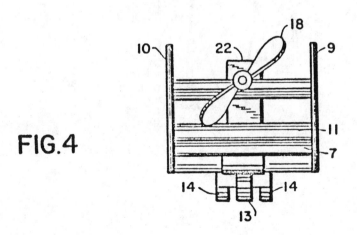

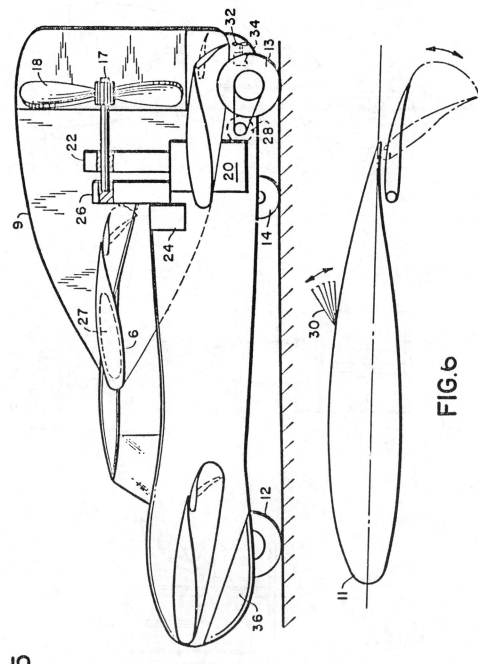

FIG.5

FIG.6

1

GROUND-AIR-WATER CRAFT

BACKGROUND OF THE INVENTION 1. Field of the Invention

The invention relates to an air-land-sea vehicle having a box wing configuration. 2. Description of the Prior Art

The NASA Technical Memorandum TM-75872 titled "The High Lift Characteristics in the Case of the V-Wing Concept" written by H. Zimmer and published in Nov. 1980 discloses in FIG. 3 (substantially reproduced herein as prior art FIG. 1) several curves illustrating the ratio of induced drag for various configurations with the same lift and the same wing span. As shown therein, curve d, which is representative of a box wing configuration, has the least ratio of induced drag of any of the wing configurations shown in the figure.

Among other prior art references of some relevance to the present invention are the following:

U.S. Pat. No. 1,058,983 discloses a flying machine having a biplane configuration with movable canards.

U.S. Pat. No. 1,839,194 shows a canard-type airplane having a single main wing.

U.S. Pat. No. 2,553,952 shows a combined land vehicle and airplane having a demountable single main wing and conventional tail surfaces.

U.S. Pat. No. 3,371,886 teaches an aircraft adapted for highway usage having a single main wing and canard wing units.

U.S. Pat. No. 4,627,585 discloses a combination road vehicle and aircraft having a foldable main wing and a pusher-type propeller mounted behind the center of the fuselage to the rear of the main wing.

U.S. Pat. No. 3,960,103 shows a marine skimmer craft (not an airplane) with two main wings and a canard. The main wings are attachable in panels to provide the desired lift.

Other prior art references considered to be of lesser interest with respect to the present invention include the following:

U.S. Pat. No. 1,495,031 describes an airplane having a plurality of wings configured for improved lifting capability.

U.S. Pat. No. 1,523,386 describes an airplane having a biplane wing configuration, and small wings on opposite sides of the engine to provide added lift to the engine during landing.

U.S. Pat. No. 1,705,904 describes an airplane having a multi-wing configuration to increase or reduce the lift in accordance with the load.

U.S. Pat. No. 2,681,773 describes a roadable aircraft with folding wings.

U.S. Pat. No. 3,258,228 describes an aircraft with a separate flight unit and payload unit coupled together.

U.S. Pat. No. 2,147,968 describes an acrobatic aircraft having a wing configuration which provides a minimum gliding ratio as well as buoyancy.

U.S. Pat. No. 3,931,942 is of interest relative to the invention of the present application in its description of an aircraft convertible to an automobile wherein the transition from the ground effect mode to the flight mode is made in flight by simultaneously lowering the tandem of the air foils, lifting the rear wall and altering the angle of attack of the forward air foil.

U.S. Pat. No. 3,954,231 is of some relevance to the invention of the present application in showing a arrangement for lifting, stabilizing, and flight controlling

2

wing surfaces placed near the front of an aircraft with the main lifting wing surfaces placed toward the rear.

U.S. Pat. No. 3,134,560 discloses an aircraft convertible to a ground vehicle with foldable outer wing sections.

French Pat. No. 1,039,983 describes a combination automobile and a detachable airplane with a single wing.

SUMMARY OF THE INVENTION

Among the primary objects of the present invention are to provide a ground-air-water craft which, when operating in the flight mode, provides for landing as slowly as possible and climbing as steeply as possible. Landing slowly is a desirable feature because it minimizes the kinetic energy of the vehicle and thus allows the vehicle to make turns of the smallest possible radius. Steep climbs are desirable because they allow for the maximum obstacle clearance and thus increase the margin of safety and also the number of locations available for take-off.

Another primary object of the present invention is to provide a ground-air-water craft which may be conveniently converted from air to ground, or from air to water, service without folding, dismantling or otherwise changing any of the craft's wing structures.

The ground-air-water craft of the present invention incorporates a box wing/canard aircraft configuration with a total wing span of less than 10 feet; propulsion means comprising a pusher configuration with a clutched propeller, turboprop or turbine; landing and ground running gear of conventional, bicycle or tricycle configuration; and means for hydroplane water operation.

The box wing configuration of the ground-air-water craft increases the effective aspect ratio of any given wing and, as a result, increases the maximum lift coefficient and thus the maximum lift to drag ratio. The lift coefficient determines the slowest landing speed for the plane. A maximized coefficient minimizes the landing speed. Since the lift to drag coefficient determines the maximum angle of climb for a given horsepower and weight, maximization of the lift to drag coefficient results in maximization of the angle of climb. In the inventive craft of the present invention, the propeller is positioned over the rear lifting wing of the box configuration. This positioning of the propeller provides several advantages. First, it provides an enhancement of lift due to a channel wing effect. Also, it provides some protection to the propeller from erosion due to water or particles. An additional advantage which is that provides containment of the propeller and drive train to limit accidental access and fragmentation damage.

The vehicle of the present invention is designed to work effectively in all three of its operating media, i.e. on the ground, in the air and on the water. The propeller is used primarily to provide thrust for air operations. It is designed to be declutched when the craft is stationary or on the ground so as to eliminate the safety hazard of rotating blades. The clutching feature eliminates the need for a cage around the propeller and thus decreases the vehicle's resistance and weight, therefore increasing the climb angle.

At high speeds the air resistance of a vehicle is the predominant source of energy drain but below approximately 30 miles per hour air resistance becomes relatively insignificant and rolling (ground) and wave (wa-

3

ter) friction and resistance are the major forces which must be overcome by the power plant. When the vehicle is operating at below 30 miles per hour in an automobile or boat modes, the propeller is declutched and the vehicle is powered directly through its wheels or a water propelling device, respectively. When operating above 30 miles per hour the air propeller may be engaged.

For a full understanding of the present invention, reference should now be made to the following detailed description of the preferred embodiments of the invention and to the accompanying drawings.

BRIEF DESCRIPTION OF THE DRAWINGS

FIG. 1 comprises curves from a prior art reference showing the ratio of induced drag for various wing configurations.

FIG. 2 is a side elevational view of the ground-air-water craft of the present invention.

FIG. 3 is a top view of the ground-air-water-craft shown in FIG. 2.

FIG. 4 is a elevation view of the ground-air-water-craft shown in FIG. 2.

FIG. 5 is a partly sectional elevational view of the ground-air-water craft of FIG. 2.

FIG. 6 is an elevational view of the control or canard wing for the craft.

DETAILED DESCRIPTION OF THE INVENTION

As mentioned previously, FIG. 1 shows a series of experimentally-determined curves which illustrate that a box wing configuration has a lower ratio of induced drag than other wing configurations.

As shown in FIG. 2, the ground-air-water-craft 1 of the present invention comprises a fuselage body 2 having a front end 3, a rear end 4 and a passenger compartment 5 therebetween. A box type main wing connected to the fuselage and extending outwardly therefrom comprises an upper wing 6 and a lower wing 7 which are substantially horizontal and have substantially the same wing span, between opposite lateral ends, which is in the range of 5 to 10 feet. The box type main wing also comprises, as shown in FIGS. 2 and 3, a right side member 9 and a left side member 10, with each side member extending substantially vertically and connected between the lateral ends of the upper and lower wings on the respective right and left sides of the craft.

Also, as shown in FIGS. 1 and 2, a control or canard wing 11 is connected to the fuselage and extends outwardly, on both sides of the fuselage 2, approximately equal distances. The total wing span between opposite lateral ends of the control or canard wing is less than 10 feet. The control wing and the main wing are located, with respect to each other, such that their centers of lift are on opposite sides of the center of gravity of the ground-air-water-craft in the central, longitudinal, vertical plane between the front and rear ends of the fuselage 2. Also as shown in FIGS. 1 and 2, the ground-air-water-craft 1 comprises a front wheel 12, a rear wheel 13, and a pair of balance wheels 14 symmetrically situated around the longitudinal center of the craft.

FIG. 2 also illustrates a propeller which, as shown in FIG. 4, comprises a hub 17 as well as blades 18. The propeller is powered by an engine 20 (FIG. 5), which may be a piston, Wankel or turbine engine, through the intermediary of a coupling/decoupling device 22.

4

As an alternative to the propeller, a single jet engine may be mounted above the center wing or on either side of the passenger compartment below the center wing.

With respect to the aforementioned main engine 20, it is noted that the passengers located in the passenger compartment 5 and the main engine 20 both have respective centers of gravity of their own which are respectively located on opposite sides of the center of gravity of the ground-air-water craft. Alternatively, the passengers may be located at or near the center of gravity of the craft.

With respect to FIG. 5 an electric generator or hydraulic pump 24 is mechanically coupled to the main engine 20 through the intermediary of a second coupling/decoupling device 26. One or more electric or hydraulic drive motors 28 are mechanically coupled to drive one or more wheels.

As shown in FIG. 5, at least one fuel tank 27 is mounted on the upper wing 6.

As best shown in FIG. 2, the control or canard wing 11 may be pivotable about its longitudinal axis with the respective right side and left side of the control wing 11 being pivotable together to control the pitch of the craft 1 and pivotable in opposite directions to control the roll of the craft 1. Also, or in the alternative, the control wing 3 may have moveable control surfaces 15 and 16 disposed on its trailing edges on both sides of the fuselage 2. As shown in FIG. 3, moveable control surfaces 19 and 20 are disposed on the trailing edges of the upper main wing 6 and control surfaces 21 and 23 are disposed on the trailing edges of the lower main wing 7, on both sides of the fuselage 2. The aforementioned control surfaces 15, 16, 19 20, 21 and 23 are flaps for controlling the lift of each of the wings.

As shown in FIG. 6, air spoiler means 30 are disposed on the upper surfaces of the control wing 11. Such air spoiler means may also be disposed on the upper surfaces of each of the main wings on both sides of the fuselage 2. The air spoiler means are located approximately at the 0.3 chord point, as viewed from the trailing edge of the wing, the chord being an imaginary line drawn from the leading edge to the trailing edge of the wing.

It is noted that the air propelling means shown in FIGS. 2 and 3 are mounted to the rear of the center of gravity of the craft 1 as are water propelling means 32 shown in FIG. 5.

Another feature of the invention is that at least one of the front wheel 12, rear wheel 13 and side wheels 14 can be retractable.

One of the wheel configurations contemplated by the invention includes two front wheels 12 mounted laterally on opposite sides of the central, longitudinal, vertical plane of the craft 1 with a single rear wheel 13 disposed in the longitudinal plane of the craft 1. It is also contemplated that the rear wheel 13 is steerable in this configuration.

As shown in FIGS. 2 and 5, the bottom portion of the fuselage 2 can be made watertight and includes a hydroplane bottom surface 36 which affords a reduced resistance to water when the craft is propelled across a water surface. Also with regard to the use of the craft in the water, as is shown in FIG. 5 water propelling means 32 are connected to a separate electric or hydraulic drive motor 34, which is powered by the electric generator or hydraulic pump 24. The water propelling means may be a conventional water propeller, a water jet, or some other known device for propelling the craft on the water.

There has thus been shown and described a novel ground-air-water craft which fulfills all the objects and advantages sought therefor. Many changes, modifications, variations and other uses and applications of the subject invention will, however, become apparent to those skilled in the art after considering this specification and the accompanying drawings which disclose the preferred embodiments thereof. All such changes, modifications variations and other uses and applications which do not depart from the spirit and scope of the invention are deemed to be covered by the invention which is limited only by the claims which follow.

What is claimed is:

1. A land, air and water ("LAW") craft having a center of gravity and comprising, in combination:

(a) a fuselage having a front end, a rear end, and a passenger compartment therebetween, said fuselage defining a central, longitudinal and vertical plane between said front and rear ends;

(b) a box-type, main wing connected to said fuselage and extending outwardly, on both sides of said fuselage, approximately equal distances from said longitudinal plane, said main wing including

(i) an upper main wing and a lower main wing which are substantially horizontal and have substantially the same wingspan, between opposite lateral ends, said lower main wing extending from a leading edge, which is rearward of the driver's position in said passenger compartment, to a trailing edge which substantially coincides, in longitudinal position, with said rear end of said fuselage, said upper main wing having a leading edge which is forward of said leading edge of said lower main wing; and

(ii) a right side member and a left side member, each side member extending substantially vertically and connected between said lateral ends of said upper and lower main wings on a respective right and left side of said craft;

(c) a control wing connected to said fuselage and extending outwardly, on both sides of said fuselage, approximately equal distances from said longitudinal plane, said control wing and said main wing being located, with respect to each other, such that their centers of lift are on opposite sides of said center of gravity as viewed in the direction of said longitudinal plane;

(d) front wheel means mounted on said craft forward of said center of gravity;

(e) rear wheel means mounted on said craft to the rear of said center of gravity and beneath said lower main wing at such longitudinal position that it prevents said lower main wing from contacting the ground when said craft is flying at an extreme upward pitch;

(f) prime mover means mounted on said craft;

(g) air propelling means mounted on said craft between said two side members and above said lower main wing; and

(h) first coupling means for selectively coupling said prime mover means to:

(i) at least one of said wheel means, and

(ii) said air propelling means.

2. The LAW craft defined in claim 1, wherein passengers located in said passenger compartment and said prime mover means both have respective centers of gravity of their own, and wherein said centers of gravity of said passengers, on one hand, and said prime mover means, on the other, are located on opposite sides of said center of gravity of said craft as viewed in the direction of said longitudinal plane.

3. The LAW craft defined in claim 2, wherein said center of gravity of said prime mover means is located to the rear of said center of gravity of said craft.

4. The LAW craft defined in claim 1, wherein the centers of lift of said control wing and said main wing are located, respectively, in front of, and to the rear of said center of gravity of said craft.

5. The LAW craft defined in claim 1, wherein said first coupling means include hydraulic pump means mechanically coupled to said prime mover means and hydraulic drive motor means, hydraulically coupled to said hydraulic pump means and mechanically coupled to at least one of said wheel means, for driving said at least one wheel means.

6. The LAW craft defined in claim 5, wherein said hydraulic drive motor means include a separate hydraulic drive motor disposed adjacent, and mechanically coupled to each of said front wheel means and said rear wheel means.

7. The LAW craft defined in claim 5, wherein said hydraulic drive motor means include a separate hydraulic drive motor disposed adjacent, and mechanically coupled to each individual wheel of said at least one wheel means.

8. The LAW craft defined in claim 1, wherein said first coupling means include electric generator means, mechanically coupled to said prime mover means, and electric drive motor means, electrically coupled to said electric generator means and mechanically coupled to at least one of said wheel means, for driving said at least one wheel means.

9. The LAW craft defined in claim 8, wherein said electric drive motor means include a separate electric drive motor disposed adjacent, and mechanically coupled to each of said front wheel means and said rear wheel means.

10. The LAW craft defined in claim 8, wherein said electric drive motor means include a separate electric drive motor disposed adjacent, and mechanically coupled to each individual wheel of said at least one wheel means.

11. The LAW craft defined in claim 1, further comprising at least one fuel tank located in said upper wing.

12. The LAW craft defined in claim 1, wherein said control wing is pivotable about its longitudinal axis, the right and left sides of said control wing being pivotable together to control the pitch of said craft, and pivotable in opposite directions to control the roll of said craft.

13. The LAW craft defined in claim 1, further comprising movable control surfaces disposed on the trailing edges of said control wing on both sides of said fuselage.

14. The LAW craft defined in claim 1, further comprising movable control surfaces disposed on the trailing edges of at least one of said upper main wing and said lower main wing on both sides of said fuselage.

15. The LAW craft defined in claim 14, wherein said control surfaces include flap means for controlling the lift of said at least one upper main wing and lower main wing.

16. The LAW craft defined in claim 1, further comprising movable control surfaces disposed on the trail-

ing edges of each of said wings on both sides of said fuselage.

17. The LAW craft defined in claim 16, wherein said control surfaces include flap means for controlling the lift of each of said wings.

18. The LAW craft defined in claim 1, further comprising movable air spoiler means disposed on the upper surface of said control wing on both sides of said fuselage.

19. The LAW craft defined in claim 1, further comprising movable air spoiler means disposed on the upper surface of at least one of said upper main wing and said lower main wing on both sides of said fuselage.

20. The LAW craft defined in claim 1, further comprising movable air spoiler means disposed on the upper surface of each of said wings on both sides of said fuselage.

21. The LAW craft defined in claim 18, wherein said air spoiler means are located at approximately the 0.3 chord point, as viewed from the trailing edge of said control wing, said chord being an imaginary line drawn from the leading edge to the trailing edge of said control wing.

22. The LAW craft defined in claim 19, wherein said air spoiler means are located at approximately the 0.3 chord point, as viewed from the trailing edge of said at least one upper main wing and lower main wing, said chord being an imaginary line drawn from the leading edge to the trailing edge of the respective wing.

23. The LAW craft defined in claim 4, wherein said air propelling means are mounted to the rear of said center of gravity.

24. The LAW craft defined in claim 1, wherein at least one of said front wheel and rear wheel means are retractable.

25. The LAW craft defined in claim 1, wherein said front wheel means include two front wheels spaced laterally on opposite sides of said longitudinal plane and wherein said rear wheel means include a single rear wheel disposed in said longitudinal plane.

26. The LAW craft defined in claim 25, wherein said rear wheel means is steerable.

27. The LAW craft defined in claim 1, wherein at least the bottom portion of said fuselage is watertight and includes a hydroplane bottom surface which affords a reduced resistance to water when said craft is propelled across a water surface.

28. The LAW craft defined in claim 27, further comprising water propelling means mounted on said craft for driving said craft forward when said fuselage is resting on a water surface and second coupling means for selectively coupling said prime mover means to said water propelling means.

29. The LAW craft defined in claim 28, wherein said second coupling means includes a hydraulic pump means, mechanically coupled to said prime mover means, and hydraulic drive motor means, hydraulically coupled to said hydraulic pump means and mechanically coupled to said water propelling means.

30. The LAW craft defined in claim 28, wherein said second coupling means include electric pump means, mechanically coupled to said prime mover means, and electric drive motor means, electrically coupled to said electric pump means and mechanically coupled to said water propelling means.

31. The LAW craft defined in claim 1, wherein said front wheel means and said rear wheel means each include a single road wheel, and wherein said craft further comprises balancing wheel means mounted on said craft substantially laterally in line with or to the rear of said center of gravity, said balancing wheel means including two road wheels disposed on opposite sides of said longitudinal plane.

32. The LAW craft defined in claim 1, wherein both said upper and lower main wings are mounted on said fuselage.

33. The LAW craft defined in claim 32, wherein the trailing edge of said upper main wing substantially coincides, in longitudinal position, to the leading edge of said lower main wing.

34. The LAW craft defined in claim 33, wherein said air propelling means has a central longitudinal axis which is oriented substantially in the plane of said upper main wing.

35. The LAW craft defined in claim 34, wherein said air propelling means is disposed rearward of said upper main wing.

36. The LAW craft defined in claim 1, wherein said first coupling means couples said prime mover means to said rear wheel means and to said air propelling means.

37. The LAW craft defined in claim 1, wherein said right side member and said left side member each have a downward and rearward sloping front edge, to provide a streamlined surface for impinging air and water.

38. The LAW craft defined in claim 37, wherein said leading edge of each right side member and left side member extends downwardly from a forwardmost point, which is at least as far forward as the leading edge of said upper main wing, to a lower, more rearward point, which is at least as far forward as the leading edge of said lower main wing.

39. The LAW craft defined in claim 1, wherein said right side member and said left side member each extend above the upper surface of said upper main wing.

40. The LAW craft defined in claim 1, wherein said right side member and said left side member each extend below the lower surface of said lower main wing.

41. The LAW craft defined in claim 1, wherein said right side member and said left side member each have a trailing edge which is articulated to serve as a rudder.

42. The LAW craft defined in claim 41, wherein said articulated trailing edges of said right side member and said left side member are located rearward of said air propelling means.

43. The LAW craft defined in claim 1, wherein said fuselage has a length, between said front end and said rear end, which is less than approximately 25 feet; wherein said upper main wing and said lower main wing each have a wingspan which is less than approximately 10 feet; and wherein said control wing has a wingspan which is less than approximately 10 feet.

44. The LAW craft defined in claim 43, wherein said fuselage length is in the range of 10 to 25 feet; and wherein said upper main wing and said lower main wing each have a wingspan in the range of 5 to 10 feet.

* * * * *

United States Patent [19]

Fitzpatrick

[11] **Patent Number:** 4,913,375

[45] **Date of Patent:** Apr. 3, 1990

[54] **VEHICLE FOR USE ON LAND, AIR, OR WATER**

[76] Inventor: Peter J. Fitzpatrick, 467 Kearny Ave., Kearny, N.J. 07032

[21] Appl. No.: 230,242

[22] Filed: Aug. 9, 1988

[51] Int. Cl.⁴ B64C 37/00; B64C 35/02
[52] U.S. Cl. 244/2; 244/49; 114/39.1
[58] Field of Search 244/2, 105, 49, 13; 114/39.1

[56] **References Cited**

U.S. PATENT DOCUMENTS

2,940,688	6/1960	Bland	....	244/2
3,012,737	12/1961	Dodd	....	244/2
3,134,560	5/1964	Halsman	....	244/2
3,614,032	10/1971	Purcell	....	244/2
4,269,374	5/1981	Miller	....	244/2

Primary Examiner—Galen Barefoot
Attorney, Agent, or Firm—Berman, Aisenberg & Platt

[57] **ABSTRACT**

A vehicle usable in the air, on water, or on ground is described. Outer wing portions are connected to a central portion by a mechanism which allows the outer wing portions to pivot about first axes for placing the outer wing portions in stored positions. The outer wing portions are also rotatable about a second axis for placing them in positions whereby they are useful as sails for driving the vehicle without the use of an engine. The wheels are capable of being pivoted to non-positions.

12 Claims, 4 Drawing Sheets

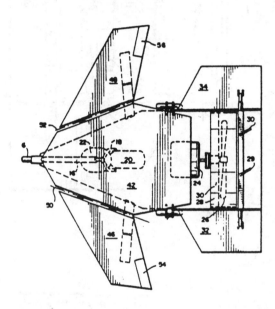

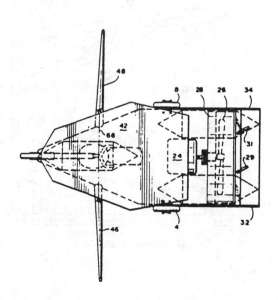

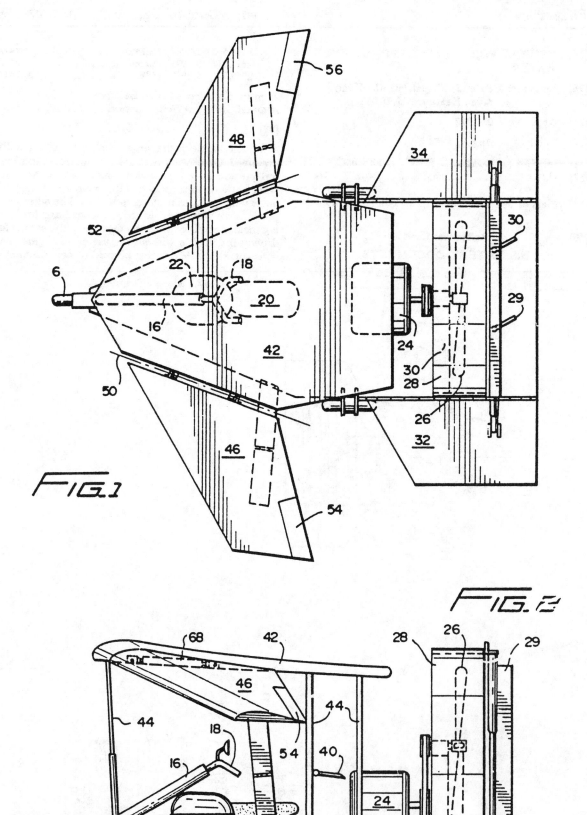

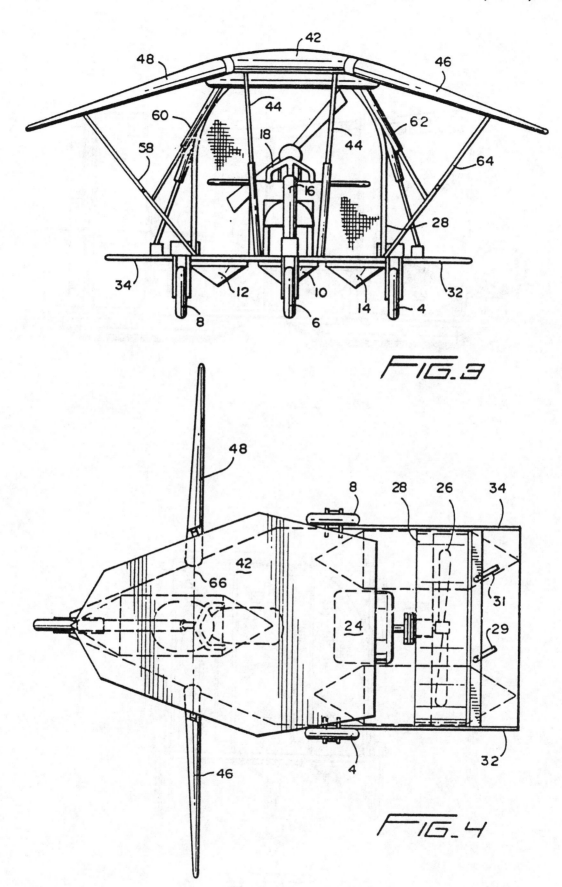

FIG.3

FIG.4

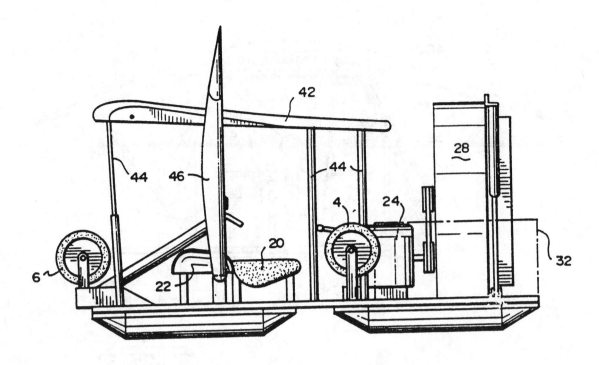

FIG. 5

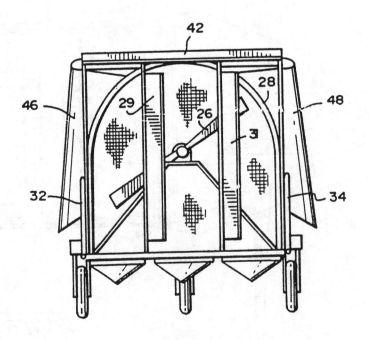

FIG. 6

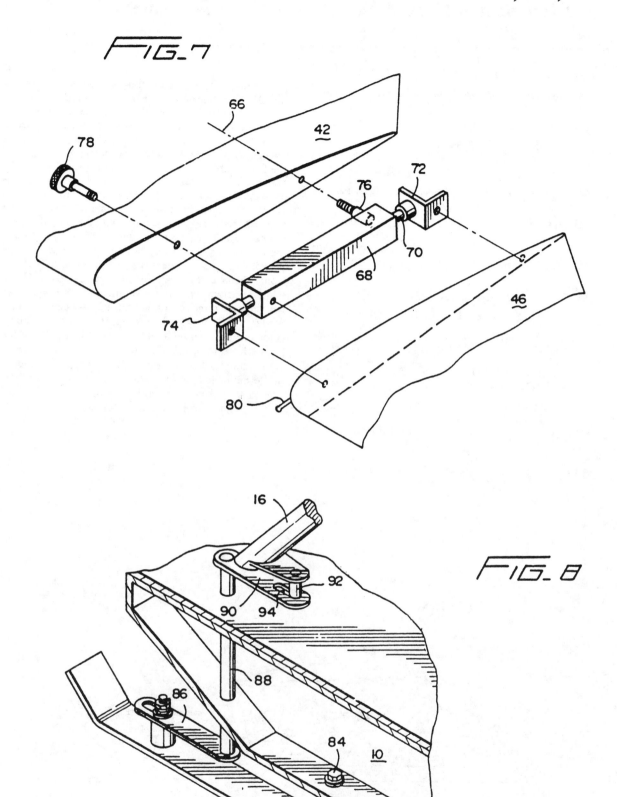

FIG_7

FIG_8

[11] Patent Number: 4,986,493

[45] Date of Patent: Jan. 22, 1991

[54] **CONVERTIBLE FIXED WING AIRCRAFT**

[76] Inventor: Branko Sarh, 2597 Devonshire Rd., Riverside, Calif. 92506

[21] Appl. No.: 279,778

[22] Filed: Dec. 5, 1988

Related U.S. Application Data

[62] Division of Ser. No. 141,096, Jan. 5, 1988, Pat. No. 4,881,700.

[51] Int. Cl.^{5} B64D 37/00
[52] U.S. Cl. 244/2; 244/46; 244/50; 244/201
[58] Field of Search 244/46, 50, 2, 201, 244/208

[56]   **References Cited**

U.S. PATENT DOCUMENTS

3,026,066	3/1962	Coates	244/208
3,361,395	1/1968	Apostolescu	244/50
4,269,374	5/1981	Miller	244/2
4,537,373	8/1985	Butts	244/50
4,579,297	4/1986	Ayoola	244/50

Primary Examiner—Charles T. Jordan
Assistant Examiner—Rochelle Lieberman
Attorney, Agent, or Firm—Herbert E. Kidder

[57]   **ABSTRACT**

A fixed wing aircraft that can be converted to an automotive vehicle, comprising a generally rectangular planform fuselage having four wheels as in conventional automobile practice, and a telescopic wing which retracts into a housing in the roof of the fuselage. Telescopic horizontal and vertical stabilizers are provided at the rear end of the fuselage, as well as a retractable pusher propeller that is driven by an engine mounted on the front end of the fuselage. Both the propeller and the rear wheels are connected by a transmission box to the engine, so that either can be driven to operate the vehicle as an aircraft or as an automobile. On take-off, the rear wheels are partially retracted so as to place the aircraft at a proper angle of attack at the same time that the elevators are raised by pulling back on the control wheel. The control wheel is also connected to both the front wheels and the ailerons, and when turned 90° to the left or right while in the flight configuration, causes the ailerons to move to their extreme angular positions while the front wheels are turned only a minimal amount. Further turning of the control wheel causes the front wheels to turn to their full angular position, without causing further movement of the ailerons. The wing is also movable longitudinally with respect to the fuselage so as to trim the aircraft for shifts in the center of gravity with varying load conditions.

8 Claims, 22 Drawing Sheets

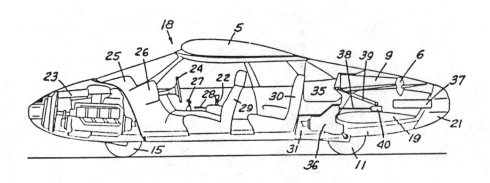

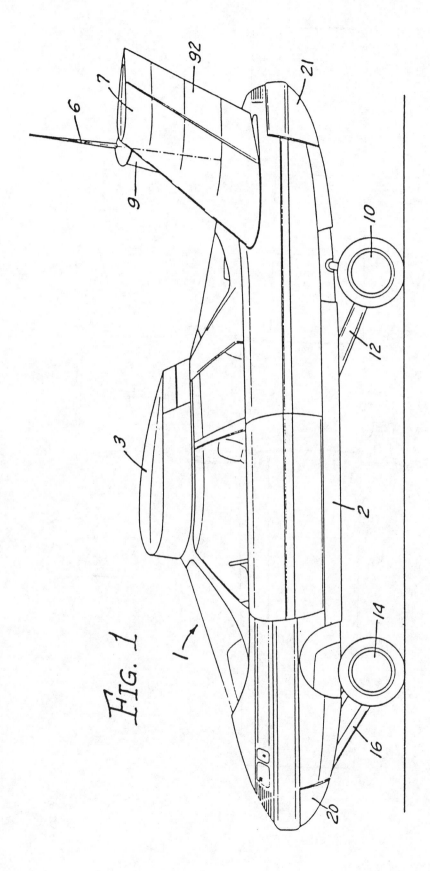

Fig. 1

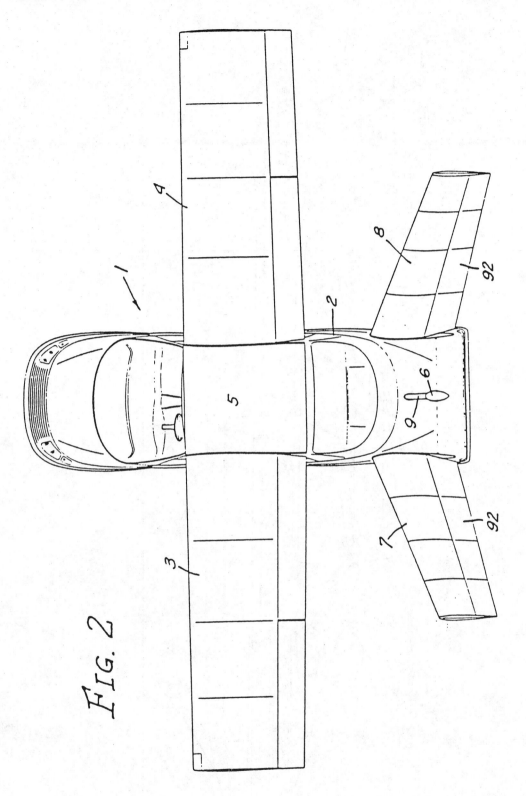

Fig. 2

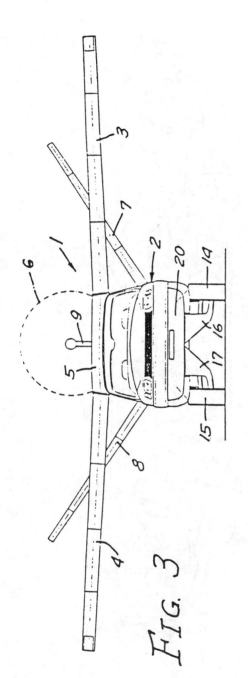

Fig. 3

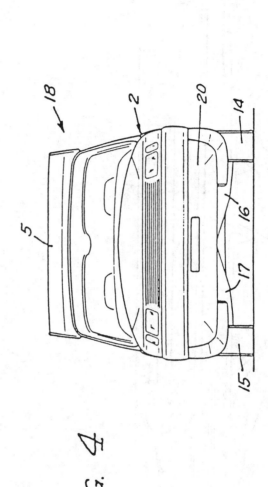

Fig. 4

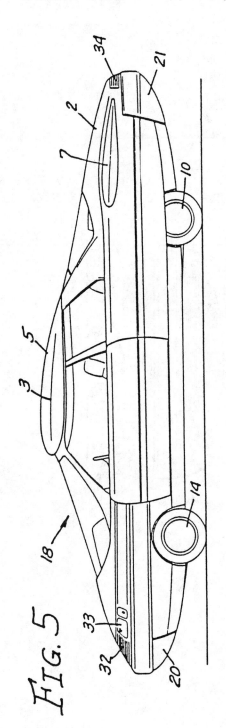

FIG. 5

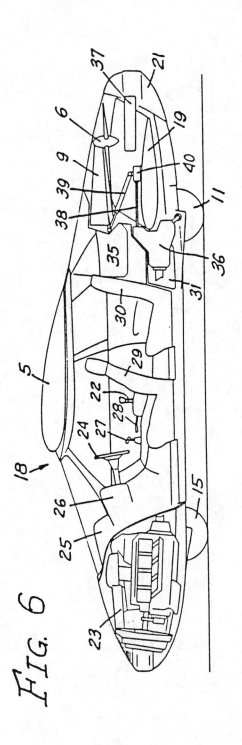

FIG. 6

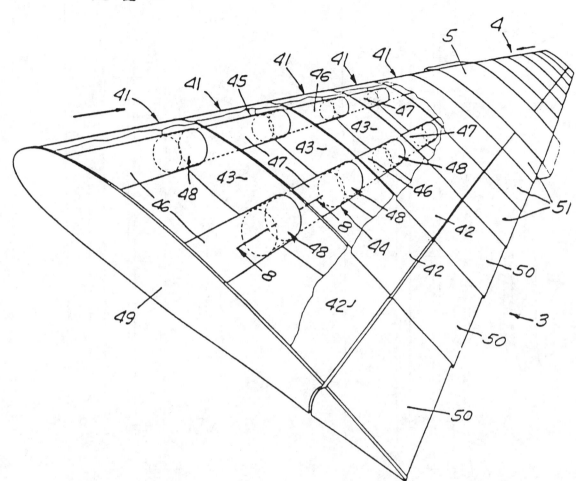

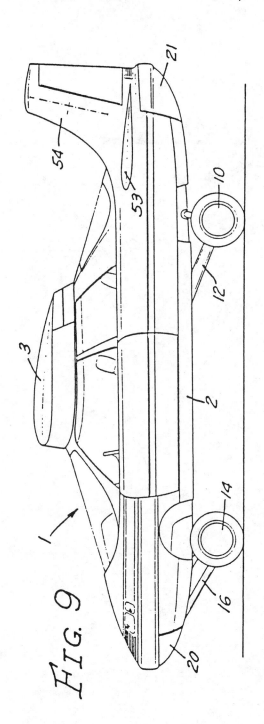

FIG. 9

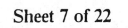
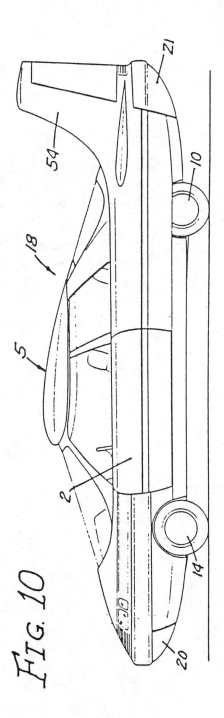

FIG. 10

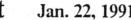

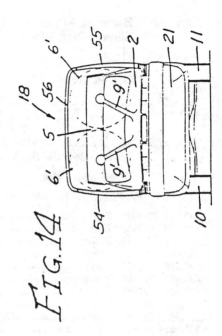

FIG. 14

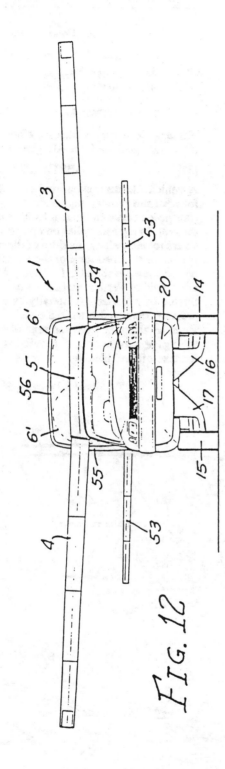

FIG. 12

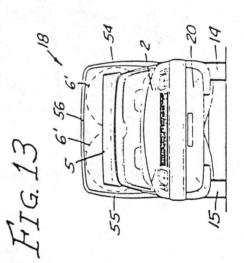

FIG. 13

United States Patent [19]

Miller

[11] Patent Number: 5,050,817

[45] Date of Patent: Sep. 24, 1991

[54] **COMBINED ROAD AND AIRCRAFT VEHICLE**

[76] Inventor: Harvey R. Miller, 3655 E. Amazon, Eugene, Oreg. 97405

[21] Appl. No.: 421,672

[22] Filed: Oct. 16, 1989

[51] Int. Cl.⁵ B64C 37/00
[52] U.S. Cl. 244/2; 244/49; 244/120; 244/50
[58] Field of Search .... 244/49, 50, 2, 102 R, 244/104 R, 104 FP, 89, 120

[56] **References Cited**

U.S. PATENT DOCUMENTS

2,573,271	10/1951	Perl	244/2
2,609,167	9/1952	Gero, Jr.	244/104 R
2,811,323	10/1957	Rethorst	244/2
2,893,661	7/1959	Aylor	244/2
2,940,688	6/1960	Bland	244/2
3,083,936	4/1963	Rethorst	244/49
3,371,886	3/1968	Schertz	244/2
4,269,374	5/1981	Miller	244/2
4,627,585	12/1986	Einstein	244/2
4,638,962	1/1987	Gunter et al.	244/102 R
4,899,954	2/1990	Pruszenski, Jr.	244/2

4,915,324	4/1990	Foreau et al.	244/102 R

FOREIGN PATENT DOCUMENTS

994341	11/1951	France .
2591559	6/1987	France .
330809	10/1935	Italy .
433102	4/1948	Italy .

Primary Examiner—Galen Barefoot
Attorney, Agent, or Firm—Eugene M. Eckelman

[57] **ABSTRACT**

A vehicle chassis is supported on front and rear wheels for road and runway engagement. A propeller assembly is disposed between the front and rear wheels and faces the rear. Wing assemblies on opposite sides of the chassis are foldable along the sides of the chassis to form side panels for the road form of the vehicle. A tail assembly on the chassis is shiftable forwardly and rearwardly and has a pair of vertical stabilizers connected together at the top by a horizontal laterally extending stabilizer. A pressure regulated retractable stabilizing wheel is provided between the front and rear wheels and is arranged to engage a runway and provide stabilizing functions for take off and landing.

7 Claims, 3 Drawing Sheets

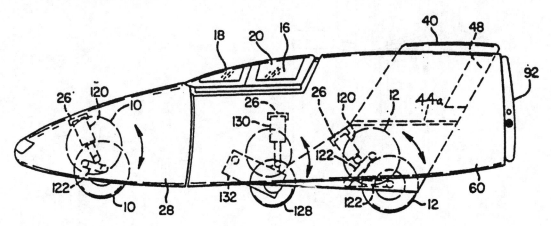

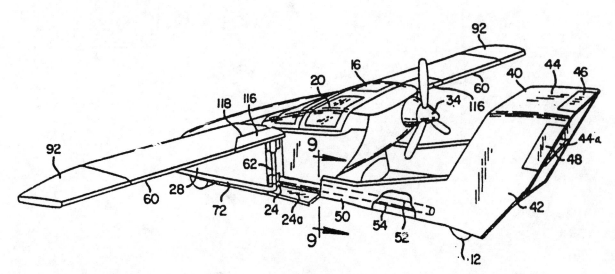

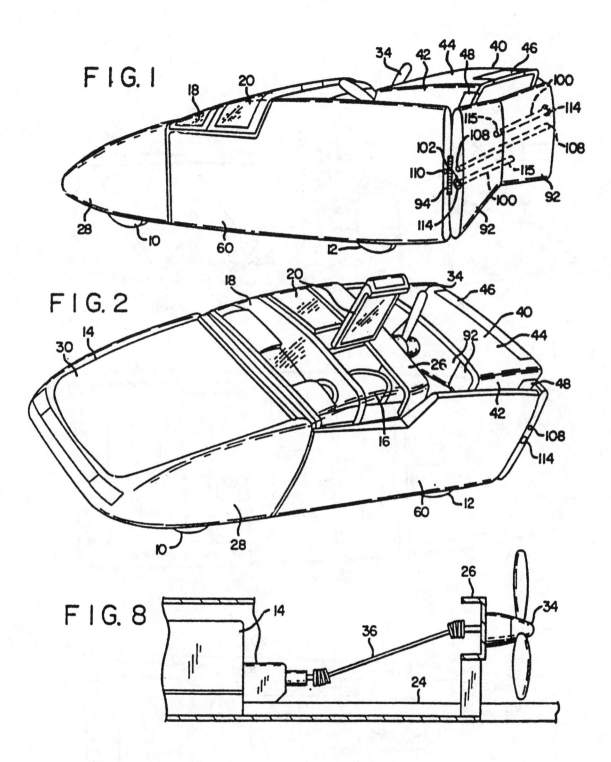

FIG. 1

FIG. 2

FIG. 8

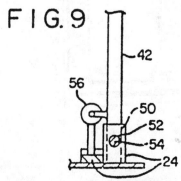

FIG. 9

F.I.G. 3

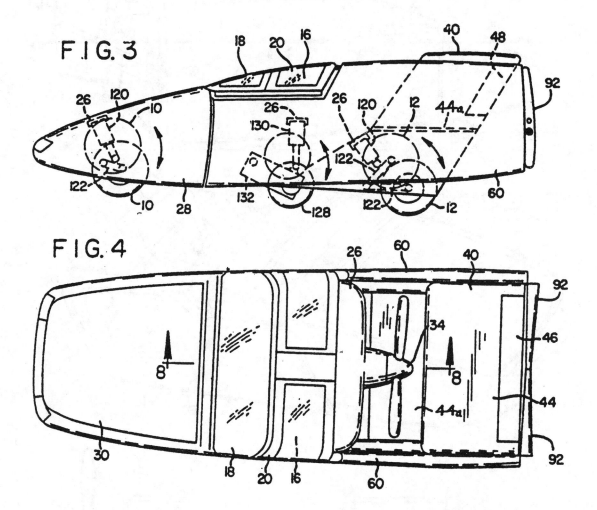

F I G. 4

F I G. 5

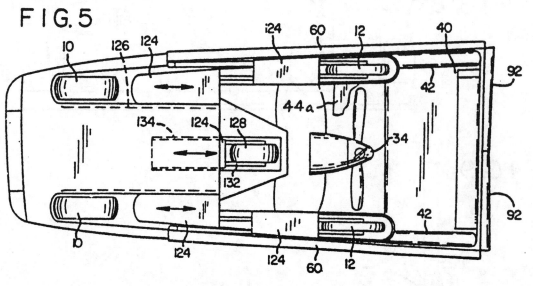

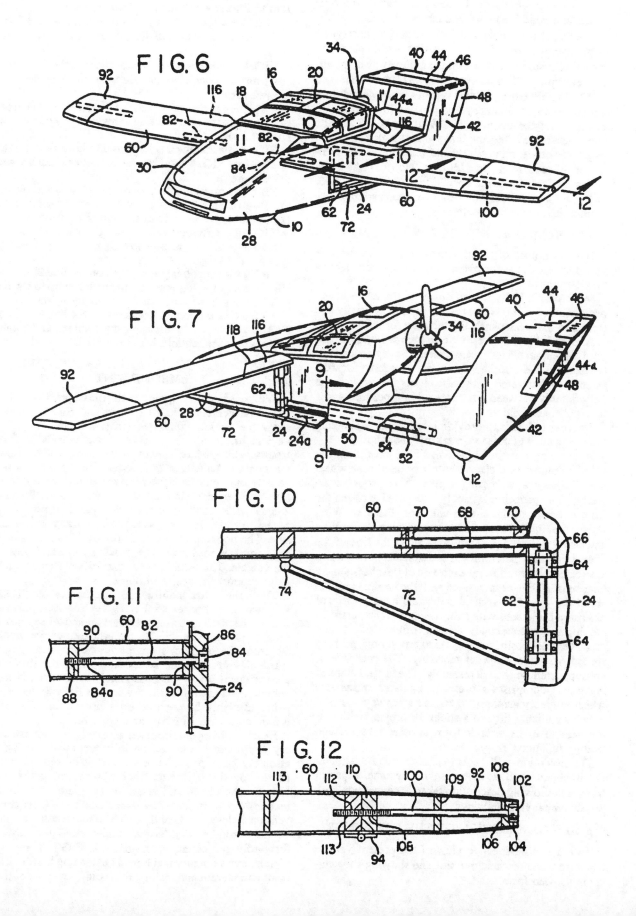

1

COMBINED ROAD AND AIRCRAFT VEHICLE

BACKGROUND OF THE INVENTION

This invention relates to new and useful improvements in a combined road and aircraft vehicle.

Combined road and aircraft vehicles have heretofore been provided wherein by converting certain elements, the vehicle can be operated on the highway or in the air. For example, U.S. Pat. Nos. 2,811,323, 2,940,688 and 3,083,936 illustrate structures which are converted from aircraft to road vehicles by folding the wings either into or on top of the body. In U.S. Pat. No. 2,573,271 the wings are folded into the body and also this structure employs a compacting tail structure to shorten the vehicle in its road form. In U.S. Pat. No. 3,371,886, the wings are folded to stand upright in the road form. U.S. Pat. No. 4,269,374 provides foldable wings which store them in inner side compartments.

SUMMARY OF THE INVENTION

It is an object of the present invention to provide improvements in a combined road and aircraft vehicle type structures.

More particularly, it is an object of the invention to provide wing sections that readily pivot rearwardly and form side and rear panels for the road form of vehicle.

Another object is to provide an improved tail assembly wherein stabilizer means thereof have vertical and horizontal portions, the vertical portions have forward extensions associated with shift means for moving the tail assembly between a retracted flying position and a forward road position.

Another object is to provide intermediate stabilizing wheel means which assist in takeoff and landing.

In carrying out the objectives of the invention, the vehicle comprises a chassis with front and rear wheel means, a central stabilizing wheel, and a propeller assembly. The propeller assembly is disposed between the front and rear of the chassis and faces the rear. Wing assemblies fold between an outward aircraft position and a folded stored position lying along the side of the chassis in the road form. A tail assembly includes a vertical stabilizer adjacent each side of the chassis and a horizontal stabilizer integrated with the vertical stabilizers at the top. The vertical stabilizers have a forward extension associated with shift means on the chassis for moving the tail assembly from a forward compacted road vehicle position to a rearward flying position spaced from the propeller assembly. The rear wheels are supported on the tail assembly. The central stabilizing wheel comprises a pressure regulated retractable wheel assembly arranged to engage a runway and provide a stabilizing lift and a shock absorbing landing as the vehicle in its aircraft form initiates take off and landing functions, respectively.

The invention will be better understood and additional objects and advantages will become apparent from the following description taken in connection with the accompanying drawings.

BRIEF DESCRIPTION OF THE DRAWINGS

FIG. 1 is a perspective view of the present vehicle taken from the rear and one side and showing the vehicle in its road form.

2

FIG. 2 is a perspective view of the vehicle taken from the front and top and also showing the vehicle in its road form.

FIG. 3 is a side elevational view of the vehicle in its road form, portions of this view being shown in phantom to illustrate retracting wheel structure.

FIG. 4 is a top plan view of the vehicle in road form.

FIG. 5 is a bottom plan view of the vehicle in its road form.

FIG. 6 is a perspective view of the vehicle taken from the front and one side and showing the vehicle in its aircraft form.

FIG. 7 is a perspective view of the vehicle taken from the rear and one side and also showing the vehicle in its aircraft form.

FIG. 8 is a fragmentary sectional view taken on the line 8—8 of FIG. 4 showing the propeller assembly and drive therefor.

FIG. 9 is a fragmentary sectional view taken on the line 9—9 of FIG. 7 showing drive means for shifting the tail assembly between road and aircraft positions.

FIG. 10 is a fragmentary sectional view taken on the line 10—10 of FIG. 6 and showing pivot support structure for the wings.

FIG. 11 is a sectional view taken on the line 11—11 of FIG. 6 and showing locking means for supporting the pivotal wing in its horizontal aircraft form; and

FIG. 12 is a sectional view taken on the line 12—12 of FIG. 6 showing foldable wing tip sections and means for locking such sections in the horizontal aircraft form.

DETAILED DESCRIPTION OF A PREFERRED EMBODIMENT

With particular reference to the drawings, FIGS. 1–5 show the vehicle in its road form and FIGS. 6 and 7 show the vehicle converted to its aircraft form. The vehicle has front wheels 10 and rear wheels 12. The front wheels are steerable by any suitable conventional mechanism. An engine 14 is located at the front of the vehicle and immediately behind the engine is the operator's compartment 16 including a windshield 18 and a T-bar and butterfly-type roof 20 capable of providing access to and from the operator's compartment at each side. The doors in the roof are removable to provide a convertible mode for both the road and aircraft forms of the vehicle. The vehicle has a streamlined shape which helps support its weight in flight.

The vehicle has longitudinal side frames 24, FIGS. 6–9, and cross frames 26, FIGS. 2–4 and 8, to form a sturdy chassis. The frame members 24 and 26 support a suitable paneling or skin 28, including an engine hood 30, from the operator's compartment forward. Rearward of a cross frame 26 at the rear of the driver's compartment is a propeller assembly 34 for driving the vehicle in its aircraft form. As seen in FIG. 8, the propeller assembly is mounted on a cross frame 26 and driven by a shaft 36 from the engine 14.

Rearwardly of the propeller assembly is a tail assembly 40 for use of the vehicle in its aircraft form. This assembly has a pair of side vertical stabilizers 42 connected together at the top thereof by an integral horizontal stabilizer 44 and at an intermediate point by a second horizontal stabilizer 44a. Stabilizer 44 has conventional elevators 46 and vertical stabilizers have conventional rudders 48. Vertical stabilizers 42 have lower forwardly projecting extensions 50, FIGS. 7 and 9, which have a longitudinal bore 52 extending in from the front end thereof and leading to a point just short of the rearward end of the stabilizer. The bores 52 slidably receive elongated rigid support rods 54 projecting integrally in a rearward direction from the frame of the vehicle. In this arrangement, the tail assembly is supported and is capable of being moved to an inward position close to the propeller, as seen in FIGS. 1-5, for compacting the vehicle in its road form. When the vehicle is to be converted to aircraft form, the tail assembly 40 is moved rearwardly, FIGS. 6 and 7, for spacing it from the propeller. This rear spacing of the stabilizers 42 and 44 obtains a proper moment arm with the propeller drive for efficient and smooth flying and when moved forwardly keeps the road vehicle body in proper proportion. Inward and outward movement of the tail assembly as well as locking positioning thereof in such positions is accomplished by a fluid operated piston cylinder assembly 56, FIG. 9, connected between the extension 50 of the tail assembly and the vehicle frame 24.

The vehicle employs wings 60 capable of being folded to lie along the vehicle in the road form and capable of being extended out laterally in the aircraft form. The wings are supported on upright rods 62, FIGS. 6, 7 and 10, having vertical rotatable support in upper and lower journals 64 secured integrally to the frame of the vehicle. Each rod 62 has an integral collar 66 that provides the support thereof on the upper journal. The upper end of the rod has an integral angled extension 68 projecting rotatably through reinforced cross frame portions 70 in the wing. The rod extension 68 and frame portions 70 provide sturdy support of the wing in its outward flying position and also allow it to be rotatable on a horizontal axis for folding, to be described. The lower end of support rods 62 also has an integral extension 72, such extension angling upward and outwardly and being secured at its upper end to an outer portion of the underside of the wing by a universal connection 74 laterally aligned with the support rod 62. Extension 72 serves as a reinforcing and anchoring strut for the wing in the extended flying position of the wing. By means of this pivot support for the wing, the front edge of the wing can be brought up to flying position by turning it on the horizontal axis 68, or the wing can be turned with its front edge down to position the wing vertically. It can then be rotated on the axis 62 to lie along the side of the vehicle chassis in the road form.

The wings are held in the level aircraft flying form at their rear portion by the pivot rod 62 and at the front by locking support bars 82, FIGS. 6 and 11, extending into the inner end of the wing from inside the motor compartment portion of the chassis. Each of these bars has a head portion 84 arranged to be received in a recess 86 in a frame portion 24 of the chassis and a threaded end 84a arranged for threaded engagement with a tapped bore 88 in an inner reinforced cross frame portion 90 of the wing.

A tip portion 92 of each wing 60 is hingedly secured to the main portion of the wing, as by hinges 94, FIG. 12, which lie along the adjacent ends of the main wing and tips 92 and allow the latter to fold toward the underside of the wing. A threaded locking support bar 100 extends inward from the outer end of portion 92. This bar has a head portion 102 arranged to be received in a recess 104 in an end frame portion 106. The bar 100 extends in a snug but slidable fit through a bore 108 in the recessed frame portion 106, through an intermediate cross frame portion 109 and the bore 108 in an end cross

frame portion 110 at the hinge end of the tip 92. Bar 100 then extends into threaded engagement with a tapped bore 112 in a cross frame portion 113 at the end of the wing. When threaded in place in the tip 92 as shown in FIG. 12, rod 100 holds the tip rigidly in alignment with the wing. When removed, the tip portions can fold.

As noted above, the wing support rods 62, upon removal of the locking support bars 82, will allow the wings to drop down to a vertical or edge upright position and the wings can then be rotated rearwardly on the rods 62 to lie along the sides of the chassis in the road form of the vehicle. As best apparent in FIG. 7, the chassis includes side support surfaces 24a such as lateral extensions on frame 24, for the folded wings. In this road form of the vehicle, the tail assembly 40 is moved inwardly on the support rods 54 and the tips 92 of the wings are folded inwardly toward each other, as best seen in FIG. 1, after first removing the locking support bars 100.

The wing tips 92 are provided with apertures 114, shown diagrammatically in FIG. 1, offset vertically from the apertures 108 for the bar 100 in its wing tip support position. The outer ends of the wing tips in alignment with the vertically offset apertures 114 have a threaded insert 115 with a threaded bore similar to bore 112 in cross frame portion 113. Thus, the locking support bars 100 can be reinserted in reverse, namely, through the bore 108 in frame portions 110 and 106 at the hinged end of the tips 92 and then into threaded engagement with inserts 115 of the other wing tip.

Wings 60 have flaps 116, FIG. 7, that assist in take-off and landing in a conventional manner. Importantly, however, these flaps are in cutout portions 118 at the inner end of the wings and can be turned down and back under the wings to leave a recess in the wings when folded back, FIGS. 1-3, for contributing to the design of the road vehicle and also for allowing easier access to the driver's compartment.

It is desirable that the front and rear wheels be retractable upwardly and for this purpose, conventional retracting means may be employed. As an example, fluid operated cylinders 120, FIG. 3, connected between frame members 26 and lever arms 122 that support the wheels can be employed to raise and lower the wheels. It is preferred that the bottom openings to the wheels be closed in the flying form of the vehicle, and for this purpose panels 124, FIG. 5, slidably mounted in longitudinal guide grooves 126 are employed for opening and closing the wheel wells. These slide panels can be power operated if desired, as by a conventional fluid operated cylinder means, not shown.

The present vehicle also employs a central landing wheel assembly 128. This wheel assembly is also retractable such as by a fluid operated cylinder assembly 130 secured between a frame member 26 and a lever arm 132 pivotally connected to the frame of the vehicle and having travel that supports the wheel down below wheels 10 and 12. This wheel is also associated with a panel 124 having sliding support in side recesses 134 arranged to cover the bottom opening to the wheel well when the wheel is retracted.

Cylinder 130 comprises a pressure regulated shock absorber type cylinder having a selected force that will stabilize the vehicle during take off and landing. That is, the holding force of the cylinder 130 for the wheel 128 is less than the weight of the vehicle but has stabilizing function during take off and landing, as will be described more fully hereinafter.

In the operation of the present vehicle in its road form, the wings 60 and tip portions 92 thereof are folded to the FIG. 1 position in the road form and a locking support bar 100 inserted in its reverse position in the tip portions 92 to hold the said portions together to form the rear panel of the road vehicle. Support bar 100 serves to hold the main wing portions against the side of the vehicle chassis and form the side panels.

In the road form of the vehicle, the tail assembly 40 is moved inwardly in the compacting position. Horizontal stabilizer 44 serves as a spoiler.

To convert the vehicle to flying form, the wing tips 92 are disconnected from each other at the rear of the vehicle and the bars 100 inserted as shown in FIG. 12 to hold the wing tips in the flying position. The wings are swung outwardly around the upright rods 62 while in their vertical or edge position to an outwardly extended flying position. The wings are then pivoted on the horizontal axis bar extension 68 by bringing the front edge thereof up to a horizontal wing position and then installing locking bars 82 as shown in FIG. 11. Thereupon, the tail assembly 40 is shifted rearwardly to provide a proper moment arm with the propeller for smooth flying and good maneuverability.

In the takeoff condition of the vehicle, all the wheels are extended, including the center stabilizing wheel 128. As the takeoff proceeds and the wings commence their lift of the vehicle off the ground, the front and rear wheels 10 and 12 will lift but since the stabilizing wheel 128 is lower than the wheels 10 and 12, it will remain in ground contact until full wing support is achieved. This provides stability in takeoff. Conversely, as the aircraft approaches landing, the stabilizing wheel 128 will engage the runway first, and since the cylinder 130 is designed so as not to fully support the vehicle, the aircraft will settle down gradually on the front and rear road wheels.

According to the present invention, a combined road and aircraft vehicle is provided which is readily convertible from one form to the other. Such conversion is accomplished by a single person if necessary and without special tools and in a reasonably time. All the parts of the vehicle are intact and merely pivot or slide into place during conversion. The retracting tail assembly provides for novel compaction into the road form and when extended provides a good moment arm with the propeller for accomplishing maneuverability. The wings when folded form side panels for the road vehicle. Also, these wrap-around wings give sufficient wing area for efficient lift and also allow efficient length compaction of the vehicle for road travel.

It is to be understood that the form of my invention herein shown and described are to be taken as a preferred example of the same and that various changes in the shape, size and arrangement of parts may be resorted to without departing from the spirit of my invention, or the scope of the subjoined claims.

Having thus described my invention, I claim:

1. A combined road and aircraft vehicle comprising:
a chassis having front, rear and side portions,
a propeller assembly for driving the vehicle in the air, said propeller assembly being disposed between the front and rear of said chassis and facing the rear,
wing assemblies on opposite sides of said chassis for supporting the vehicle in the air,

folding support means for said wing assemblies arranged to support said wing assemblies in an outward aircraft form of the vehicle or in a folded stored position lying along the side of the chassis in a road form of the vehicle,
a tail assembly on said chassis,
shift means arranged to slidably shift said tail assembly alternately between a forward compacted road vehicle position and a rearward aircraft position spaced from said propeller assembly,
first wheel means on the front of said chassis providing front end support of the vehicle on a road and runway,
and second wheel means on said tail assembly providing rear end support of the vehicle both on a road in the road form of the vehicle and on a runway in the aircraft form of the vehicle.

2. The combined road vehicle and aircraft of claim 1 including stabilizing wheel means intermediate said front and rear wheel means, said stabilizing wheel means comprising a pressure regulated retractable wheel arranged to engage a runway and provide stabilizing lift and shock absorbing landing as the vehicle in its aircraft form initiates take off and landing functions, respectively.

3. The combined road and aircraft vehicle of claim 1 wherein said tail assembly comprises lower forwardly leading extensions with longitudinal socket means and the chassis comprises integral rearwardly extending guide and support rods slidably engageable in said socket means providing slidable guide and support means for said tail assembly.

4. The combined road and aircraft vehicle of claim 1 wherein each of said wing assemblies has a hinged end extension arranged to extend outwardly in the plane of said wings in the aircraft form of the vehicle and arranged to extend angularly relative to said wings on a vertical axis in a compacted road vehicle position of the tail assembly and a folded position of the wings forming a rear panel for the chassis in its road form.

5. The combined road and aircraft vehicle of claim 4 including removable lock bars at said hinged end extension for holding said extensions outwardly in the plane of the wings and for engaging opposite folded end extensions of the wings when forming the rear panel for the chassis.

6. The combined road and aircraft vehicle of claim 1 wherein the folding support means for each of said wing assemblies comprises a vertical support rod pivotally supported at the side of said chassis, a right angle horizontal extension on said support rod pivotally engageable with the wing assembly longitudinally adjacent a rear edge thereof, whereby said wing assembly is arranged to pivot on said horizontal extension to turn it up edgewise and to pivot rearwardly to said stored position lying along the side of the chassis in the road form of the vehicle, and a horizontal locking support bar supported on said chassis and removably engageable with said wing assembly adjacent a front edge thereof for supporting said wing assembly in its outward aircraft form.

7. The combined road and aircraft vehicle of claim 6 including an angled support strut connected integrally to a lower end of said vertical support rod and universally connected to an outer portion of said wing assembly.

* * * * *

United States Patent [19]

Moller

[11] **Patent Number:** **5,115,996**

[45] **Date of Patent:** **May 26, 1992**

[54] **VTOL AIRCRAFT**

[75] Inventor: **Paul S. Moller, Dixon, Calif.**

[73] Assignee: **Moller International, Inc., Davis, Calif.**

[21] Appl. No.: **472,696**

[22] Filed: **Jan. 31, 1990**

[51] Int. Cl.⁵ **B64C 29/00**
[52] U.S. Cl. .... **244/12.5; 244/23 D;**
244/52; 239/265.19; 239/265.27; 239/265.25
[58] Field of Search .... 244/12.5, 23 D, 2, 23 R,
244/23 A, 52, 219; 415/148, 150, 167;
239/265.13, 265.19, 265.25, 265.27, 265.29,
265.31

[56] **References Cited**

U.S. PATENT DOCUMENTS

2,923,494	2/1960	Strong	244/2
3,061,242	10/1962	Zurawinski et al.	244/52
3,081,597	3/1963	Kosin et al.	244/52
3,087,303	4/1963	Heinze et al.	244/52
3,206,929	9/1965	Marchant et al.	244/52
3,259,338	7/1966	Schmidt	244/52
3,262,511	7/1966	Carr	244/52
3,265,142	8/1966	Winter	244/52
3,291,242	12/1966	Tinajero	244/2
3,292,864	12/1966	Edkins	244/52
3,486,577	12/1969	Jackes	244/23 R
4,071,207	1/1978	Piasecki et al.	244/12.5
4,804,155	2/1989	Strumbos	244/52

FOREIGN PATENT DOCUMENTS

1223854	7/1987	Canada	244/23 R
457705	12/1924	Fed. Rep. of Germany	244/23 R
2054536	5/1972	Fed. Rep. of Germany	244/23 D
1281653	12/1961	France	244/23 R
1136331	12/1968	United Kingdom	244/12.5

Primary Examiner—Joseph F. Peters, Jr.
Assistant Examiner—Anne E. Bidwell
Attorney, Agent, or Firm—Rosenblum, Parish & Bacigalupi

[57] **ABSTRACT**

A VTOL aircraft including a fuselage with four nacelles, three vertical stabilizers and a horizontal stabilizer attached to the fuselage. The fuselage and the nacelles are lifting bodies that are configured to jointly form an aerodynamic lifting body which cooperates with the horizontal stabilizer to provide aerodynamic lift to the aircraft in forward flight. Each nacelle contains two rotary engines directly driving corresponding fans which face each other and operate in counter-rotating directions. Each nacelle also contains a system of vanes located at the rear opening thereof, and actuators for extending and retracting the vanes to deflect the airflow over a predetermined range of angles from the horizontal. Each engine utilizes the dynamic pressure of the air behind the fans to provide a source of air for cooling the rotors and exhaust system. A triple redundant computerized flight control system maintains the stability of the aircraft as it transitions from one flight regime to another as well as in flight. The system of vanes alone can also be used as an apparatus for gas or fluid stream directional control.

38 Claims, 15 Drawing Sheets

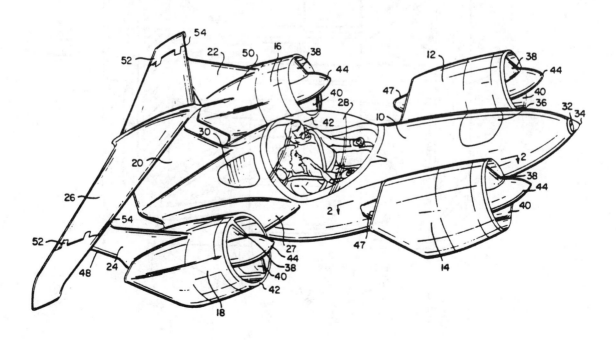

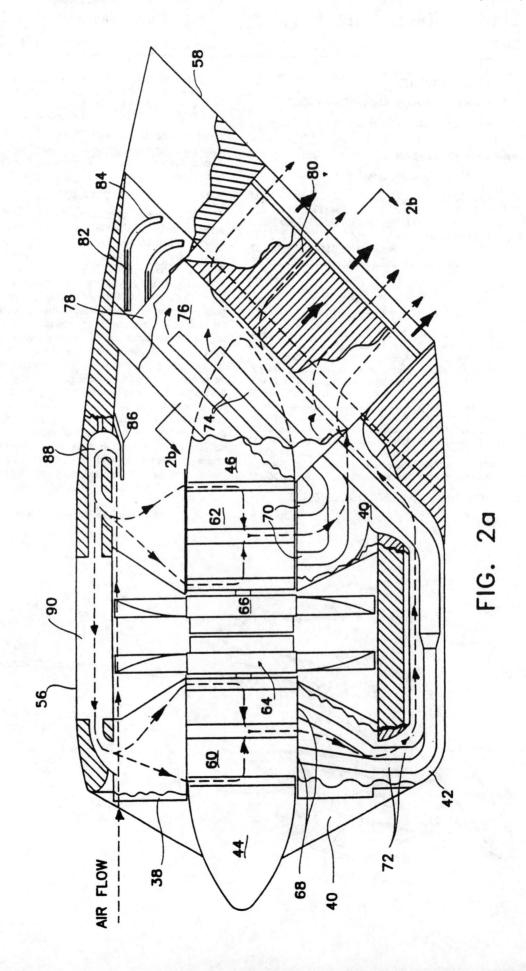

FIG. 2a

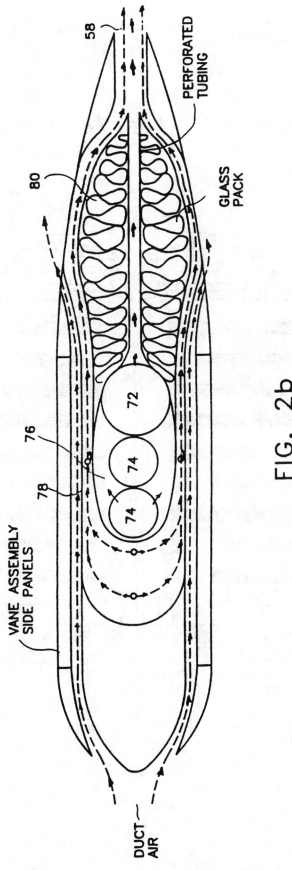

FIG. 2b

FIG. 3a

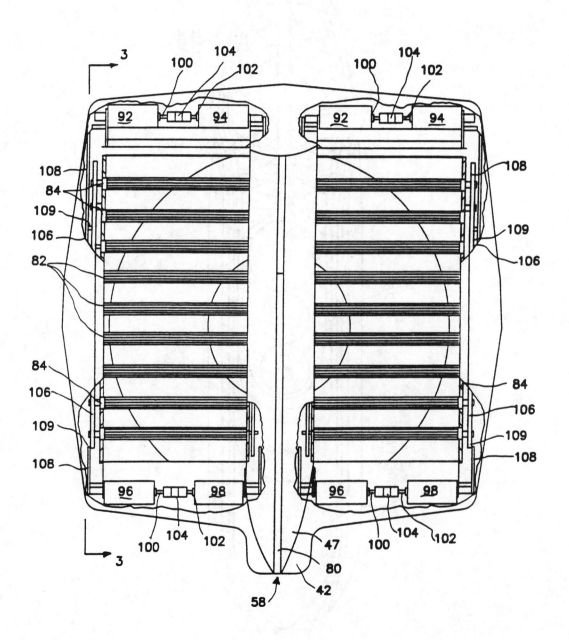

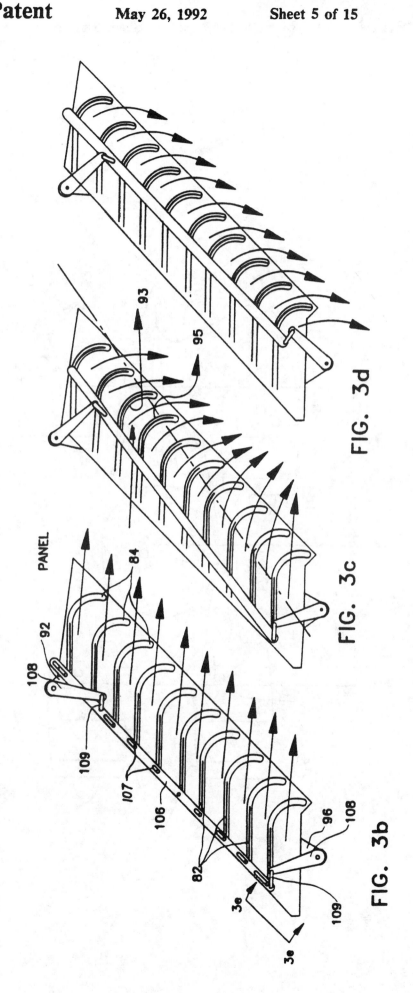

FIG. 3d

FIG. 3c

FIG. 3b

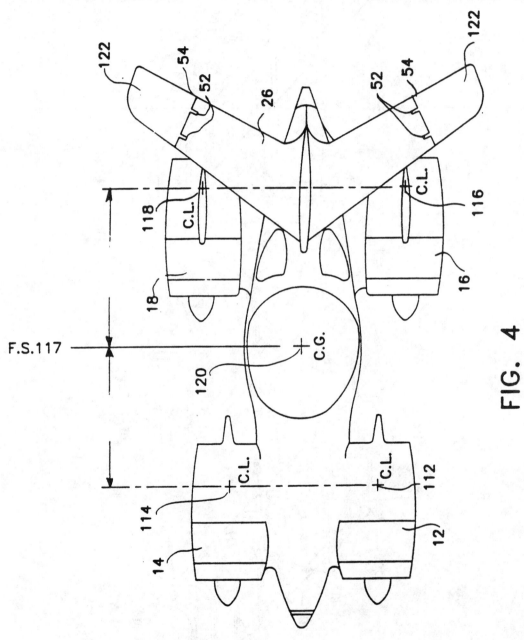

FIG. 4

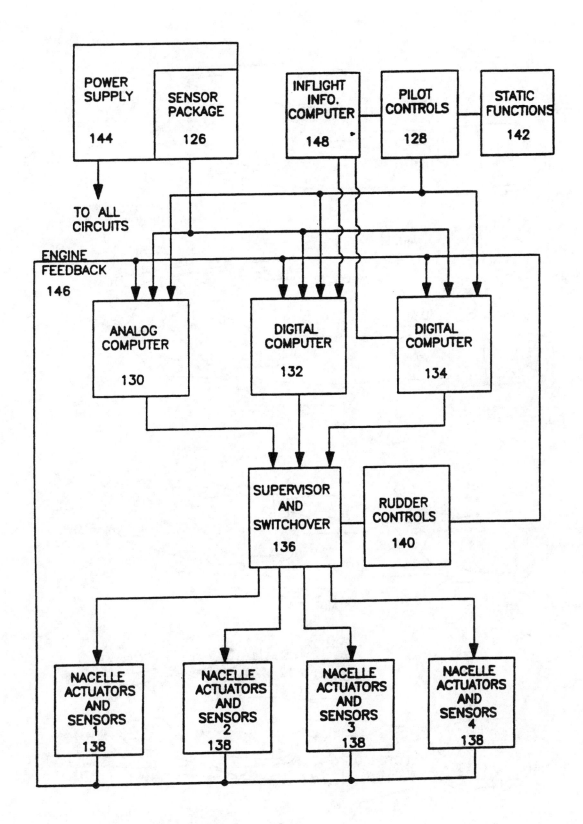

FIG. 6a

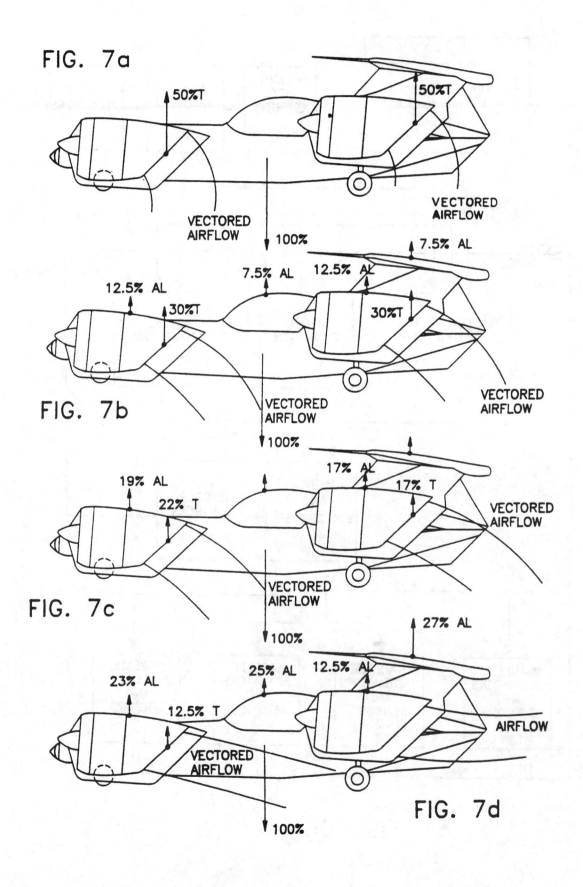

FIG. 7a

FIG. 7b

FIG. 7c

FIG. 7d

VTOL AIRCRAFT

BACKGROUND OF THE INVENTION

1. Field of the Invention

The present invention relates generally to VTOL aircraft, and more particularly to an improved VTOL aircraft and ducted fan propulsion system wherein the ducts housing the engines remain stationary with their axial center lines approximately parallel with the center line of the fuselage, and the thrust is selectively vectored by adjustable vanes mounted in the aft portion of each duct.

2. Brief Description of the Prior Art

Over the past 53 years, inventors have attempted to create a vehicle that could be flown in the air as well as driven on land. According to an article in the February 1989 issue of Smithsonian Magazine, more than 30 designs for flying cars have been submitted to the U.S. Patent Office since 1936. These early designs combined elements of the automobile with those of the airplane. Since the fuselage of the craft was large, usually the size of a passenger compartment of a car, a huge, powerful engine and large wings were needed to generate enough thrust and lift to make the craft airborne. On the ground, the huge engine was unnecessary and thus inefficient, the exposed propeller (if one was used) was a safety hazard, and the large wings had to be removed and stored prior to driving the craft on the road.

The present invention is an aircraft that can be used as a land vehicle efficiently and without modification. A major difference between the present invention and the prior car/plane inventions is that the present invention is all one structure so it provides efficiency in the air as well as on the ground. Ducted fans are used instead of exposed propellers so safety is not compromised. Half of the engines can be shut down for fuel conservation and efficient operation of the aircraft while being driven on land. Additionally, the outboard segments of the short wings are hinged to be folded easily, and thus do not have to be removed from the craft prior to driving.

Another feature of the present invention is that it is capable of vertical takeoff and landing (VTOL) by vectoring the fan thrust from the ducted fan engines. Previous VTOL efforts have relied on fixed orientation of the duct centerlines vertically for hover and then re-directing their thrust with vanes for transition into forward flight. This method was used with rigid re-directing vanes that would stall the airflow at angles above 15 degrees. This rigid vane approach resulted in a limited ability to generate a significant transverse force for acceleration. The alternative has been VTOL aircraft that have tilted the entire duct or the exposed propeller, whichever was used, in order to vector the thrust. A tiltable duct or propeller requires complex structural, electrical and mechanical connections. Furthermore, the tilting duct or propeller experiences off-axis flow into the inlet during transition into forward flight, resulting in flow separation at the upstream inlet lip. The rotation of the duct or propeller is inherently slow to react and cannot be modulated to provide the fast response time that is required for longitudinal control. Additionally, the tilting duct is not an efficient annular airfoil, and therefore additional wing area must be provided for aerodynamic lift. This greater wing area results in additional drag.

U.S. Pat. No. 4,358,074 shows a propulsion system for VTOL aircraft having stationary ducts which vec-

tor the airflow by utilizing a movable, fixed camber, cascading vane system in addition to a slotted flap system. The airflow within the nacelle is divided into twin airstreams. One of the airstreams is directed downwardly through the fixed camber vane system. The other airstream is exhausted through an aft nozzle at the outlet, against a slotted flap system mounted on a wing located immediately behind the duct. The fixed camber vane system can only direct a limited amount of airflow through very modest angles before the flow separates creating large pressure and thrust losses. The divided airstream system is required because it would be difficult to deflect the full airstream through large angles by utilizing the wing flap system alone.

Variable camber flow deflector blades, in which each blade (similar to a vane) is capable of resiliently deforming to affect airflow direction, are the subject of U.S. Pat. No. 4,235,397. In this patented invention, the leading edge of the blade is anchored and the trailing edge of the blade is affixed to a mechanism which pulls the trailing edge downward in an arc, so that the blade is effectively bent, thereby re-directing the airflow. This configuration requires that the blade be great enough in width to house an effective leaf spring member and it also limits the materials that the blade skin and filler can be made of. Another type of airfoil variable cambering device is the subject of U.S. Pat. No. 4,247,066. Both of these patented inventions utilize mechanical parts that are subject to high stress loads. These complex mechanical devices are slow to react due to the particular interaction of the mechanical parts and cannot provide the fast response times desirable for attitude and altitude control.

OBJECTIVES OF THE PRESENT INVENTION

It is therefore a primary objective of the present invention to provide an improved ducted fan VTOL aircraft capable of vertical takeoff and hover, forward flight and all regimes of transition between hover and forward flight.

Another objective of the present invention is to provide a VTOL aircraft having multiple nacelles, with a powerplant configuration within each horizontal nacelle combining two rotary engines, each driving a fan, with the fans facing each other and counter-rotating.

A further objective of the present invention is to provide a VTOL aircraft having multiple nacelles, each of which includes a system of extendable, retractable and flexible vanes capable of selectively deflecting the airflow out of the nacelles downwardly to an angle substantially perpendicular to the lateral axis of the nacelle.

An additional objective of the present invention is to provide a general purpose apparatus having a system of vanes capable of redirecting and controlling a large velocity stream of gas or liquid with little actuation power and little thrust or pressure losses.

Yet another objective of the present invention is to provide a ducted fan driven VTOL aircraft having an exhaust system that utilizes the dynamic pressure of the air behind the fans to cool the rotors, the exhaust pipes and the baffle structure.

A still further objective of the present invention is to provide a multi-engine, ducted fan VTOL aircraft of the type described above, having a triple redundancy flight control system which regulates the thrust of each engine and the amount of deflection of each set of vanes in order to provide a stable platform in all flight regimes.

SUMMARY OF THE PREFERRED EMBODIMENT

Briefly, a preferred embodiment of the present invention includes a fuselage with four nacelles, three vertical stabilizers, and a horizontal stabilizer attached to the fuselage. The fuselage and the nacelles are configured to jointly form an aerodynamic lifting body which cooperates with the horizontal stabilizer to provide aerodynamic lift to the aircraft. Each nacelle contains two rotary engines, each of which directly drives a fan. The fans face each other and operate in counter-rotating directions. Each nacelle also contains a system of vanes located at the rear opening thereof, and means are provided for extending and retracting the vanes to deflect the airflow over a predetermined range of angles from the horizontal. Each engine utilizes the dynamic pressure of the air behind the fans to cool the engine's rotors and exhaust system. A triple redundant computerized flight control system maintains stability of the aircraft as it transitions from one flight regime to another, as well as in flight.

ADVANTAGES OF THE INVENTION

An important advantage of the present invention is that it provides an aircraft which smoothly and easily transitions between takeoff or hover modes and forward flight, without any transient decrease in stability.

Another advantage of the present invention is that it includes ducted nacelles which are stationary and thus need no complex structural, mechanical and electrical connections.

An additional advantage of the present invention is that each nacelle includes a system of vanes which are adjustable to deflect airflow out of the nacelle over a range of more than 90 degrees with only a slight decrease in the airflow cross section, therefore minimizing the loss of thrust in transition from one extreme to another.

The use of two engines and fans in each nacelle provides the benefit that failure of one engine will result in only a partial reduction of thrust from that nacelle if the remaining engine is operated near its maximum output.

Yet another advantage of the present invention is that the fans face each other and counter-rotate, thereby cancelling the gyroscopic moments which might otherwise interfere with pitch, yaw, and roll control. Also, the swirl in the flow induced by the first fan is cancelled by the second counter-rotating fan so that swirl energy, normally lost, is recovered.

It is another advantage of the present invention that one engine in each nacelle can be shut down when maximum speed or power is not required, thereby increasing the range and operating efficiency.

Another advantage of the present invention is that the shrouded fans are buried deep in their ducts and counter-rotate, thereby keeping fan noise to a minimum.

An advantage gained by the present invention is that it provides a powerplant design having improved rotor and exhaust cooling features needing no auxiliary pump to accomplish the necessary cooling.

Another advantage of the present invention is that it includes a computer operated flight control system which, through feedback from inertial sensors and actuator response sensors in the nacelles, keeps the vehicle balanced during flight and implements the pilot's commands for desired pitch, yaw and roll motion.

Yet another advantage of the present invention is that two engines are used in each nacelle thereby providing that adequate pitch and roll control can be maintained through power modulation should one engine in a nacelle fail.

An advantage of the present invention is that a heavy firewall between the engines and cockpit is not necessary, due to the utilization of engines with a small frontal profile which can be mounted in a nacelle that is attached to the fuselage, rather than having the engines within the fuselage near the cockpit.

These and other objects and advantages of the present invention will no doubt become apparent to those skilled in the art after having read the following detailed description of the preferred embodiment which are contained in and illustrated by the various drawing figures

IN THE DRAWING

FIG. 1 is a perspective view of a presently preferred embodiment of a VTOL aircraft according to the present invention.

FIG. 2a is a longitudinal cross sectional view through the nacelle taken along the line 2—2 of FIG. 1.

FIG. 2b is a partial top view of a nacelle showing a cooling system for the exhaust chamber and baffle structure, which is contained within the dividing strut.

FIG. 3a is a diagram showing a rear view of the nacelle shown in FIG. 2.

FIGS. 3b through 3d are partial cross-sectional views through the nacelle taken along the line 3—3 of FIG. 3a, showing the interior wall of a vane guide containing panel of the nacelle together with the vane control mechanisms and vanes in various control positions.

FIGS. 3e and 3f are side views of a vane guide containing panel taken along lines 3e—3e of FIG. 3b.

FIG. 3g is a side view of a vane showing the vane segments and connecting membrane.

FIG. 3h is a partial bottom view of a vane with the membrane broken away illustrating details of vane construction.

FIG. 4 is a top view of the preferred embodiment illustrating the location of the center of gravity of the aircraft and the center of lift of each nacelle in a hover mode.

FIGS. 5a, 5b and 5c are plan, rear, and side views respectively, illustrating details of the horizontal stabilizer of the aircraft shown in FIG. 1.

FIG. 6a is a block diagram illustrating the triple redundant computerized flight control system of the preferred embodiment.

FIG. 6b is a block diagram representing the various actuators and sensors contained within each nacelle block shown in FIG. 6a.

FIGS. 7a through 7d are four side views showing the aircraft of FIG. 1 in transition from takeoff through forward flight.

FIG. 8a is a perspective view of an apparatus for effecting flow stream directional control.

FIG. 8b is a diagram showing a vane and bidirectional guide slot assembly.

FIGS. 8c and 8d are partial cross sectional views through the apparatus taken along the line 8—8 of FIG. 8a, showing the interior wall of a vane guide containing panel of the apparatus together with the vane control mechanisms and vanes in two extreme positions.

United States Patent [19]

Lay

[11] **Patent Number:** 5,141,173

[45] **Date of Patent:** Aug. 25, 1992

[54] **PRESSURE-JET AND DUCTED FAN HYBRID ELECTRIC CAR**

[76] Inventor: **Joachim E. Lay**, East Lansing, Mich.

[21] Appl. No.: 743,753

[22] Filed: **Aug. 12, 1991**

[51] Int. Cl.5 .... B64C 29/04; B64C 37/00
[52] U.S. Cl. .... 244/2; 244/23 R; 244/52; 244/23 A; 180/2.2; 180/117; 180/65.3
[58] Field of Search .... 244/2, 23 R, 23 A, 23 B, 244/58, 53 R, 52; 180/2.2, 116, 117, 65.3

[56] **References Cited**

U.S. PATENT DOCUMENTS

1,469,264	10/1923	Lubeck	180/65.3
2,989,271	6/1961	Bohr	244/23 A
3,152,776	10/1964	Tresilian et al.	244/23 R
3,265,330	8/1966	Conway et al.	244/2
3,276,528	10/1966	Tucknott et al.	
3,486,718	12/1969	Marchal et al.	
3,494,575	2/1970	Budworth	
3,499,163	3/1970	Verreault	180/2.2
3,774,865	11/1973	Pinto	244/23 C
4,043,421	8/1977	Smith	180/117
4,141,425	2/1979	Treat	180/65.3
4,171,784	10/1979	Eickmann	
4,218,624	8/1980	Schiavone	180/65.3
4,768,738	9/1988	Weinert	244/58
4,955,560	9/1990	Nishina et al.	244/58

Primary Examiner—Galen Barefoot
Attorney, Agent, or Firm—Ian C. McLeod

[57] **ABSTRACT**

A hybrid electric vehicle (10) capable of ground travel and air travel is described. The vehicle provides for movement over the ground by wheel motors (20) mounted at each of four ground engaging wheels (14 and 16). The wheel motors are supplied with electric power by a battery pack (24) or an electric generator (32) powered by a combustion engine (22). The combustion engine is also geared to vertically oriented ducted fans (40) and a horizontally oriented ducted fan or propeller (76) for providing the vehicle with the capability of travel through the air. Pressure jets (62), supplied with compressed air from a compressor (66) driven by the combustion engine, augment the lift of the ducted fans and provide steering for the vehicle. The vehicle can also be provided with photo-electric cells (82) for supplying a portion of the electric power for the vehicle.

25 Claims, 6 Drawing Sheets

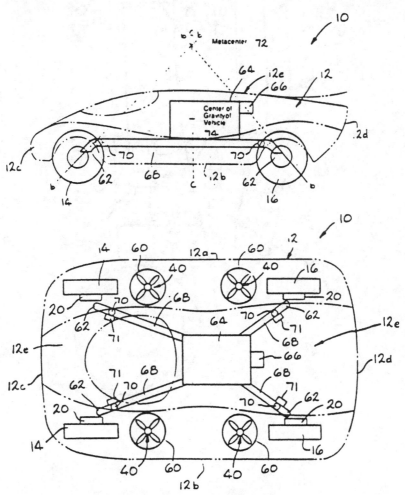

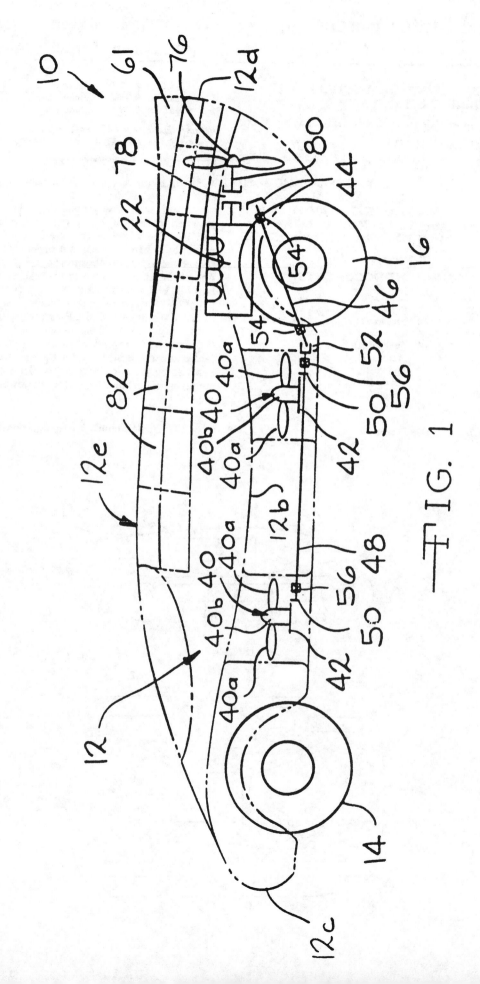

FIG. 1

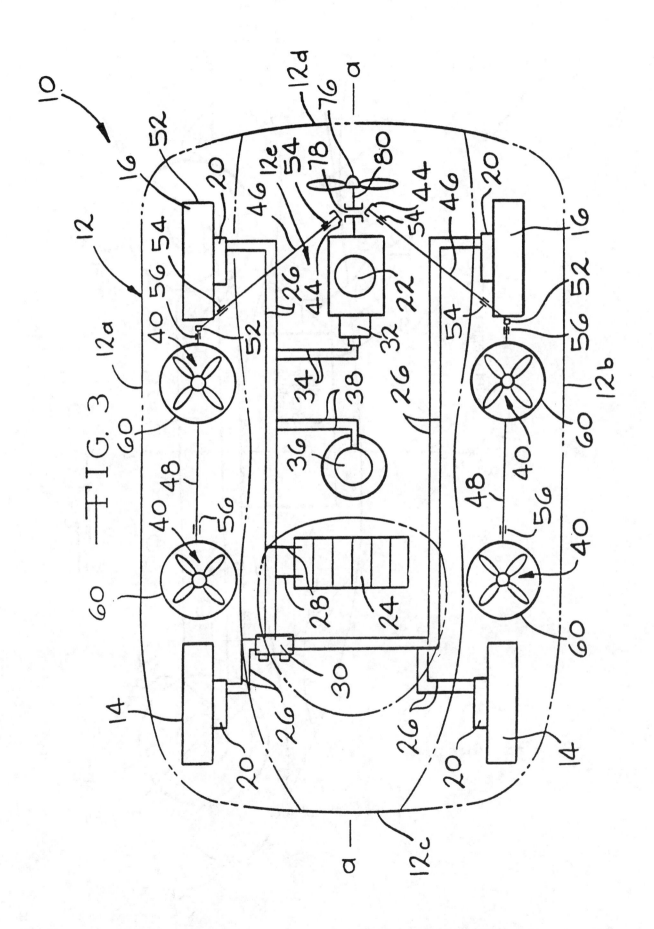

FIG. 3

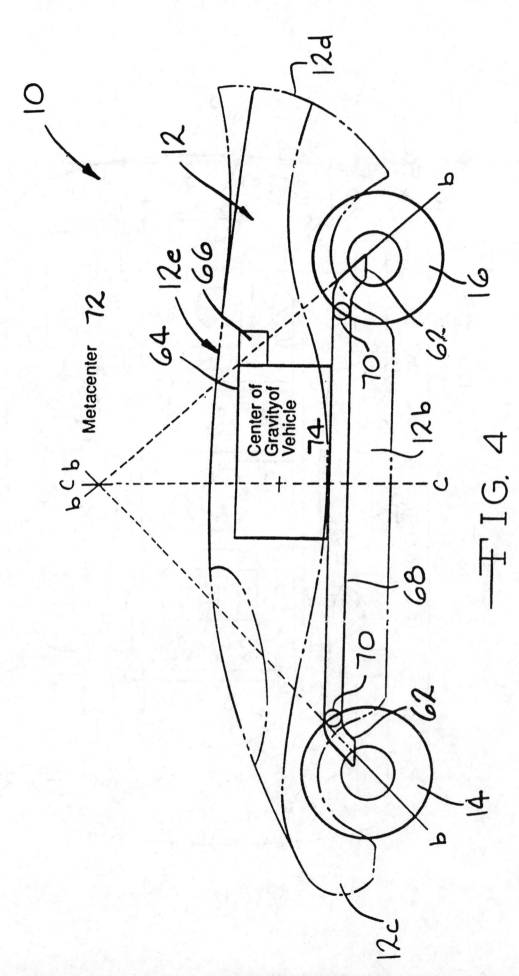

FIG. 4

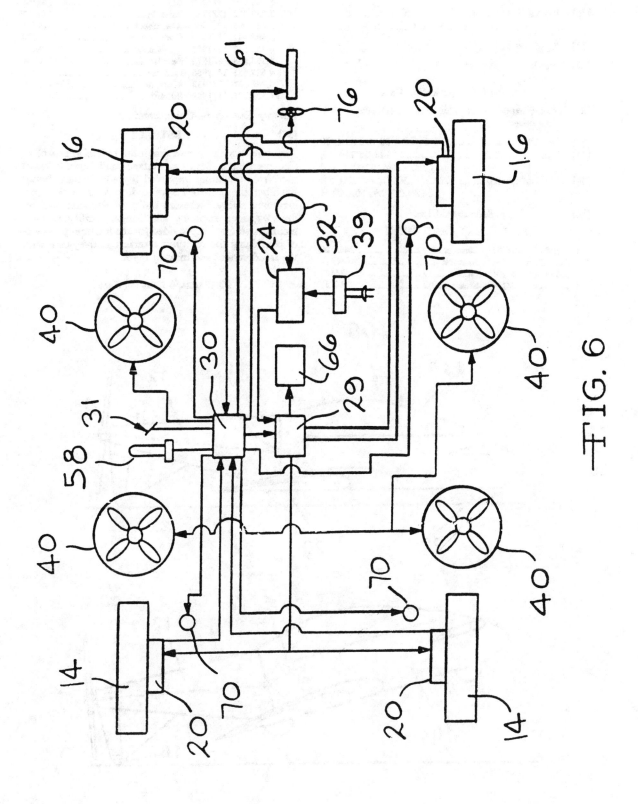

FIG. 6

United States Patent [19]

Wooley

[11] **Patent Number:** **5,201,478**

[45] **Date of Patent:** **Apr. 13, 1993**

[54] **AIRPLANE EFFICIENCY, SAFETY AND UTILIZATION**

[76] Inventor: **Don H. Wooley, 252 Las Miradas Dr., Los Gatos, Calif. 95030**

[21] Appl. No.: **725,217**

[22] Filed: **Jun. 26, 1991**

Related U.S. Application Data

[63] Continuation-in-part of Ser. No. 505,413, Apr. 6, 1990, abandoned.

[51] Int. Cl.⁵ B64C 37/00; B64C 1/30
[52] U.S. Cl. 244/2; 244/49; 244/89; 244/120
[58] Field of Search .... 244/2, 49, 120, 51, 244/52, 89, 50, 102 R

[56] **References Cited**

U.S. PATENT DOCUMENTS

1,828,026	10/1931	Cline et al.	244/120
2,271,226	1/1942	Johnson	244/45 A
2,434,068	6/1948	Geisse	244/2
2,478,847	8/1949	Stuart	244/51
2,624,530	3/1953	Hanssen	244/2
2,767,939	11/1956	Taylor	244/2
3,054,579	9/1962	Bary	244/51
3,222,012	12/1965	Piasecki	244/51
3,281,096	10/1966	Konecheck	244/51
3,966,142	6/1976	Corbett et al.	244/120
4,358,072	11/1982	Williamson	244/2
4,598,888	7/1986	Beteille	244/45 A
4,627,585	12/1986	Einstein	244/49
4,746,081	5/1988	Mazzoni	244/45 A
4,881,701	11/1989	Bullard	244/49

Primary Examiner—Galen Barefoot

[57] **ABSTRACT**

This invention involves a simple but radical approach to airplane design. Many advantages and benefits result therefrom including improved flight efficiency, better handling and control response, less tail area required, increased safety, increased utility of airplanes, and reduced ground handling and hangar facility requirements. A solution is provided for the inherent problems of combining the utility of a surface conveyance with the freedom and swiftness of flight.

20 Claims, 6 Drawing Sheets

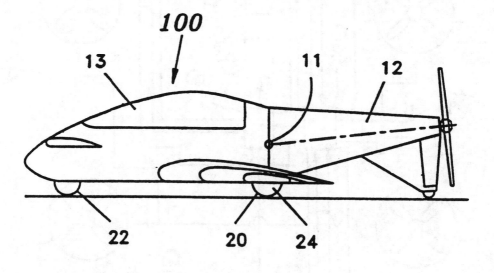

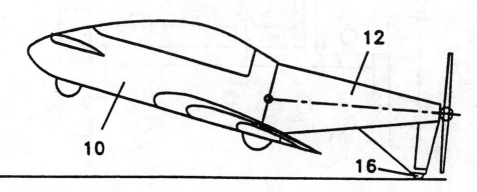

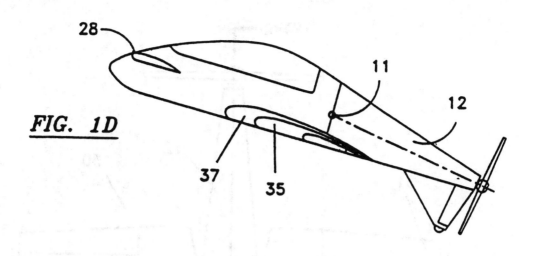

FIG. 1D

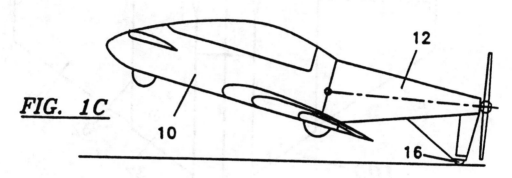

FIG. 1C

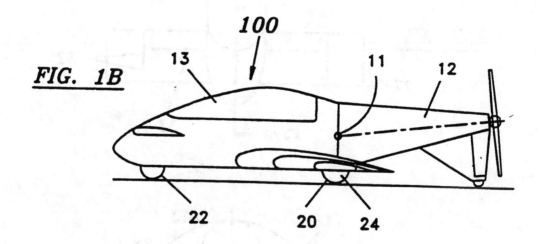

FIG. 1B

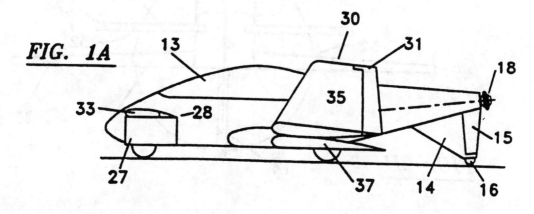

FIG. 1A

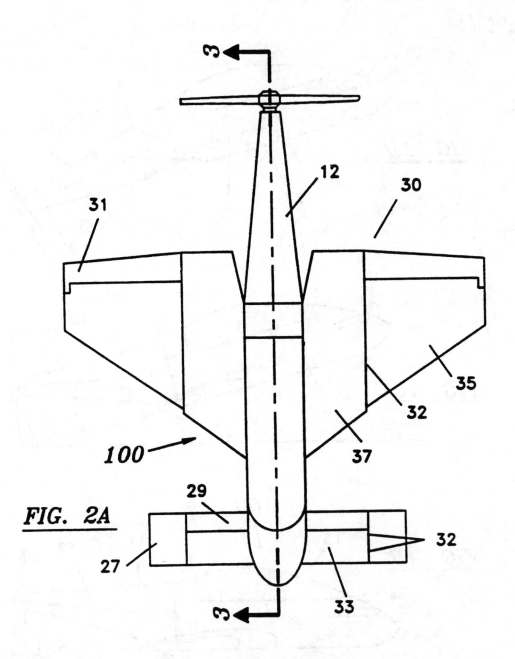

FIG. 2A

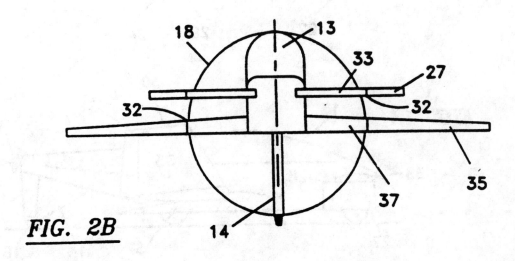

FIG. 2B

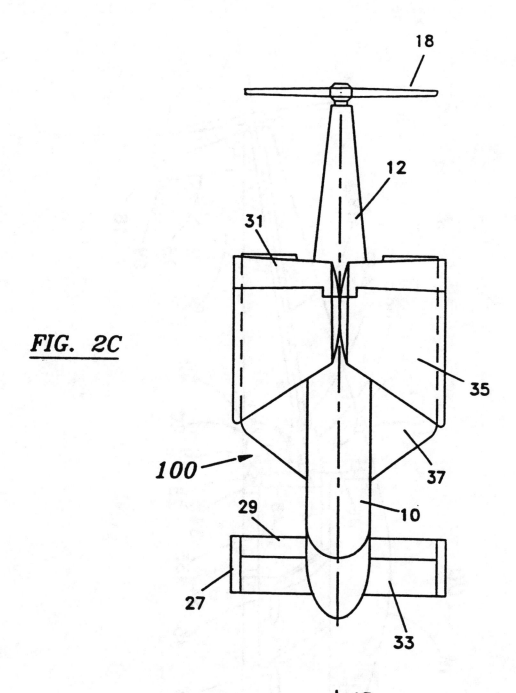

FIG. 2C

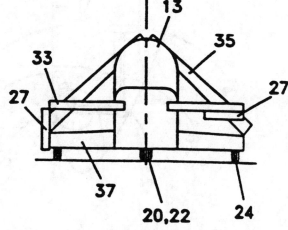

FIG. 2D

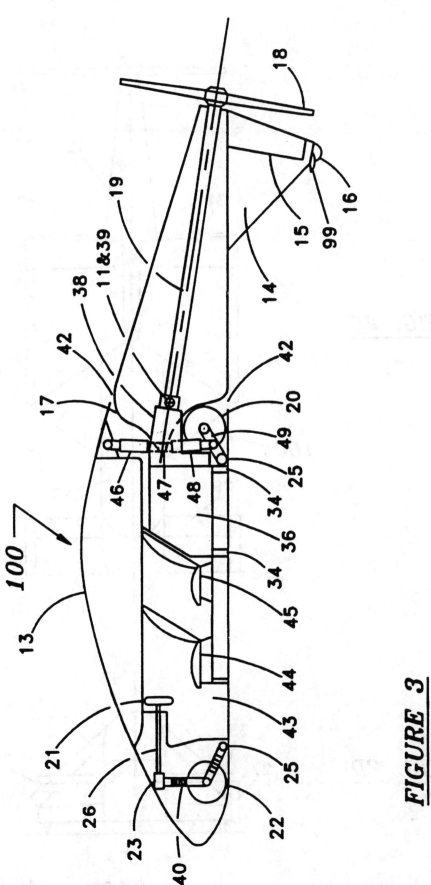

FIGURE 3

1

AIRPLANE EFFICIENCY, SAFETY AND UTILIZATION

This is a continuation-in-part Application of Application Ser. No. 07/505,413 filed Apr. 6, 1990, now abandoned.

BACKGROUND—FIELD OF INVENTION

This invention involves a simple but radical approach to airplane design. Many benefits and advantages derive therefrom. More effective flight control, greater flight efficiency, improved safety and greater utilization of aircraft result from this invention. The concept was originally conceived to provide a solution to the inherent problems of combining the utility of an automobile with the freedom and swiftness of flight. However, the advantages of the concept can be applied to airplanes from commercial airliners down to the smallest personal airplane. Although the concept is simple involving few parts its impact is incalculable as to airplane safety, airplane use by the general public and its effect on the efficiency of commercial aircraft and thus its effect upon our national resources.

Also, integral with and dependent upon the basic invention are a number of special features and benefits that are not possible with conventional design. These special features and benefits include:

1. automatic retraction and extension of the landing gear without operator assistance and with no additional components required;

2. automatic high volume air cooling while on the ground and automatically restricted air flow during flight with no operator assistance required and with no additional parts required;

3. variable thrust vector alignment for optimum flight performance with no additional parts required;

4. positive yaw/roll coupling instead of adverse coupling as is the case with conventional design;

5. overall airplane efficiency and performance significantly increased compared to conventional design;

6. up to 100% aerodynamic ground effect is automatically provided, but only when needed, during takeoff and landing operations;

7. improved control response and handling quality with less tail area required over conventional design;

8. greatly reduced height and profile resulting in reduced ground handling and service facility requirements;

9. increased safety with simple arresting device.

STATEMENT OF A PROBLEM

Airplane design has always been confronted with a challenge as to how to design a streamlined, efficiently shaped fuselage and yet provide ground clearance for the body and propellers or jet units. This is especially critical during takeoff and landing rotations. Presently, huge airliners down to the smallest airplane show that this problem has not been resolved. The conventional design of the fuselage of a commercial airliner shows that not only is the aft portion of the fuselage not aligned with the airflow but actually the aft body shape during cruise and related phases of flight is creating a negative or downward lift. Thus, present day airplanes are designed for a phase of operation that takes a few seconds of time and not a flight that consumes hours of time. This inefficient design not only wastes fuel but the upward tilted aft body presents others problems as well.

2

Current design requires an immense vertical tail jutting skyward resulting in an airplane requiring high scaffolding and tall hangars to service and accommodate them. However, more important than the increased cost to operate and service such aircraft is the reduced effectiveness that such a tail provides. During takeoff and landing the lower part of the vertical tail is in the turbulent wake of the fuselage. Also, when the rudder is deflected it creates a roll moment opposite to the desired direction of the yaw turning force due to its high position. This contributes to the large tail area requirement.

Aside from ground clearance requirements, if an aircraft could be designed with an aft body aligned in the direction of the downwash airflow then the drag force would be reduced. Also, if the vertical stabilizer and rudder could be oriented to project downward beneath the aft end of the fuselage then the tail area could be reduced because the tail would be more effective. The present invention would eliminate these problems as explained herein and a more efficient and better controlled airplane would result.

Note that the radical design change described herein will affect pitch trim compared to conventional design. Increased positive trim can be gained by reflexing the main wing camber or simply by raising both ailerons slightly upward equally. These changes would supplement canard lift or aft horizontal tail loading to offset the main wing negative moment if it is required.

BACKGROUND—DESCRIPTION OF PRIOR ART

Over the years numerous attempts have been made to devise a way to combine the utility of an automobile with the advantages inherent with the freedom and swiftness of flight. Previous attempts have concentrated on how to fold and store the wings and other flight components, then, either to carry the flight gear on the vehicle while traveling on land or to secure the flight gear at the landing site requiring a return trip to continue the flight. Neither of these two methods has proven to be practical for reasons explained herein. However, there is one known example of a third method of achieving a practical combination vehicle in which the flight components are folded into a unit comprising a trailer that can then be towed behind the auto unit that is thus shed of the components that make land travel impractical. While this method appears to be the most practical and usable vehicle its acceptance in the marketplace demonstrates that it is not much more than a novelty. The reason is that basic inherent problems of such a combination were not addressed nor remedied resulting in an airplane with a 300 pound weight penalty requiring more than a 50 percent increase in power to handle the airplane.

The above auto-trailer concept was proposed by M. B. Taylor in U.S. Pat. No. 2,767,939 to Aerocar, Inc. (1956) entitled "Flying Automotive Vehicle Assembly." U.S. Pat. No. 2,434,068 to Geisse (1948) entitled "Roadable Airplane with Folding and Detachable Wings" combines the features of both of the first two above mentioned concepts, namely a vehicle that can fold and carry the flight components on the automobile or can detach the folded components and leave them behind as desired. U.S. Pat. No. 2,624,530 to J. H. Hanssen (1953) entitled "Vehicle Comprising an Auto-Airplane Combination" was designed to leave the flight gear at the airport with the automobile unit capable of traveling on the roads being limited in use to people who travel mainly between one town or area and another and returning back to the origination point of the trip.

All of the prior attempts have fallen short of their objective of a practical and usable combination vehicle because they have not solved the basic problems inherent in such a combination. These inherent problems are, and the concept's solution follow:

(a) A most fundamental problem of combining an auto with an airplane is that of propeller clearance which requires at least a part of the vehicle must be elevated from the ground which means it is in conflict with requirements of a stable, low center of gravity for the automobile. All prior art has not successfully solved this problem because of weight penalties or time and effort requirements in making a changeover from one mode of travel to the other. However, the placement of the propeller at the aft end of the fuselage provides a means by which a relatively small portion of the structure need be so elevated. This was employed by the above U.S. Pat. No. 2,767,939, auto-trailer combination and has proven to be a reliable means of providing thrust to the airplane. One of the drawbacks to this concept is that the thrust vector is actually oriented downward and the aft fuselage is not aligned with the airflow which both reduces fuel efficiency and handling quality of the airplane. The proposed concept eliminates these problems as explained below.

(b) Prior attempts to fold, retract, collapse, detach, and related means of ridding the vehicle of unwanted flight surfaces have resulted in claims of quick conversion from one configuration to the other and back again with little needed effort or time spent. U.S. Pat. No. 2,767,939 claims that the flight gear is easily assembled into a trailer in only a few minutes. However, in that scheme as with other prior art, the operator must exit the vehicle to accomplish this changeover which is an unacceptable procedure. For the vehicle to be readily useful by the general public under all normal weather and road conditions the changeover must be made by a simple procedure without the operator having to leave the vehicle at any time. The proposed embodiment of the combined machine would employ a simple folding of only the outer panels of the airplane by hand operated means without the operator leaving the vehicle. The entire tail assembly including the propeller and vertical tail would remain as is without any changeover required in the conversion. Thus the conversion is made without stopping the vehicle at any time.

(c) Prior efforts have resulted in vehicles that have a relatively high center of gravity that makes ground travel unstable and therefore limited in performing as an automobile. No solution to this problem has heretofore been offered. The jointed fuselage concept solves this problem by allowing the road clearance of the vehicle to be at the minimum legal limit. This means that the center of gravity of the road vehicle can be brought down to an acceptable height above the road because the wing, engine, operator and other major weight items can be placed lower than heretofore was possible. An additional benefit of this minimum vehicle ground clearance is the aerodynamic ground effect or air cushion effect of having the wing close to the ground.

(d) Prior combined vehicle configurations have not adequately solved the requirement to have a small, low side profile with the vehicle in the land travel mode. The prior attempt to have an auto towing a trailer has resulted in an unwieldy, large elevated side area that is not safe or practical for road use, especially considering the lightness of the towed structures. The articulated fuselage concept allows placement of all heavy components at or near minimum levels during all phases of road travel and thus the profile is low and smaller in size.

(e) Some of the prior attempts to carry the large, light weight flight structures have been made by simply carrying them on airframe and undercarriage of the airplane with some of the structure being cantilevered out from the undercarriage support. U.S. Pat. No. 2,767,939 solved this problem with the trailer concept. Thus, the problem of carrying such structures on the road where roadway air turbulence and cross-wind forces exist was reduced. The invention presented herein likewise employs a third wheel configuration but accomplishes it without the large side area or elevation or conversion tasks of the prior art.

(f) The prior U.S. Pat. No. 2,767,939 had a flight configuration in which the aft fuselage was canted upward to the rear with a propeller oriented so that forward thrust was aimed slightly downward. Both of these orientations were undesirable but necessary because of the fixed position of the aft fuselage structure. The jointed fuselage feature allows the thrust vector of the propeller to be directed in the optimum direction depending on the flight condition. A fixed position of the thrust vector is at best a compromise and in the above cited prior art together with the upward rearward slope of the body was necessitated by the requirement to provide propeller ground clearance at liftoff. Thus, for a phase of operation that consumes less than a few seconds of time a flight of hours is compromised.

(g) There is an old saying in aircraft design and construction that "Hell holds an awful fate for those who add a little weight." This is a basic and fundamental problem with the subject combination vehicle. Any of the prior art attempts can be shown to have a weight penalty that must be borne by the vehicle in its flight mode. The addition of special hardware to fold, detach, store, secure, and related requirements of the road vehicle all add "a little weight." In the prior art there appears to be no significant attempt to compensate for this weight penalty. The articulated fuselage all but eliminates fuselage or body weight carrying structure because the low wing-engine-operator-main load support wheel-power transmission and related gear are all coupled together with minimal or no space separating these major heavy items thus providing the flight vehicle with a significant weight reduction of lengthy high load path structure. Also, there is another aspect of the proposed invention that reduces weight. That is the above mentioned ground effect that aids in lowering liftoff and touch down speeds and rollout distances which in turn means that a smaller wing of lighter weight can be employed, all other conditions being the same.

A number of unique features that are meaningless or impossible without the jointed fuselage are not discussed here. These special features (see the "Unique Features" section) have no prior art as they are peculiar to the radical design of this invention.

OBJECTS AND ADVANTAGES

The objects and advantages of the articulated fuselage concept are:

(a) to provide the lowest possible placement of the propeller relative to the ground while providing assur-

WHERE ARE THEY NOW?

Vehicle	Location
AC 35 (Pitcairn)*	Smithsonian Garber Facility Silver Hill, Maryland (Appt Req'd)
Aerobile (Waterman)	Smithsonian Garber Facility Silver Hill, Maryland (Appt Req'd)
Aerocar prototype (Taylor)	Experimental Aircraft Association Oshkosh, Wisconsin
Aerocar I(102D) & II (Taylor)	Ed & Sandra Sweeney Black Forest, Colorado
Aerocar I(Taylor)	Privately owned in Southern CA
Aerocar I(Taylor)	Silverwood Theme Park Athol, Idaho
Aerocar III (Taylor)	On loan to the Museum of Flight Seattle, Washington
Aircar (Martin)	Forney Transportation Museum Denver, Colorado
Airphibian (Fulton)	Smithsonian Garber Facility Silver Hill, Maryland (Appt Req'd)
Convaircar (Hall)	Aerospace Museum (Models Only) San Diego, California
Flying Corvair (Stockwell)*	Erwin Stockwell Orange, Massachusetts

*No related patents in book

BIBLIOGRAPHY

Borovec, Ronald D. "Roadable Aircraft Magazine" Bimonthly about
    20 pages per issue starting with July/August 1992. $15 per
    year in U.S. $21 other. Back issues $3 in U. S. $4 other.
    338 8th Ave S., Edmonds WA 98020-3412. Only current
    publication devoted to this field. Many articles too numerous
    to mention. Excellent coverage of the movement which is
    resurging. He also runs forums at Oshkosh.

Bryan, Leland "Dewey" "Mechanix Illustrated" November 1955
    pp109-111. Description of his first roadable. Ten pictures.

Bowers, Peter M. 1990 "Unconventional Aircraft" pp207-215. Intro,
    advantages,disadvantages Curtiss*,Waterman**, Pitcairn*,
    Stout/Spratt*, Fulton**, Hall(Convaircar)*, Zuck**, Taylor(I)**,
    Bryan(II)*. TAB Books, Blue Ridge Summit, PA, ISBN 0-8306-
    2450-3

Bullard, Gary, "Land Air" info pack 6pages, 9 figures. Two place
    tandem canard pusher with wings hinged at mid span to fold
    over on top of fuselage. $8 Land Air, P.O. Box 1373, Salisbury
    MD 218802-1373. Also a patent in Stiles book.

Chana, William F. "Projecting Future Designs from Current Models"
    "Professional Pilot" September 1989.

    "Air Trails" August 1949, p23, One picture of his flying auto in
    three configurations.

Chant, Christopher 1984 "Fantastic Aircraft"pp56-58. Curtiss,
    Pitcairn, Waterman, Hall(Convaircar)*. W. H. Smith Publishers,
    Inc, New York, ISBN 0-8317-3189-3

Clark, "Air Trails" August 1949, p21,23. Four sketches with captions:
    two place side by side, twin boom pusher. Wings and
    empenage stow above fuselage for ground travel.

BIBLIOGRAPHY

Coleman, J.F. "Skeets" "Skeets Coleman's Aeromarine" by
     JosephVolney in "Flying"December 1955pp36,7f. Four place
     delta wing pusher concept with wing tip rudders. Wings
     double hinged to fold twice over rear fuselage. Amphibious.

Corn, Joseph 1983 "The Winged Gospel" pp91-111,and picture
     section following p70. Chapter is titled "An Airplane in   Every
     Garage?"   Broken promises and unfullfilled dreams,
     history, Waterman***, Pitcairn**, Fulton***, Taylor* and others.
     Oxford University Press, New York, ISBN 0-19-503356-6

Crow, Dr Steven C. "Star car design and GPS Control" see SAE
     "Conceptual Design of a Starcar"see SAE
     "Engineering Design of Starcar 3" see SAE
     "Differential GPS Control" (and Frank Manning) January 27,
     1992, Institute of Navigation. 19 pages, 7 photos, 11 figures,
     very thorough report on navigation research project using GPS.

Curtiss, Glenn "Autoplane" see EAA

Experimental Aircraft Association 1991 "Molt Taylor's Aerocar-
     Giving the Automobile its Wings"(VHS video) 35 minutes Bio,
     post war(WWII) situation, Fulton's inspiration, Taylor
     interviews, shop and flight footage, Ed Sweeney interview. EAA,
     P.O. Box 3065, Oshkosh, WI 54903, 1-800-843-3612.

     Roadable Aircraft /Flying Auto articles in EAA publications. See
     attached sheet.

Farmer, James see IRAA

Faulconer, Thomas P., see Stiles and Hall

Fox, Kenneth ,see Stiles

Fulton, Robert Edison, Jr. "The Airphibian" in "Air Facts" January 1,
     1947 pp9-21, 9 photos, "Fulton's Airphibian" in "Air Facts"
     July 1, 1950, pp52-74, 20 photos, both by Leighton Collins. "I
     Fly My Automobile", "Air Facts" July 1, 1950, pp11-27, 11
     photos, 1 figure. Very extensive articles on his two place side
     by side four wheel tractor design with detachable flight section
     and prop. This was the first to be certified by the CAA.

BIBLIOGRAPHY

"The One Man Caravan of Robert E. Fulton, Jr." VHS done by Fulton and his sons. Three half hour segments originally done for French television. Several minutes on the Airphibian. Very professional and inspiring. Robert Fulton Company, Flying Ridge, 18 Platts Hill Rd., Newtown, CT 06470. $25(?). Also one patent in Stiles book.

Hall, Theodore P. "SAC Aerocar" in "Fabulous Flying Flops" an "Air Classics" special report 1985. Article (no author listed) about Hall"s first design(with Faulconer), a three wheel, tractor prop, single engine, two place side by side, with twin boom high wing detachable flight section which must be left at airport. 4 pages and 4 pictures. Challenge Publications, Inc., 7950 Deering Ave., Canoga Park, CA 91304. See Chant. Also two patents in Stiles book.

Holland, Wismer, "At Last a Roadable Ercoupe" by Nonie Horton in "Air Facts" February 1, 1949, pp28-9, 6 figures. Wings stowed on top of fuselage, aircraft taxis down road. Also two patents in Stiles book.

IRAA (International Roadable Aircraft Association)12444 Powerscourt Dr., St. Louis, MO 63131. Write for list of publications.

Kosanchick, Mel, Jr. see IRAA and Stiles

Krassin, Yuriy A, "A view from Moscow", "Kit Planes" November 1989 pp28-9, 4 pictures of a model. Concept is a triphibious canard, long range, high aspect ratio, high thrust line, contra rotating rear mounted tractor props, and foldable, towable flight section.

Miller, Harvey and Smurthwaite, Robert "Avi Auto" promotional videotape of 4 wheel two place side by side twinboom pusher (RC model) Outer portions of horizontal stabilizer fold down, booms telescope forward, wings prtate about spar then fold back along fuselage. Avi Auto, P.O. Box766, Baker City, OR 97814. Also two patents in Stiles book.

Moller, Paul Info pack on the M400 Volantor Skycar, a 4 place concept with 4 ducted fans and deflectors, two Wankel engines per duct, vertical takeoff. Video and "Popular Mechanics"

BIBLIOGRAPHY

Jan"91,Moller International, 1222 Research   Park Drive,
Davis, CA 95616.

Roadable Aircraft Magazine See Borovec

Roby, John "Roadable Aircraft Literature List" Out of print and
current. Send SASE and $1 to 3703Y Nassau Dr., San Diego,
CA92115

SAE(Society of Automotive Engineers) 400 CommonwealthDr.,
Warrendale, PA 15096-0001. Each paper about $6.
Crow, Steven C., "Conceptual Design of a Starcar" #911021
"Starcar Design and GPS Control" #921569
"Engineering Design of Starcar 3" #932602
Czajkowski, Mike, "Design and Analysis of a Telescopic Wing"
#932605
Goldsworthy, Brandt, "The Convaircar Flying Automobile"
#921566
Knepp, John E. and Mullen , R. L. "Conversion of Production
Automotive Engines for Aviation Use" #932606
Sarh, Branko "Design Concepts and Market Opportunities for
Flying Automobiles" #921570
"Design Methodology and Infrastructures for
Flying Automobiles" #932604
Stiles, Palmer "History and Future of Flying Automobiles"
#9211568
"Carnard -A New Roadable Aircraft Concept" #932601
Taylor, Molt "The Aerocar 'Flying Automobile'" #7403393
Weiss, Merkel F. "Design and Styling of an Advanced Flying
Automobile" #9322603

Sarh, Dr. Branko See SAE. Also one patent in Stiles book.

Smith, A.J. "AeroCaballo info pack" A two place two wheels in front
and one in back vehicle with an airfoil shaped fuseladge. Two
vertical stabilizers with a horizontal stabilizer on top and the
trailing edge of the fuselage form a box enclosing two small
overlapping props. Each prop is powered by a small auto
engine through a long drive shaft. two small high wings pivot
backward in a horizontal plane for ground storage on top of
fuselage. A.J. Smith, 615 E. Douglas St., O'Neill, NE 68763
(402) 3364-1941.

BIBLIOGRAPHY

Stiles, Palmer C., ed, "Flying Auto and Roadable Aircraft Patent Search" 2nd Edition,   perfect bound. $20 plus P&H see below.

"Molt Taylor Video Interview"   Done at his office and workshop in 1988. His career, Aerocars, other homebuilts, model of Aerocar IV, tour of workshop, honors, awards, Aerocar III at Museum of Flight in Seattle. Approximately 2 hours. VHS. $15 plus P&H see below.

"Tom Faulconer Video Interiew " Done at San Diego Yacht Club August 1992. Personal history. Southern Aircraft and Convaircar flying autos combined effort with Ted Hall. Approximately one hour. VHS. $15 plus P&H see below.

"Mel Kosanchick, Jr. Video Interview"   Done at P. Stiles office August and December 1992. Personal vision of future trans- portation. Founding of International Roadable Aircraft Association and Autonomous Vehicle Institute.Legal reasons for using philosophy of roadable aircraft instead of flying autos. Legal precedents. Approximately 2 hours. VHS. $15 plus P&H see below.

"Joe Yasecko Video Interview" Inquire

"Harvey Miller and Robert Smurthwaite Video Interview" Inquire

"Michael Siewart Video Interview" Inquire

"CarNard Video"   A concept flying auto using canard layout. A 1/24th scale model based on a Lamborghini shown in 50 frame animated sequence at 10 frames per second. Vehicle drives on Interstate highway, deploys wings and canard while moving, rotates and takes off. $7 plus P&H see below.

"CarNard Model"   A 1/24th scale conceptual model based on a Lamborghini. Ed Sweeney says, "This is the second best flying auto design concept." Diecast body with aluminium flight components, Inquire about availability.

"Bibliography on Flying Autos and Roadable Aircraft" $2

BIBLIOGRAPHY

"Flying Auto and Roadable Aircraft Chronology" $1

"Where Are They Now?" Location of existing vechicles. $1

For above Stiles items include postage and handling: $3 first item, $1 each additional. Overseas airmail add $10 per order. 5580 N. U.S. Highway 1, Melbourne, FL 32940 Enclose check in U.S. funds or Visa or Mastercard number with expiration date and signature.

Strong, Richard A. 1973 "Strongmobile Development Report Volume One Summary" 25 pages, 15 figures. Richard Strong, 7514 Belle Plaine Drive, Huber Heights, OH 45424-3229. (513) 236-0361. Also two patents in Stiles book.

Taylor, Molt "Molt Taylor Video Interview"See Stiles. Also one patent in Stiles book.
"The Aerocar 'Flying Automobile'" see SAE
"Molt Taylor's Aerocar - All you ever wanted to know about flying automobiles" 20 pages, about 12 figures, history, philosophy, Bryan*, Smolinski (AVE Mizar)*, Fulton*, Waterman*, Pitcairn*, Curtiss, Zuck, Stout, Hall, Taylor***, Aerocar IV info. $22.50. Molt Taylor P.O. Box 1171, Longview, WA 98632 (206) 423-8260 or 425-9874.

Waterman, Waldo 1988 "Waldo Pioneer Aviator"(with Jack Carpenter)492 pages, soft. Complete story of Waldo with about 25% on the Arrowbiles. About $20. Arsdalen Bosch and Co., Box F, Carlisle, MA 01741. ISBN 0-9600736-0-4

Yenne, Bill 1990 "The World's Worst Aircraft" pp116-119. Curtiss, Waterman*, Boggs*, Stout, Spratt, Hall (SAC)**&(Convaircar)*, Zuck (II)*,Hervey (Travelplane)*. Brompton Books Corp., 15 Sherwood Place, Greenwich, CN 06830. ISBN 0-88029-490-6

Zuck, Daniel R. 1958 "An Airplane in Every Garage" 192 pages, many figures, hard. History, philosophy, Planemobiles I&II. (out of print). Also three patents in Stiles book.

*Denotes the number of pictures
Second Edition Copyright Palmer Stiles 1994

ROADABLE AIRCRAFT/FLYING CAR ARTICLES IN EAA PUBLICATIONS

YEAR	MONTH	PAGE	MAG	TITLE
54	03	08	SA	Taylor Roadable Aircraft Design Considerations
55	08	10	SA	Combination Auto/Airplane Envisioned within 3 Years
56	12	20	SA	Can a Roadable Airplane be Designed?
57	02	04	SA	The Roadable airplane-Background
62	09	20	SA	Taylor Aerocar Design in Logic
63	10	50	SA	Brian Special
63	12	19	SA	Inner Workins of the Aerocar
64	08	25	SA	Roadable Delta
66	09	22	SA	A Design in Logic - (Flying Auto)
67	10	19	SA	An Opinion - How to Change the World (Flying Auto)
71	06	13	SA	The Corvair powered Corvair
78	05	06	SA	(NOTE ONLY) - Dewey Bryan Roadable Aircraft Award
80	03	20	SA	Thereby Hangs the Tail (Taylor Aerocar)
82	05	09	SA	More Interest Shown in Flying Auto
83	02	56	SA	Autos that Fly
83	08	06	SA	Roadable Aircraft Association Formed
83	12	91	SA	Private Flying in 2000 (Roadable Aircraft)
87	08	32	SA	1917 "Auto Car" Takes to the Air

* Some of the articles listed above may be just brief notes. Back issues are available as follows: All SPORT AVIATION (SA) magazines are $2.00 postpaid. All other magazines are $1.50 each postpaid. If the magazine you wish is out of stock, the article will be copied for you if you provide the issue and page number. Notes are very brief items. Countries outside the U.S. should ask for a quote on postage based on their order; specify Air or Surface mail.

Roadable Aircraft Association
Kenneth Fox

0588H
12/04/90
Ben Owen
Information Services
djm

Roadable Aircraft

the magazine of flying automobiles and roadable aircraft

This is the magazine for flying automobile and roadable aircraft experimenters and enthusiasts. We have published **Roadable Aircraft Magazine** every two months since July, 1992.

The purpose of **Roadable Aircraft Magazine** is to support, inform, amaze and just plain entertain people who are interested in machines which can both fly and drive. We want to help fellow enthusiasts, experimenters and interested people share information, solve problems and popularize flying automobiles and roadable aircraft.

The reason for roadable aircraft and flying automobiles is expanded utility. We are looking for aircraft and automobiles that are more useful. We already know that roadable aircraft can be answers for ground transportation when a pilot is away from home, or during bad weather on a cross-country flight, when many pilots would be grounded at the airport. At any time, roadable aircraft or flying automobiles give you the option of driving or flying. These machines can be the breakthrough permitting lifestyles now hardly imagined.

We admit the technical, economic and social problems regarding flying cars or roadable aircraft can be formidable. Before success these issues must be addressed. Up to now no one vehicle or solution has resolved all the problems. But now the issue of high cost is being tackled head on by people working in the homebuilt aircraft-kitcar arena. The amateur built solution promises to bring to market many different designs at reasonable prices. There are also commercial projects with large financial resources who plan to market complete vehicles or kits. We report on them all.

The most common roadable aircraft are conventional or canard airplanes. But reported roadable projects or concepts have included gyroplanes, amphibians, flex-wings, powered parachutes and others. Ground mode concepts range from fairly conventional aircraft to automobiles, trikes, motorcycles and sneakers.

One fascinating aspect of roadable aircraft is that these vehicles are not all figured out. There is no one consensus - the answers are not cast in concrete. Possible new solutions and ideas are appearing all the time.

Professional papers presented at national engineering conferences are reprinted in **Roadable Aircraft Magazine** when appropriate. Such papers from the Society of Automotive Engineers have included: The History and Future of Flying Automobiles by Palmer Stiles and Design Concepts and Market Opportunities for "Flying Automobiles" by Dr. Branko Sarh.

Every issue includes coverage of historical vehicles, current projects, design concepts, new ideas, technical issues and reader concerns. Reader input is strongly encouraged. We constantly look for new ideas, concepts and points of view. A regular feature is "Blue Sky" ideas - fresh, even far-out ideas worth presenting. We actively search for new, more effective and cheaper ways to solve the problems of flying and driving one vehicle.

At **Roadable Aircraft Magazine**, we do not take a particular position about a "right solution". We support and will report on any project with merit, in or out of the mainstream. The editor, Ron Borovec, is a mechanical engineering consultant and a licensed Professional Engineer. He takes great interest in projects and ideas, but makes every attempt not to impose a point of view.

This is an exciting period for roadable aircraft and flying cars. There is a resurgence of interest coming at a time when the means to develop successful vehicles has never been better.

Thank you for taking a look at **Roadable Aircraft Magazine**. We look forward to having you be a subscriber and explore with us the world of flying automobiles and roadable aircraft.

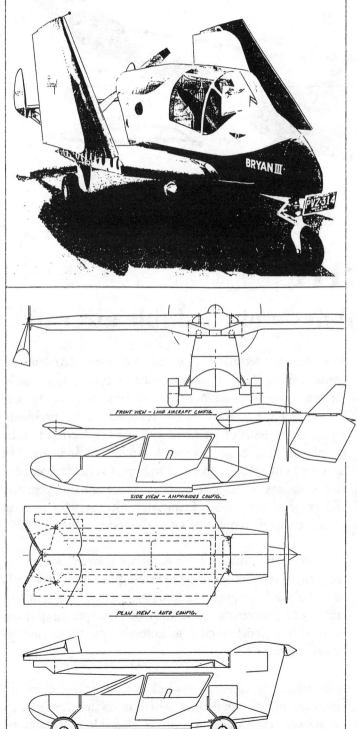

July/August 1993
Volume 2
Number 4
$3.00

The Search for Utility

Roadable Aircraft

"Seagull" Roadable Amphibious Airplane Concept by William Schugt

Cover of July/August 1993 issue

Roadable Aircraft Magazine

Model of Molt Taylor's Aerocar IV. Feature article on this design appeared in the January/February 1994 issue.

Roadable Aircraft Magazine first appeared with the July/August 1992 issue, and has been published every two months since then. The following summary will indicate the range of **Roadable Aircraft** content.

Back issues of **Roadable Aircraft** are available. Turn this page for subscription and back issue details.

Feature Articles from Back Issues:

July/August 1992   Issue 1; Vol. 1, No. 1
The future of roadable aircraft and the purpose of the magazine
Ground, Air & Full Roadables - Defining roadable aircraft by air and ground capabilities
Commuter Aircraft - Predicting the future of personal transportation - by David Whitlow
1992 SAE Conference - The flying automobile
Questionnaire - What do you think?

September/October 1992   Issue 2; Vol. 1, No. 2
AC-35 - Historic roadable autogiro
Wooley Roadable - A new roadable aircraft configuration
Whitlow Roadable Aircraft Classifications
Stemme S-10 Chrysalis Motor Glider - Retracting propeller and folding wing solutions

November/December 1992   Issue 3; Vol. 1, No. 3
The Bryan Roadables - Three airplanes licensed for the highway and driven for years
History and Future of Flying Automobiles - A professional paper from the 1992 SAE Future Transportation conference

Land-Air GB 2000 - A canard roadable airplane now under development

January/February 1993   Issue 4; Vol. 2, No. 1
Roadable Aircraft Patent Search - A new book by Palmer Stiles
Flying Cars or Roadable Planes - Harry Einstein's roadable aircraft designs
All Terrain Roadable Aircraft - Applying VTOL to a roadable
Defining the Personal Commuter Roadable Aircraft - by David Whitlow
Questionnaire Results - What do we want in a roadable airplane?

March/April 1993   Issue 5; Vol. 2, No. 2
The AviAuto - A new flying car design
Don Parham's Gyrocar - Gyroplane and 3 wheeled car
Mainair Skybike - Flex-wing trike and motorcycle
The Approach Control Problem - Aerodynamics of the Roadable Commuter Part 1 - David Whitlow looks at the design of the personal air commuter
Blue Sky - The sky is the limit for ideas
1992 Index to **Roadable Aircraft Magazine**
Complete listing of articles

May/June 1993   Issue 6; Vol. 2, No. 3
Design Concepts and Market Opportunities for "Flying Automobiles" - Part 1 - SAE paper by Dr. Branko Sarh
Easy Propeller Analysis - David Whitlow shows how to apply the powerful Fred Weick method
Powered Parachutes - Carry this plane in your trunk

continued

Roger Williamson's homebuilt ROADRUNNER design is currently under construction. This and other Williamson concepts were covered in the November/December 1993 issue.

Subscription information:

A subscription to **Roadable Aircraft** is $15.00 per year for 6 issues in the U.S., and $21.00 for foreign subscribers. New subscribers immediately receive the current issue by first class mail.

Back Issue information for new subscribers:
Issues 1 - 12 of **Roadable Aircraft** are available. As a special offer to new subscribers back issues of Roadable Aircraft are available for $2.50 each, including first class postage and will be quickly mailed together with your copy of the current issue. Please specify which **Issues**. See below for foreign orders and regular back issue prices.

Regular Back Issue Prices:
$3 each for one, two or three copies sent by first class mail in the U.S.
Four or more copies are $2.50 each and are sent by third class mail in the U.S. Add $1 per large order in the U.S. for first class mail.
Foreign orders for back issues must add $3 extra per order for postage. Magazines will be sent air mail. Foreign orders send US Postal Money Order. No foreign checks please.

Mail to:
Roadable Aircraft Magazine:
P.O. Box 38
Edmonds, WA 98020-0038

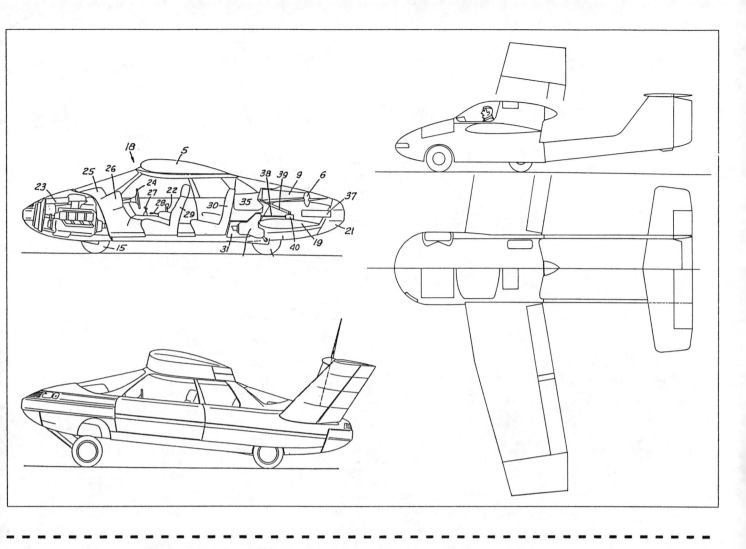

SUBSCRIPTION ORDER FORM

Yes, I want to subscribe to **Roadable Aircraft Magazine**.

☐ $15 for 1 year (6 issues) in the U.S.

☐ $21 for 1 year to all other countries.
(U.S. funds please. Outside U.S. send International Postal money order.)

☐ $3   Send me a sample issue in the U.S.

☐ $4   Send me a sample issue to any other country. (U.S. funds please.)

Roadable Aircraft Magazine
338 8th Ave. S.
Edmonds, WA 98020-3412

If there is no label on the reverse side please print your name and address here very legibly.

Name: _____

Address: _____

Address: _____

City: _____ State: ____ ____ Zip: __ __ __ __ __ - __ __ __ __

(Optional) Your interest: _____

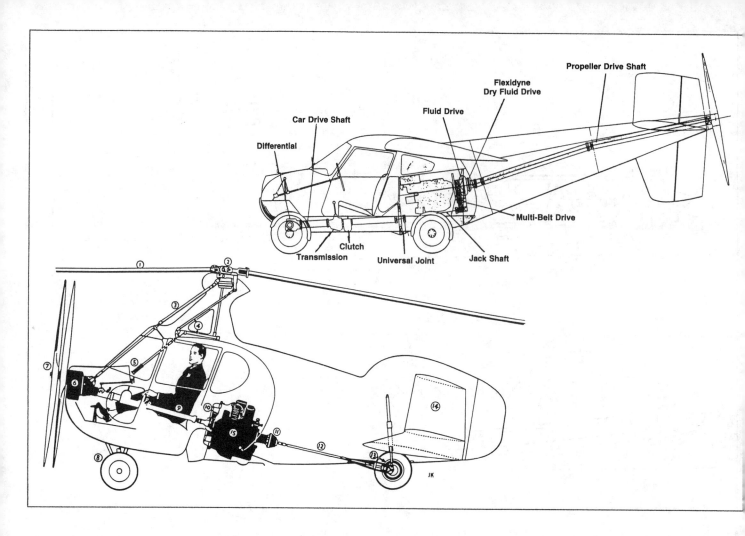

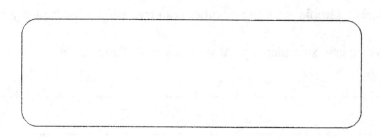

ROADABLE AIRCRAFT MAGAZINE
338 8 AVE S
EDMONDS WA 98020-3412
U.S.A.

ORDER FORM

QUAN		PRICE	TOTAL
	Roadable Aircraft: *From Wheels to Wings*	$20.00	
	Florida residents State Sales Tax	6%	
	Shipping & Handling North America	3.00 each	
	Priority Mail - 2 day delivery USA only	4.00 each	
	Shipping & Handling Outside North America	5.00 each	
	Airmail	13.00 each	
		TOTAL	**$**

☐ Check enclosed   ☐ MC   ☐ VISA   expiration date _____

\#_____

Sig_____

Name _____

Address _____

City _____ Zip _____

MAKE A COPY, FILL OUT, AND MAIL TO: Custom Creativity, Inc.
5580 N. US 1
Melbourne, FL 32940